1/2 Nat. size

LEOPARD

JACKAL

JUNGLE CAT

HYENA

THE DEER AND THE TIGER

THE DEER
AND THE TIGER

A STUDY OF WILDLIFE IN INDIA

GEORGE B. SCHALLER

THE UNIVERSITY OF CHICAGO PRESS

CHICAGO AND LONDON

Library of Congress Catalog Card Number: 66–23697

THE UNIVERSITY OF CHICAGO PRESS, CHICAGO & LONDON
The University of Toronto Press, Toronto 5, Canada

TO JOHN T. EMLEN

CONTENTS

PART III THE PREDATORS

ILLUSTRATIONS

PLATES

All photographs except Nos. 8, 13, and 14 were taken in Kanha National Park.

FIGURES

TABLES

THE DEER AND THE TIGER

PART I

**INTRODUCTION,
STUDY LOCATIONS,
AND METHODS**

CHAPTER 1

INTRODUCTION

India is remarkable for the variety of its large mammals, a richness in species exceeded by few countries in the world. From the rain forest of Assam to the snows of the Himalayas and the deserts of Rajasthan, from the deciduous forests of the central highlands to the mangrove swamps of the Sunderbans, India presents a great diversity of vegetation types, each with its unique faunal assemblage. The immense sweep of the Himalayas harbor sheep such as the bharal[1] and urial as well as wild goats — the markhor, tahr, and ibex; and there are takin and goat antelopes such as the serow. Snow leopards stalk musk deer in the rocky gorges, and black bears prowl the forested slopes. Many of these species belong to the palaearctic faunal region, and the mountains represent the most southerly part of their range in India. The peninsula has its own distinctive mammals, with some, such as the blackbuck, nilgai, and chital, being almost wholly confined to it. The thorn forests and other open habitats are or were the home of the Asiatic lion, cheetah, Indian gazelle, and others; the grass jungles of the Gangetic basin hold wild buffalo, barasingha, hog deer, and the great Indian rhinoceros; the forests harbor elephant, sloth bear, leopard, gaur, barking deer, sambar, pig, and the unique four-horned antelope. And many of the forests contain the tiger, an animal which perhaps more than any other over the years has become the symbol of India's wildlife heritage.

The Western world was largely unaware of the variety and abundance of the mammals in India until the nineteenth century, although the four principal Vedas (2000–1500 B.C.) mention the tiger, lion, wild pig, and twenty-seven others (Rao, 1957) and the Mogul emperors from the thirteenth to the sixteenth century were famous as

[1] Scientific names may be found in Appendix A.

hunters. Akbar the Great is said to have kept three thousand trained cheetahs with which to hunt antelope, and his successor Jehangir shot, among other animals, a total of 889 nilgai (Ali, 1927). With the advent of British rule, and particularly after the consolidation of the whole country following the mutiny of 1857, many hunters penetrated all parts of the country. Books by Rice (1857), Shakespear (1860), Baker (1890), Forsyth (1889), and Kinloch (1892), among others, give a vivid picture of the great herds of hoofed animals and the numerous large predators that occurred even in the parts heavily populated by man. Jerdon (1874) reported herds of blackbuck in the Punjab numbering ten thousand animals; "traveling through almost any district, you will come across them, sometimes in large herds, and herd after herd" (Aflalo, 1904). Rhinoceros and wild buffalo still existed at the foot of the Himalayas, and "swamp-deer, hog deer, sambhur, and other cervine species, herd together in the tall grateful cover of the friendly jungle grass — and wild pig, porcupine, wild fowl, game fowl, and other animals, dear to the sportsman, are to be met with in incredible numbers" (Inglis, 1892).

These herds are no more. The cheetah is extinct in India, the last ones having been shot in 1951 (Talbot, 1960). The great Indian rhinoceros, which was hunted in the Indus valley by the Moguls as late as 1519 (Rao, 1957), survives only in a few isolated sanctuaries in India and Nepal. The population of Kashmir stag has been reduced to fewer than two hundred fifty individuals (Gee, 1962a). The Asiatic lion, once found throughout the dry open forests north of the Narmada River, now occurs only in the Gir Forest of Gujarat, where fewer than three hundred animals remain (Gee, 1962a). Probably no more than two thousand wild buffalo exist in scattered remnants (Daniel, pers. comm.). Of the "herds of thousands" of barasingha seen by Pollock and Thom (1900) in Assam and Bhutan only some four thousand survive in the country and in the world. Where Forsyth (1889) observed herds of blackbuck "which must have numbered a thousand or more individuals," none are now seen and this species once so abundant is reaching a critical stage in its survival. The other large mammals — the Indian gazelle, nilgai, chital, gaur, and so forth — which were exceedingly common have all declined drastically in number. The ubiquitous tiger has become scarce in most parts of the country. The Himalayan fauna has suffered a similar fate (Dang, 1964a,b). What has been the cause for the decline?

Direct shooting has been an important factor in the decrease of wildlife. Many British civil servants were inveterate hunters, as were the maharajas, for whom it was a major form of recreation. Animals of any age and sex were bagged indiscriminately. Hunting was not just a sport but a symbol of status, the criterion for the latter being the number of animals, especially tiger, shot. In Cooch Behar (1908) the caption on one photograph reads: "A record day's bag of bison — 3 bulls and 8 cows"; books by Rice (1857), Shakespear (1860), and Smythies (1942) contain representative descriptions of this type of hunting. By the end of the past century the decline had accelerated to such an extent that some hunters grew concerned. The rhinoceros was gone from most of its former haunts, and the lion was nearly exterminated, although one was shot in central Madhya Pradesh as late as 1851 (Forsyth, 1889). Russell (1900), after bagging twenty-four blackbuck in one outing, noted the general scarcity of the species in the area. Baldwin (1877) wrote: "In former years tigers were doubtless a scourge, now they are becoming rare even in the wooded parts of the country, where in days of yore they abounded, and where once a dozen could be shot by a party in the hot weather with but little difficulty, two or three now will only be bagged over the same ground, and these not without great exertion and perseverance." Attempts were made to regulate the shooting, with acts for the preservation of animals being passed in 1887, 1912, and 1935. The Nilgiris Game Association was founded in 1877 and the Bombay Natural History Society in 1885, both designed to promote the conservation of wildlife. A number of reserves were established, prominent among them the Banjar Valley Reserve, Corbett National Park, and Kaziranga Sanctuary. However, the decline of the wildlife continued, and Champion (1953) wrote in 1934: "Animals like blackbuck and chital and game-birds, both in the plains and particularly the hills, are literally being wiped out at an increasingly rapid rate and one wonders if there will be anything left except monkeys and jackals after another two or three decades." Yet in spite of the apparent apathy with which the government viewed the protection of the large mammals (Stebbing, 1912), and the great amount of damage done by army personnel during the Second World War, India retained a considerable amount of its wildlife until 1947.

Independence ushered in a period of destruction that could almost be compared to the slaughter on the American prairies in the 1880's. Rejecting shooting regulations as a form of colonial repression and released from restraint, Indians shot down wildlife everywhere, including sanctuaries and private estates. As a result of food shortages the government initiated a national drive to protect crops from the depredation of wild animals, and guns were issued freely to farmers, an action which literally doomed almost all animals near cultivation. For instance, G. Singh, Conservator of Forest in Punjab, wrote to me in 1964: "Blackbuck was found in large number in central and southern parts of the Punjab state until 15 years ago. Then it was treated as a crop pest and killed in large numbers. This resulted in virtual extermination of the species." A new type of hunter emerged, too, a motorized one who drove in jeeps along forest roads at night and shot at any eyes that reflected the beam of his light. For about five years the destruction continued unabated. In 1951 Bombay state passed the Wild Animals and Wild Birds Protection Act; in 1952 the Indian Board for Wildlife was formed and in 1958 the Wild Life Preservation Society of India. Conditions improved slowly with each state government making serious attempts to preserve its fauna and to strengthen the existing shooting regulations. A number of fine but small reserves were established. But enforcement against poaching on the local level remained inadequate, with the result that the wildlife continued in its decline.

Coupled with the outright destruction of wildlife by shooting was the indirect method of eliminating the habitat. As late as the sixteenth century rhinoceros, elephant, buffalo, and other animals characteristic of fairly moist conditions occurred in parts of western India that are now covered with dry thorn scrub (Rao, 1957), indicating a rapid dessication of the habitat undoubtedly caused by misuse of the land by man (Puri, 1960). Chinese pilgrims in A.D. 600 talked of the dark jungles in the Gangetic basin, and even three centuries ago large areas of Uttar Pradesh were still covered with virgin forest (Robertson, 1936). Today, the heavily populated Gangetic basin retains sizable patches of forest only at the base of the Himalayas, areas that were uninhabitable earlier because of malaria. Tremendous tracts of grass and reeds in the valley of the Brahmaputra River were put under the plow, and Kaziranga Sanctuary remains as one of the few remnants of a habitat that once covered thousands of square miles. Forests were cleared throughout India for cultivation, and the timber was cut for use in railroad construction. After independence the drive for more food and the unchecked increase in the population resulted in the cultivation of most marginal land. The natural vegetation cover of India is forest, but less than a quarter of the country is still covered with it.

A great scourge of India's land is the vast numbers of domestic animals which are undernourished, diseased, and unproductive, yet are permitted to exist for religious reasons. The plains of West Bengal, for instance, had in 1961 a human population of 1,031 per square mile and a cattle and buffalo population of 351 per square mile. The animals received only one third of their estimated daily nutritional requirements, and annual mortality due to disease was about 15 percent (Anon., 1962). India had an estimated 204 million cattle and buffalo and 94 million goats and sheep in 1956, of which 21 million of the former and 13 million of the latter grazed exclusively in the forests (Venkataramany, 1961). Livestock is permitted to graze without restrictions in virtually all forests and most sanctuaries, and serious damage to the vegetation culminating in widespread erosion is common particularly in the thorn and deciduous forests. The carrying capacity of many forest areas and other uncultivated lands is so far exceeded by livestock alone that a substantial amount of wildlife could not support itself even if it were protected from shooting.

Livestock diseases, especially rinderpest and foot-and-mouth disease, also affect the wild ruminants. There are numerous records of gaur, chital, and others contracting diseases from cattle and dying in large numbers, whole populations having been wiped out in this manner (Brander, 1923; Ali, 1953). The health of domestic and wild hoofed animals is mainly a function of the quality of the range, and animals in poor condition as a result of malnutrition become highly susceptible to parasites and disease, making the problems of range condition and disease inseparable.

In one hundred years the combination of land clearing, uncontrolled slaughter, habitat destruction by livestock, and disease have reduced one of the world's great wildlife populations to a small remnant. Yet in spite of a realization that wildlife represents the country's fastest vanishing asset, no detailed studies of any kind have been attempted on the large mammals. Published information consists for the most part of incidental observations collected in the course of shooting the animal, the majority of books, even the better ones like Forsyth (1889), Sanderson (1912), and Champion (1927), presenting only general life history notes. Articles in the *Journal of the Bombay Natural History Society*, the *Journal of the Bengal Natural History Society*, and others are either cursory or consist of notes and anecdotes of unusual encounters. The books on Indian mammals — Jerdon (1874), Sterndale (1884), Blandford (1888–91), Lydekker (1924), Prater (1948) — although providing useful summaries, do little more than repeat the information first published in the books by hunters. By far the best single book on Indian wildlife is by

Brander (1923), who, though occasionally in error, presents a good deal of accurate data. E. P. Gee is virtually the only person in India who has in recent years consistently gone into the field and published first-hand accounts of certain mammals, particularly of the threatened ones like the Indian rhinoceros and Kashmir stag (Gee, 1953; 1962a,b; 1963), and he has also been the major voice in drawing international attention to the plight of the wildlife. His book *The Wild Life of India* presents a useful introduction to the animals and his work. So far even the most rudimentary forms of ecological research, such as making accurate annual censuses and determining rates of reproduction and mortality, have yet to find a place in the plans of the state forest departments and the Zoological Survey of India, the two governmental services with direct responsibility for this type of work.

In 1961 the Johns Hopkins Center for Medical Research and Training was established in Calcutta, West Bengal, under the direction of Dr. F. Bang, School of Hygiene and Public Health, Baltimore. Although the center is medically oriented, as the name implies, the organizers have realized that a meaningful program of disease studies is possible only in a broad ecological context, one in which the behavior of the vectors and of the possible hosts of the disease organisms also is studied in detail. To gather such data, the program formed an ecological unit headed by Dr. C. Southwick. Some of the projects completed or in progress include work on the biology of flying foxes, rhesus monkeys, and various rodents, as well as the present study of deer and tiger.

At first I intended to study primarily the chital deer, but it soon became apparent that the most fruitful approach, the one that would yield the most information not only for the program but also from the standpoint of conservation and management, would be to collect a broad spectrum of facts on a number of different species in one locality. After considerable searching I decided on a relatively undisturbed forest area in central India, the Kanha National Park in the state of Madhya Pradesh, as the site for the study. Fourteen months were devoted to research on the large mammals in this sanctuary, the remaining six months of the project being used to obtain comparative information in other areas. A broad study has one severe disadvantage — the danger of superficiality, of failure to collect the quantitative data needed for proper evaluation of the observed facts. On the other hand, a broad approach provides a better understanding of the interrelationship between species, which in the study of one area may be highly important. At Kanha Park, for example, observations on the chital automatically included the barasingha, with which they were often associated, and the tiger, which preyed on both. I hope that I have managed to present a reasonable compromise between the two approaches.

This report is concerned largely with the ecology and behavior of the major hoofed animals in Kanha Park — the chital, barasingha, sambar, blackbuck, and gaur — and with the life history of the tiger, the most important predator in the area. The main purpose of placing all this information under one cover is not only to present new material about the habits of these animals but also to stress similarities and differences in aspects of behavior, such as the time of mating and bearing of young, and to attempt to answer such questions on predator-prey relations as, What is the effect of tiger predation on the hoofed animals in Kanha Park? The report, furthermore, provides a summary of the available information about these species in the wild in India, indicating how little has been and is still known about them and how much research needs to be done in the near future if the large mammalian fauna is to survive in appreciable numbers. In India, perhaps more than in most countries, the basic problems of animal and human ecology are intimately related, and a solid body of facts is desperately needed if conservation and management practices satisfactory to man, his livestock, and the wildlife are to be initiated in time to save the last from complete extermination. If this report acts as a stimulus for other studies it will have served its purpose.

CHAPTER 2

STUDY LOCATIONS AND METHODS

The wildlife was studied in a number of localities under different ecological conditions. This chapter of the report presents my itinerary and describes the general study techniques employed. It also discusses India's physiography, vegetation, and seasons with special emphasis on Kanha National Park.

Study Locations

I arrived in India on September 2, 1963, and departed on May 9, 1965. The work during this period fell into several stages.

Zoo Study

The first one and a half months of the project were devoted chiefly to the study of a herd of twenty-three chital deer in the Calcutta Zoological Garden to determine which aspects of social behavior were important to quantify in the wild, to record details of social interactions such as dominance, and to trace the development of fawns of known age in order to establish a basis for comparison with free-living animals. Observations were continued by assistants after I began work in the field, but the condition of the herd unfortunately deteriorated as a result of malnutrition and disease, and most data had to be discarded.

Surveys

Parts of northern India were toured from October 20 to November 16, 1963, to search for a suitable study site and to become familiar with the ecological conditions existing there. The journey included visits to some of the major wildlife areas and vegetation types in the states of Bihar, Uttar Pradesh, Rajasthan, and Madhya Pradesh (see

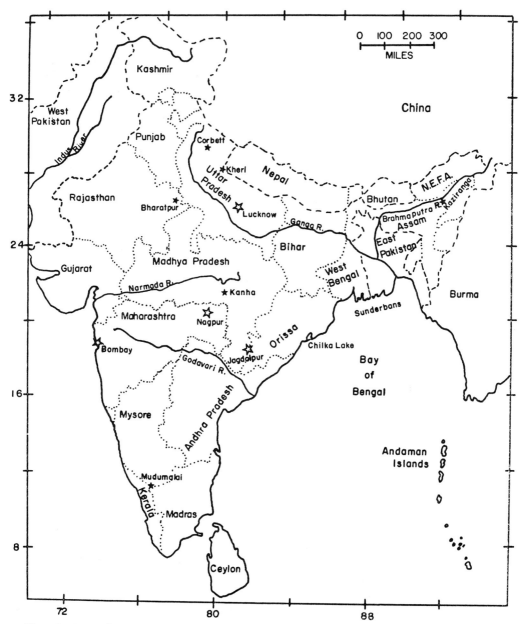

Fig. 1.—Map of India showing states and main study areas.

Fig. 1). It soon became apparent that a wildlife study such as I had in mind was feasible only in a sanctuary because the animals in the unprotected forests were usually so shy and sparse that prolonged observations proved difficult. It was also desirable to locate a site with low human and livestock populations as well as one where the possibilities of viewing the wildlife were adequate throughout the year. Most of the areas visited were unsuitable for one reason or another: Hazaribagh National Park in Bihar and Chandraprabha National Park in Uttar Pradesh contained very little wildlife; the South Kheri Forest Division and the whole stretch of forest in and along the foothills of the Himalayas, including Corbett National Park, had ample wildlife in a few localities, but for six months of the year the grasses are ten to fifteen feet high in many places, making it difficult to see the animals much less to observe them at length; the sanctuaries of Rajasthan supported a vast livestock population; and the high mountain fauna was inaccessible because of unsettled political conditions. Shivpuri National Park in Madhya Pradesh was a possible site, but by far the best one proved to be Kanha National Park in the same state. Gee (1961) considered it to be the finest reserve in India, and Brander (1953) wrote after a visit in 1928:

In 1900 this tract contained as much game as any tract I ever saw in the best parts of Africa in 1908. I have seen 1,500 head consisting of 11 species in an evening's stroll. It is nothing like that now, but it is probably true to say that it contains more numbers and more species than any other tract of its size in the whole of Asia.

Additional surveys were made in West Bengal — in the Sunderbans at the mouth of the Ganges from October 3 to 7, 1963, and the hill forests in the vicinity of Darjeeling from December 4 to 7, 1963.

THE MAIN STUDY

Observations in Kanha Park were carried out from December 20, 1963, to January 17, 1965, and from March 11 to 31, 1965, a period of almost fourteen months. The bulk of the data in this report were collected in the central part of Kanha Park, and unless specifically stated otherwise all facts and generalizations pertain to this area alone. It is important to keep this fact in mind not only because the behavior of a species in such aspects as the season of rut and food habits may vary considerably from locality to locality but also because the ecological conditions in my study area were in many respects ideal. There were fairly large ungulate and predator populations, the forest was not cut for timber, and the grass was only lightly grazed by livestock, a situation very unusual in India today. The population

TABLE 1

LARGE MAMMALS OF KANHA NATIONAL PARK

Scientific Name*	Common Name Used in This Report	Other Common Names
Primata		
Presbytis entellus	Common langur	
Lagomorpha		
Lepus nigricollis	Indian hare	Black-naped hare
Rodentia		
Hystrix indica	Indian porcupine	Crested porcupine
Carnivora		
Canis aureus	Asiatic jackal	
Cuon alpinus.	Indian wild dog	Red dog, dhole
Vulpes bengalensis	Bengal fox	
Melursus ursinus	Sloth bear	
Herpestes edwardsi	Grey mongoose	
Hyaena hyaena	Striped hyena	
Felis chaus.	Jungle Cat	
Panthera pardus	Leopard	Panther
Panthera tigris†	Tiger	
Proboscidea		
Elephas maximus	Indian elephant (domesticated only)	
Artiodactyla		
Sus scrofa	Wild pig	
Tragulus meminna	Mouse deer	Spotted chevrotain
Axis axis†	Chital	Axis deer, spotted deer
Cervus duvauceli†	Barasingha	Swamp deer, gond
Cervus unicolor†	Sambar	
Muntiacus muntjak	Barking deer	Indian muntjac
Antilope cervicapra† . . .	Blackbuck	Indian antelope
Tetracerus quadricornis . .	Four-horned antelope	Chousingha
Boselaphus tragocamelus . .	Nilgai	Blue bull
Bos gaurus†	Gaur	Indian bison

* Nomenclature follows Ellerman and Morrison-Scott (1951).
† Mammals treated in detail in this report.

dynamics of the species may have been influenced considerably in such respects as the rate of reproduction and survival of young by these habitat conditions.

Table 1 lists the large mammals found in Kanha National Park. Brander (1953) recorded Indian gazelles near the boundaries of the park, but none have been seen there in recent years. Wild elephants and buffalo were regular visitors to the area during the rainy season in 1900 (Brander, 1923); today neither species occurs within a one-hundred-fifty-mile radius.

COMPARATIVE STUDIES

To obtain some material with which to compare the data from Kanha, and to add to my knowledge of several species, I spent from one to two weeks in the following four different wildlife areas.

Two days were spent in obtaining age and sex counts of the un-

Location	Dates	Species Studied
Corbett National Park, U.P.	Jan. 23–Feb. 8, 1965	Chital, hogdeer
Keoladeo Ghana Sanctuary, Bharatpur, Rajasthan	Feb. 11–23, 1965	Chital, blackbuck, nilgai
West Kheri Forest, U.P.	Feb. 25–Mar. 5, 1965	Chital, barasingha, hogdeer
Kaziranga Sanctuary, Assam	Apr. 30–May 7, 1965	Barasingha, hogdeer

gulates in the Vanbihar Sanctuary, Rajasthan, and part of a day was devoted to the blackbuck in a 700 × 1,500 foot enclosure at Akbar's Tomb, Sikandra, about five miles north of Agra. J. C. Daniel of the Bombay Natural History Society conducted a census of the wild buffalo west of Jagdalpur in the West Bastar District, Madhya Pradesh, from April 1 to 10, 1965, and I assisted him in this. My assistant De studied the blackbuck at Chilka Lake, Orissa, from November 8 to 15, 1964, a site which I also visited for one day on April 13, 1965.

Study Methods

The techniques used in gathering data on the various species are discussed at the appropriate places in the report, but some of the main points are enumerated below.

GENERAL OBSERVATIONS

The animals were usually observed with the aid of 7 × 50 binoculars and a 20 × spotting scope at distances of 100 to 800 feet depending on the circumstances. At Kanha Park, as well as in Corbett Park and the Keoladeo Ghana Sanctuary, much of the work was done from the inside of a Land Rover or on its roof, because the wildlife tended to disregard the presence of a car whereas it fled from a man on foot. I usually cruised along meadows and over forest roads until a herd of animals was spotted, then parked and observed it for varying lengths of time. This technique was particularly useful at night and during the three hours after dawn and before dusk when the wildlife was active. A considerable amount of work was also done on foot — searching for remains of animals killed by tigers, transecting forests to estimate abundance of wildlife at various times of the year and in different parts of the park, collecting plants and making notes on the vegetation, and just wandering about for the pleasure of it. From mid-June to mid-November all roads in Kanha Park were impassable because of the monsoon rains, making observations on foot a necessity. Most work at West Kheri and in the Kaziranga Sanctuary was done from the back of an elephant because of the tall dense grass.

Kanha Park is 123 square miles in size, and it was obviously not possible to study the whole sanctuary in detail. Although all parts of it were visited, most observations were made in a sample area of 20 square miles in the center of the park which was relatively undisturbed by man and livestock. The study area contained much of the wildlife in the park, including all the blackbuck, two-thirds of the chital, and seasonally most of the barasingha and gaur. Park headquarters, where we lived, was located within this area.

Observational conditions varied greatly with the seasons and with the habits of the animals. From September to December the grass was high and the wildlife scattered in the forest, making the collecting of data difficult. But after the burning of the grasses in January, chital and barasingha congregated on the meadows and remained readily observable until August. The gaur and sambar appeared on the meadows primarily during the hot time of the year. As a consequence the emphasis of the study shifted somewhat with the seasons, with, for example, January being devoted particularly to the barasingha and April to the gaur. Detailed observations on the main ungulate species at Kanha were made for the following numbers of hours, which do not include numerous brief encounters: barasingha, 242 hours; chital, 227 hours; blackbuck, 133 hours; gaur, 82 hours; and sambar, 15 hours.

Tigers were occasionally seen, but rarely for more than half an hour at a time. Prolonged observations were possible only when the tiger was on its kill, but since most of its prey was relatively small and was eaten up in a day or two, it was rarely possible to obtain information in that fashion. Only when a tiger killed a large animal, such as a domestic buffalo or a gaur, was I able to obtain data on feeding habits, social interactions, and so forth, by watching the kill from the cover of a tree trunk or other hiding place. Domestic livestock dead from disease or other causes was occasionally placed out at specific places and the behavior of the cats observed from a blind 80 to 150 feet away. A total of sixteen head of livestock, principally buffalo, was staked out alive to attract tigers, a method commonly employed by hunters in India. One male tiger and two tigresses, each with cubs, tended to disregard my presence in the blind and ignored the beams of flashlights and spotlights, making accurate night observations possible. I spent twenty-four whole nights and numerous partial nights in waiting for tigers and in watching them. Tigers were observed for 129 hours, a number which does not include the many hours in a blind with the tiger resting nearby but out of sight.

POPULATION STUDIES

The forest department has conducted a yearly wildlife census in Kanha Park during late May or early June since 1953, the only such sustained effort in India. Since 1958 the census technique has been relatively standardized, the animals being counted in a drive census by villagers who walk through the forest, spread out at four men to the mile, and tally the number and kinds of animals they see. Only twenty square miles are covered in this fashion, but since the sam-

TABLE 2

FOREST DEPARTMENT CENSUS FIGURES
FOR THE LARGE UNGULATES IN KANHA NATIONAL PARK

Year	Chital	Barasingha	Sambar	Blackbuck	Gaur
1938.	2,844	3,023	324	168	35
1958.	1,726	577	36	44	176
1959.	1,579	411	52	52	159
1960.	1,259	260	96	38	181
1961.	1,253	254	87	44	01
1962.	1,292	244	194	46	259
1963.	1,471	173	126	30	297
1964.	623	94	77	16	97
1965.	1,146	109	139	20	239

pled areas include all the known wildlife concentrations, the figures obtained are thought to give a good idea of the size of the populations in the park (Table 2). I was able to obtain reliable counts on the chital, barasingha, and blackbuck populations in my study area during 1964, and these figures, together with my estimates for gaur and sambar, provided a check on the reliability of the forest department census during the same year. The number of tigers and leopards are estimated by the forest department on the basis of footprints at water holes. The resulting figures are discussed later in detail for the respective species.

Between February 12 and 16, 1965, Spillett and I censused the Keoladeo Ghana Sanctuary by transecting the entire area on foot in parallel lines 150 to 300 feet apart (Schaller and Spillett, 1966).

A particular effort was made to determine the status of the few surviving barasingha populations in the world. In addition to corresponding extensively with persons who know or might know about the animal in a particular area, I visited several parts of its range and made censuses in two of them. In the Kaziranga Sanctuary, the deer remained primarily on the short grass bordering the ponds where they could be counted readily from the back of an elephant. The last known large herd of barasingha occurs on private farm land and in the Kheri Forest Division of Uttar Pradesh. Since a census on foot through the swamps and high grass was impossible, five elephants walking in parallel lines about 200 feet apart were used to tally the animals as they flushed (Plate 8, facing p. 000).

Classification counts were made of all species to ascertain the relative number of males, females, and young in the population. All single animals and herds were classified whenever it was possible to distinguish every individual clearly. If only a few members of a herd were visible, then no count was made except in a few instances. The total number of animals tallied usually exceeded the number in the area because some were recorded repeatedly in the daily counts.

DISEASE STUDIES

It was not possible to collect a series of specimens for detailed autopsy. However, endo- and ectoparasites as well as blood samples were obtained from 3 chital, 2 killed by predators and 1 by poachers. In addition, 9 chital were tranquilized with a sleep-inducing drug (Sernylan) and checked for ectoparasites. Some blood was extracted from the jugular veins of these animals and later tested for disease antibodies (Shah et al., 1965). A few parasites were also obtained from carcasses partially eaten by tigers. Eleven fresh tiger feces and 3 leopard feces were preserved in formalin and later checked for parasite ova. The mammalian ectoparasites, collected by Mitchell, Spillett, and myself from rodents, carnivores, and ungulates, comprised 8 species of ticks, 19 species of mites, 5 species of suckling lice, 3 species of fleas, and 1 species of hippoboscid fly. The potential disease relationships and other information regarding these parasites have been discussed in a separate paper (Mitchell et al., 1966). Mitchell and Nadchatram (1966) described 7 new species of chiggers from Kanha Park, and Maa (1965) a new species of hippoboscid fly.

FOOD HABIT STUDIES

The food habits of the ungulates were determined mainly by identifying the species of plants eaten while the animals were actively foraging on them. I obtained some quantitative data by collecting rumen samples from deer and gaur killed by predators. About one to two pounds of material, gathered at the kill site, were preserved from each animal. The sample was washed to eliminate the fine material, and the residue was separated into three broad plant types — browse, fruit, and sedge grass. After being drained, each type was measured volumetrically by water displacement. A total of twenty-six samples, representing four species, were analyzed.

To determine the extent of predation on the various prey species, kills were sought throughout the study area, fresh ones sometimes being advertised by the behavior of jungle crows and vultures. The lower jaw was collected for later determination of relative age, based on the eruption of and wear on the premolar and molar teeth; and the sex was noted from skull characteristics. De and I found a total of 100 animals believed to have been killed by tiger, leopard, and perhaps wild dog, and the villagers brought in an additional 128 jaws. The cranium and lower jaw could not both be found in many instances. Predators frequently carry the remains of their prey from site to site, and their habit of dragging the victim into a ravine to feed there in seclusion results in the bones' being washed away during the rains; young animals are usually eaten so completely that only a few bone splinters are left. Even though we found the remains of 82 chital, barasingha, and sambar at Kanha, both the age and sex of only 46 of these could be determined.

A careful examination of the animal remains in the fecal droppings of tiger and leopard revealed the food habits of these two cats. Each pile of droppings was dissected thoroughly, and the hair and sometimes hooves were then compared with reference material from known specimens obtained earlier at kill sites. The hairs of most species, including those of langur, porcupine, pig, cattle, and chital, differed sufficiently in color, length, and thickness to make identification possible with the unaided eye. Barasingha hair, however, was occasionally difficult to distinguish from sambar hair in that manner; but since the cuticle of hair in each species has a diagnostic scale pattern, the hairs of the two species could readily be distinguished when examined under a microscope. The central portion of the barasingha's guard hairs were found to have large irregular scales with contiguous edges, whereas those of the sambar were comparatively smaller and not in direct contact with each other. In a few instances it was difficult to separate domestic buffalo from gaur, but since few of the former were killed in the area during 1964, the possible slight error will have had little effect on the percentages. A total of 335 tiger and

22 leopard feces were analyzed. A number of jackal, jungle cat, and sloth bear droppings were also checked for ungulate remains.

Description of the Study Areas

Although most work was done in Kanha National Park, brief studies were also carried out in other areas. The following brief description of the major physical features and vegetation types of India places my study area into a broader perspective and serves as a background for comparing the various ecological conditions under which the wildlife exists.

PHYSIOGRAPHY AND VEGETATION OF INDIA

The one and a quarter million square miles of India are divisible into three major physical regions. Between the headwater gorges of the Indus and Brahmaputra rivers rises the tremendous mountain barrier of the Himalayas. For 1,500 miles these mountains arc across the northern frontier of the country in a series of parallel ranges varying in total width from as little as 100 miles in the east to nearly 300 miles in the west. The Himalayas are a young range, built mainly between the Eocene and Pleistocene, and activity has not yet subsided. The inner range — the snow peaks — is composed of granites and gneisses; the outer range, consisting of forested mountains some 6,000 to 10,000 feet high, has a sedimentary origin. Bordering the outer range are the Siwaliks, low hills of ancient river deposits stretching from the Punjab to Assam (Randhawa, 1958).

The Indo-Gangetic plain, including the valley of the Brahmaputra River, skirts the Himalayas like a moat. This great plain with a width of over 250 miles along parts of the Ganges River was once a deep depression formed by the elevation of the Himalayas and until the Eocene was occupied by an arm of the sea (Ripley, 1964). Covered now with fertile alluvium to a depth of over 6,000 feet, the region has over the centuries been the principal site of India's history and the source of its wealth. Today an average of four hundred persons per square mile crowd into this monotonously flat plain.

The Indian peninsula rises from the southern end of the Gangetic basin in a series of terraces to a huge plateau. This plateau is one of the oldest stable land formations in the world, having apparently never been wholly submerged since the Cambrian. Its average elevation is about 1,500 feet, although it rises to 3,000 feet in Mysore. Most of the peninsula consists of Archean rocks — a mixture of gneisses, granites, and schists—which on decomposition form the rather infertile red soils that give the country a bleak and baked look during the hot season. However, in the western part, particularly in Maharashtra and western Madhya Pradesh, the underlying rock is composed of volcanic lava which produces a rich black cotton soil. The northern edge of the plateau is flanked by the Vindhya and Satpura ranges, a series of scattered and rather desolate flat-topped hills reaching an altitude of 4,500 feet. Only the higher parts of the Satpuras—the Mahadeo Hills and the Maikal Range—have the verdant aspect so delightfully described by Forsyth (1889). The Western Ghats border the western edge of the plateau. Starting near the Narmada River, they grow progressively higher toward the south until they reach an altitude of 8,000 feet in the Nilgiri Hills of Kerala and Madras. The whole plateau tilts eastward, with the result that the hills along the eastern edge, the Eastern Ghats, are usually no more than 1,000 feet high.

A number of different forest types cover India, and several detailed classifications of these exist (Champion, 1938; Puri, 1960). For the purposes of this report, however, a characterization will suffice. Figure 2 features only the major vegetation types below an altitude of about 4,000 feet. Those above that altitude show a definite zonation of temperate forests grading from (1) *Pinus* to (2) *Abies*, *Picea*, *Tsuga*, *Quercus*, and *Acer*, to (3) the conifer, *Betula*, and *Rhododendron* thickets, and finally to (4) timberline at about 12,500 feet. Although the natural vegetation of India is forest, with grasslands occurring primarily along some of the large rivers, about 75 percent of it has been cut and the land used for cultivation and other purposes. Since the majority of the large mammals are forest dwellers, one can gain a rough impression of the amount of habitat still available to them in the various states from Table 3. The figures tend to be somewhat high, for denuded and overgrazed tracts, which in some instances are simple wastelands, are also included.

Five major forest types cover most of India.

1) *Tropical wet evergreen and semi-evergreen forest*. Much of Assam, Nagaland, and Manipur, parts of West Bengal, and the coast of Orissa, as well as the west coast from the vicinity of Bombay southward through Kerala, have a hot, humid climate. The mean annual temperature is over 75°F and the minimum not below 50°F. Rains are heavy, 75 inches or more per year, with Cherrapunji in Assam receiving up to 430 inches. The trees in undisturbed evergreen forest reach a height of 150 feet, and the canopy is continuous. The

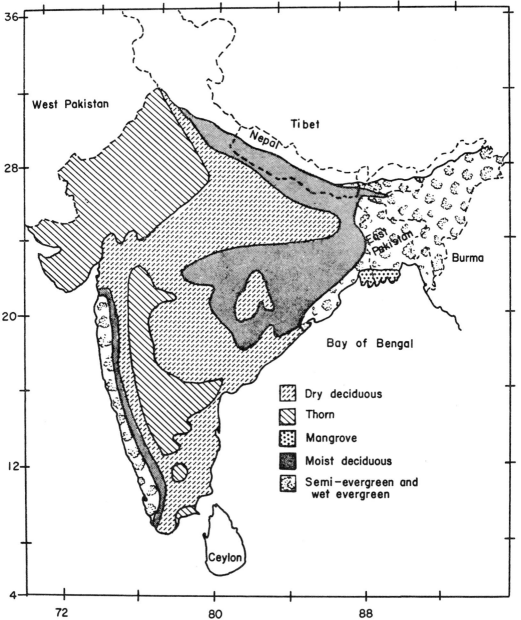

FIG. 2.—Distribution of principal forest types in India below an altitude of 4,000 feet (adapted from Randhawa, 1958, and Anon., 1961).

TABLE 3

PERCENT OF AREA UNDER FOREST IN INDIAN STATES AND TERRITORIES
AND DENSITY OF HUMAN POPULATION PER SQUARE MILE

State or Territory	Total Geographical Area in Square Miles	Percent under Forest	Density of Population per Square Mile
Andhra Pradesh . . .	106,052	24.8	295
Assam and Nagaland .	53,460	32.6	159
N.E.F.A.	31,439	59.7	159
Bihar	67,198	19.2	577
Gujarat	72,207	9.2	226
Maharashtra	118,831	21.8	271
Jammu and Kashmir .	86,024	12.9	51
Kerala	15,003	32.4	903
Madhya Pradesh. . .	171,210	41.1	152
Madras	50,132	16.5	598
Mysore	74,122	18.7	262
Orissa	60,161	42.1	243
Punjab	47,084	11.7	343
Rajasthan.	132,150	12.7	121
Uttar Pradesh	113,454	19.7	557
West Bengal	33,928	13.9	775
Delhi	573	2.3	3,044
Himachal Pradesh . .	10,879	37.3	102
Manipur	8,628	26.9	67
Tripura	4,035	60.9	158
Others	3,412	75.7	15
	Total: 1,259,983	Average: 24.0	Average: 287

After Venkataramany, 1961.

number of tree species is great, with *Michelia, Dipterocarpus,* and *Artocarpus* being common among the genera. Many trees are buttressed and draped with epiphytes. Shrubs and forbs grow sparsely in the understory, and the ground is for the most part covered with molding leaf litter. The semi-evergreen forest appears to be a subclimax to the evergreen one and differs primarily in that it contains a number of deciduous tree species. The canopy is consequently somewhat open, the undergrowth is dense in spots, and occasional bamboo thickets occur. Both types of forest grow on flat to hilly terrain, rarely above an altitude of 4,500 feet. The only large tracts of these forests survive in eastern India, particularly in the North East Frontier Agency (N.E.F.A.). Shifting cultivation is the usual method of agriculture practiced in the areas occupied by these forests, with the result that many of them present a patchwork of trees in various stages of regeneration.

2) *Mangrove forest.* The only large area of mangrove forest in India lies in the Sunderbans at the mouth of the Ganges River, but small patches also occur at the mouth of the Godavari and Mahanadi rivers. A network of sloughs and channels intersect the delta

leaving innumerable flat alluvial islands which are partially to wholly submerged during the tides. It is hot (average annual maximum, 96°F), humid (average relative humidity, 80 percent) and wet (average annual precipitation, 79 inches). The trees are for the most part low and scrubby, 20 to 30 feet high, creating almost impenetrable stands. *Ceriops roxburghiana, Excaecaria agallocha, Avicennia alba,* and *Heritiera minor* are common tree species, and patches of *Phoenix paludosa* grow along the water's edge. The ground consists mostly of mud, but grasses grow sparsely in places not reached by the sea.

3) *Tropical moist deciduous forest.* The Siwalik Hills and adjoining plains from western Uttar Pradesh eastward to northwestern Assam, and parts of Bihar, Orissa, and Madhya Pradesh are covered with a forest in which the dominant trees are deciduous. Rainfall is usually 50 to 80 inches per year, and there is, in contrast to the evergreen forest areas, a definite dry season. Temperatures range at the extremes from about 25°F to 110°F in the shade. The tree canopy in undisturbed forest is high, about 120 feet, and almost closed. Clumps of bamboo are common, but the undergrowth is often sparse because the grasses and shrubs are burned during the dry time of the year. Some moist deciduous forest is thought to be secondary, the result of shifting cultivation, but much of the area is covered with sal (*Shorea robusta*), a climax species.

4) *Tropical dry deciduous forest.* Dry deciduous forest grows in the plains and hills from Uttar Pradesh south to Madras in areas of moderate rainfall — usually 25 to 50 inches — and a prolonged dry, hot season. The trees average 40 to 60 feet in height, and the canopy coverage rarely exceeds 70 percent and is usually about 50 percent. During the dry season the majority of trees shed their leaves and remain bare until the onset of the rains. *Tectona, Anogeissus, Erythrina, Albizzia,* and *Bauhinea* are some of the common genera. Bamboo is abundant only in parts of central India. Shrubs, some of them thorny, are prominent in the understory, and so is grass. But these forests are either burned annually or are so heavily grazed by livestock that for much of the year they present a denuded appearance.

5) *Tropical thorn forest.* In the plains of Rajasthan, western Punjab, and Gujarat, as well as in the shadow of the Western Ghats, an area which fails to receive the heavy monsoon rains because of the mountain barrier, the forests consist of xerophytic, thorny plants. Rainfall is usually less than 30 inches annually and maximum tem-

peratures reach 120°F. The scattered trees average only 20 to 30 feet in height and include several species of *Acacia* and *Zizyphus*, as well as *Vachellia, Salvadora, Cassia, Mimosa, Tamarix, Prosopis*, and others. The understory contains several kinds of thorny shrubs and a sparse cover of grasses. Excessive use of these forests by man for firewood and by livestock for grazing has turned or is turning them from semidesert to desert conditions.

DESCRIPTION OF KANHA NATIONAL PARK

Kanha National Park lies in a rugged tableland in the eastern part of the Satpura Range known as the Maikal Hills, about 25 miles southeast of the district town of Mandla, at 22°45′N. latitude and 80°45′E. longitude. The park comprises 123 square miles of terrain ranging in altitude from about 1,750 feet in the valleys to 2,900 feet on the high ridge tops. The area consists for the most part of a huge amphitheater, some five miles in diameter, hemmed in by hills on three sides and beyond them by a series of lesser ridges and valleys. The shape of the park is roughly rectangular, demarcated within a continuous block of forest of over 500 square miles.

Little was known about the area before British rule came to Mandla in 1818, except that from the sixth to the twelfth centuries it was ruled by the Rajput dynasties and after that by Gond kings until it was acquired by the Marathas of central Madhya Pradesh in 1781 (Fuchs, 1960). The local tribal people, the Baigas, practiced shifting cultivation throughout the hills until prohibited from doing so by the Land Settlement Act of 1868. The management of the forests was taken over by the government in 1879. Although the district became famous as a place to hunt because of the abundance and variety of its wildlife, it was not until 1935 that 99 square miles of the area were established as a sanctuary, which was then known as the Banjar Valley Reserve. The size of the sanctuary was reduced to 51 square miles in 1942 in order that the chital deer, which supposedly destroyed sal seedlings, could be shot. About two hundred fifty chital are said to have been removed yearly from 1945 to 1952. From 1947 to 1951 the Maharajkumar of Vijayanagaram had special shooting privileges in and around the sanctuary, and he killed about thirty tigers during that time. Felling of sal trees mainly for railroad sleepers began in 1864 and continued intermittently until terminated in 1959. In 1952 the sanctuary was enlarged to 98 square miles and in 1964 to 123 square miles. On June 1, 1955, the area was declared a national park by the state government, which has sole jurisdiction over it (Nath, n.d.).

Although legal hunting and timber felling in the park has ceased, human disturbance continues to be quite heavy. Five forest villages — Raunda, Sonph, Kisli, Silpuri, and Kanha — lie within the park, but all except the last are near the periphery. Another fifteen villages lie at or within two miles of the boundaries. Each village occupies a clearing in the forest at least one square mile in size and consists of mud-walled huts, fields of rice, and grazing land for livestock. Only one rice crop is grown per year, which is planted during the rains and harvested by November. The tribal peoples roam through the forest cutting grass for thatch and bamboo for house construction, picking wild fruit, tubers, and mushrooms in season, poisoning fish in the streams, and poaching deer. Each village retains a fairly large herd of cattle and buffalo, which forage in the forests. The approximate livestock population of the villages in and immediately bordering the park is twenty-five hundred head, but a considerable number of other animals are brought into the forest illegally from farther away during the hot season. Twenty-five square miles in the basin of the amphitheatre are closed to cattle grazing, except for one small herd at Kanha village. This, together with the fact that at least five miles of unbroken forest stretch in all directions from the village, has left the central part of the park, my study area, comparatively undisturbed. Relatively few Indian and foreign tourists visit the park, and these confine themselves to the roads.

Mandla District lies in an area of transition from moist deciduous to dry deciduous forest, and both types occur in the park. The major habitats include village sites, 5 square miles; grass meadows, 18 square miles; sal forest, 30 square miles; and mixed forest (dry deciduous), 70 square miles.

Grass meadow. Grass meadows varying in size from a few acres to several hundred acres lie scattered throughout the area on ridge tops, in valleys, and along stream beds. Most if not all of the large meadows represent abandoned village sites, some of them deserted during the famine of 1874 and never reoccupied. Periodic frosts, yearly fires, and grazing by animals prevent the surrounding forests from encroaching. The species composition of the grasses has been altered considerably around the villages and near the boundaries of the park where numerous cattle and buffalo forage. Perennials like *Themeda triandra* have been largely replaced by annuals or other perennials like *Pennisetum alopecurus*, a coarse bunch grass not favored by livestock. *Zizyphus jujuba*, a thorny shrub, and several unpalatable species of forbs have also spread unhindered. At all seasons the grasses are eaten down to a short, sparse stubble.

The meadows in the center of the park present an entirely different appearance, and typical of these is the Kanha meadow on which I made many of my observations of the wildlife (Plate 1). This meadow is about three square miles in size, the largest in the park. Several stream beds transect the gently undulating terrain, and numerous small ravines, often bordered with a variety of trees and shrubs, radiate from them. Copses of trees, particularly of sal and *Lagerstomia parviflora*, interrupt the expanse of the meadow, as do rocky hillocks covered with clumps of bamboo (*Dendrocalamus strictus*). Solitary trees, from the lofty *Bombax malabaricum* to the brushy *Bauhinea racemosa* and the spreading *Ficus*, dot the meadow here and there. Its whole aspect is most pleasing and resembles a tended parkland more than a wilderness in central India.

I collected 29 species of grasses and grasslike plants on the meadow. The dominant grass along the forest's edge and other shaded sites is *Themeda triandra*, which reaches a height of 7 feet. On the dry open expanses *Heteropogon contortus, Andropogon brevifolius, Imperata cylindrica, Chrysopogon fulvus*, and *Hemarthria compressa* are common. The height of these grasses rarely exceeds 4 feet, and in the moist depressions such species as *Panicum miliare, Sporobulus diander, Cyperus iria, Eragrostis gangetica, Cyperus exaltatus*, and *Fimbristylis dichotoma* are often no higher than one to two feet. *Vetiveria zizanioides, Arundo donax*, and *Coix lachrymajobi* form dense thickets 10 feet high along some stream beds. Forbs are inconspicuous, with some, like the blue-flowered *Evolvulus alsinoides* being almost procumbent. Most shrubs, except for *Zizyphus jujuba* and *Phoenix humilis*, are associated with stands of trees.

Sal forest. Shorea robusta is largely confined to the valleys below an altitude of 2,000 feet. There it forms almost monotypic stands on flat to undulating terrain with moist loamy soil derived from the decomposition of schists, gneisses, and other metamorphic rocks. About 80 percent of the trees around Kanha village are middle-aged, 70 to 90 feet high, and 10 to 18 inches in diameter. The straight boles reach upward for two-thirds of their length before the first branches flare out to form a canopy covering 70 to 80 percent of the ground. Toward the periphery of the park, where logging has been heavy and the soil is poor, the trees are spindly, only some 40 to 60 feet high and the coverage of the canopy 50 percent or less. One of the main associates of sal is *Terminalia* sp., which on some of the low, rocky hills replaces it as the dominant tree.

The forest beneath the canopy is quite open (Plate 2). A conspicuous second story is generally absent, although stands of young sal occur in some clearings, saplings of such trees as *Cordia myxa* are scattered here and there, and bamboo forms occasional dense thickets, particularly along stream beds and on the boulder-strewn hillocks that rise from the forest floor. The dominant shrub is *Moghania stricta*, which, together with a dwarf palm (*Phoenix humilis*), several thorny vines (*Smilax zeylanica, Asparagus racemosus*), and various forbs and grasses, creates in places a tangled undergrowth to a height of 3 or 4 feet. *Bothriochloa odorata, Imperata cylindrica, Chloris dolicostachya, Themeda triandra, Eragrostis unidoides*, and *Cyperus paltestylis* are the abundant grasses and sedges. Of the forbs, the tall, broad-leafed *Curcuma ferruginea* and *Chlorophytuum tuberosum* are conspicuous, but most others (see Table 11, p. 59) are small and found predominantly among the banks of streams. In areas where the canopy is continuous or the soil heavily sprinkled with white quartzite pebbles, the ground is often bare except for leaf litter and an occasional tuft of grass.

Mixed forest. The slopes of the hills are steep, rocky, and cut by numerous ravines; the tops are often flat, forming plateaus up to several hundred feet wide. The hills consist of basalt capped with limestones, quartzites, and conglomerates. The forest is scrubby, with trees only 40 to 60 feet high, most of them deciduous. The canopy covers about 50 to 60 percent of the ground when the trees are in leaf, and there is little shade when they are not. Among the more common trees are *Anogeissus latifolia, Buchanania lanzan, Acacia torta, Cassia fistula, Bauhinea racemosa, Gardenia latifolia*, and *Terminalia* sp.; a large-leafed climber (*Bauhinea vahli*) trails from many branches.

Stands of bamboo are very abundant on the slopes. The clumped stems grow to a height of 20 feet and arch outward to form such a dense canopy in places that the ground remains bare or at most is covered with a dense mat of shade-resistant grasses (*Oplismenus burmanii, Arthraxon ciliaris*). Bamboo usually reproduces by vegetative shoots, although it flowers at intervals of 10 to 20 years and seeds gregariously, then dies. Roughly 70 percent of the bamboo in the area flowered in 1963–64 and about 5 percent in 1964–65. Consequently dead bamboo stems littered the hills and valleys, and after the onset of the monsoon, bamboo seedlings sprouted in profusion. Such flowering occurred also in 1900, 1921, 1930–31, and 1944 (Mehta, n.d.).

Shrubs (*Pogostemom plectranthoides, Colebrorkia opposilifolia*) grow densely on a few ridge tops; at other places, black basaltic boulders and rocky soil prevent much vegetation from finding a foothold. Usually, however, the ground cover consists of grasses 2 to 7 feet high, among them *Themeda triandra, Heteropogon contortus, Apluda mutica, Andropogon monticola, Spodopogon rhizophorus, Iseilema laxuus,* and *Pennisetum setosum.*

The Seasons

The whole tempo and pattern of life on the subcontinent of India is strongly affected by the seasons. The temperatures and the amount of rainfall change drastically with the time of year, and this in turn has a profound effect on the vegetation and on the habits of the animals, including man. The year at Kanha is divided into three major seasons, which are also typical of much of India as a whole, although the intensity and time of the seasonal change differ somewhat in various parts of the country.

The cool season. The cool season from November to February, sometimes referred to as "winter," has a temperate climate, with the nights crisp and daytime temperatures rarely above 85°F (Table 4; Fig. 3). Occasional frosts occur in December, sometimes severe enough to kill sal seedlings in the clearings. The lowest temperature recorded on the meadow in 1964 was 26°F, but temperatures as low as 22°F were noted in some previous years. Night temperatures in the forest are usually at least 5°F warmer than on the meadows, especially during the coldest time of the day from 0300 to 0600 hours. Relative humidity reaches 100 percent during the night (Fig. 4), with the result that the vegetation is sodden with dew in the morning and, on the meadow, sometimes covered with frost. A low blanket of fog often lies over the clearings until dissipated by the warming sun. Rain is scanty, except for occasional showers toward the end of the season (Table 4). These spring rains are part of the northeast monsoon, which in a typical year deposits two to three inches of rain in the highlands. But in some years, including 1964, the rains almost fail.

Since the cool season follows the retreat of the monsoon, the vegetation is still green and rank in the forest, but the grasses on the meadows have already gone to seed and turned yellow. The forest department then begins to burn the grass on the Kanha meadow, burning a patch here, another there, until after a month or more only a black stubble remains. In 1963 the burning began on December 28

TABLE 4

Weather Data, 1964, Kanha National Park

Date	Temperature*				Precipitation			Cloud Cover
	Average Maximum	Average Minimum	Highest	Lowest	Total Precipitation† (In Inches)	Number of Days With Rain	Approximate Number of Hours of Rain	Number of Cloudy Days
January 1–31	78.3	48.0	84	40	.00	2	3.0	0
February 1–29	82.0	53.1	92	44	.62	4	14.0	0
March 1–31	96.4	60.0	102	52	.15	2	.5	2
April 1–30	103.3	69.6	109	61	.00	2	1.5	0
May 1–31	105.2	73.5	110	69	.00	3	1.0	0
June 1–19	104.1	79.2	107	74		6	2.0	0
June 20–30	84.9	75.0	103	74	8.53	11	69.5	10
July 1–31	83.3	74.4	89	71	16.19	29	149.0	17
August 1–31	81.7	73.9	89	71	25.18	27	270.0	22
September 1–30 . . .	85.2	72.4	91	68	11.23	16	56.5	13
October 1–31	85.0	66.0	89	55	1.19	5	6.0	4
November 1–30 . . .	77.1	52.2	83	44	.00	1	2.0	2
December 1–31 . . .	74.5	45.1	79	37	.00	0	.0	0
Total					63.09	108	575	70

* Temperatures were taken in the shade of the sal forest 9 feet above ground.
† For the records of total precipitation, I am indebted to the forest department.

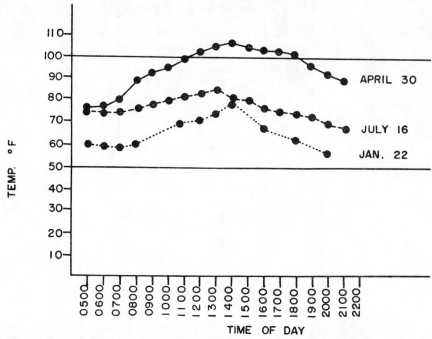

Fig. 3.—Hourly temperature readings in the shade at Kanha on a representative day in the cool (January 22), hot (April 30), and wet (July 16) seasons.

but in 1964 as early as November 30. Burning the grass apparently releases nutriments into the soil and, together with the sporadic showers, stimulates a fresh growth of green grass to appear within two weeks. The new growth is very sparse in areas that are not burned. The Kanha meadow was burned by Brander (1923) in 1902 and has probably been set afire every year since then.

By mid-January the weather resembles the European autumn as some of the deciduous trees shed their leaves, which crackle underfoot and are blown across the ground by the wind. But in February it is suddenly springtime with the nights growing somewhat warmer, the *Bombax* trees opening their large scarlet flowers, and many birds beginning to breed. Ringdoves coo, green barbets tinker with the dawn's first redness at 0600 hours, peacocks strut, and the persistent call of the brain-fever bird is heard for the first time in the year.

The hot season. From March to mid-June, the local "summer," the sun burns down from a hazy sky and temperatures reach 110°F in the shade (Table 4; Fig. 3) and considerably higher on the meadows.

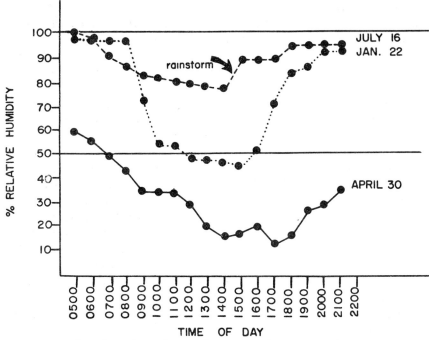

Fig. 4.—Hourly relative humidity readings in the forest at Kanha on a representative day in the cool (January 22), hot (April 30), and wet (July 16) seasons.

The sun rises as a coppery orb at 0530 hours and by 0900 the white heat blazes down until dusk brings relief. Relative humidity is low, sometimes less than 20 percent during the early afternoon (Fig. 4). Rain, if any, occurs in sporadic showers, and hail sometimes falls in March and April (I saw some stones in 1965 the size of golf balls).

The grasses almost everywhere have now withered, and toward the end of the season the green shoots on the meadows have been grazed off or have been shriveled by the sun. The sal trees bloom in early March and at the same time shed their leaves. Almost simultaneously they grow new ones, so that when the deciduous trees in the hills are bare and the ground is exposed to the full force of the sun, the sal forest is shaded by leaves of the freshest green. The forest floor everywhere is carpeted with dead leaves so brittle that even a tiger finds it difficult to walk silently.

Villagers burn the grasses and dead leaves throughout the forests from March to May, except in a few spots which inadvertently escape the fires or from which the livestock has eaten the inflammable material. The fire leaves the soil bare and black, giving the hills in particular an exceedingly bleak appearance. With almost all forage gone, the wildlife leaves the hills and concentrates in the sal forest, where some green shoots and coarse grasses remain and where the sal saplings and *Moghania* shrubs have burst into fresh leaf.

All streams cease to flow by early March, and water remains only in pools in the large stream beds and at a few seepage springs in the hills. In 1964, when the rains of the northeast monsoon almost failed, water was very scarce, with, for example, only 7 pools in an area of fifteen square miles near Kisli village. A waterhole count in my study area during late May and early June, however, revealed 253 pools of various sizes, 155 of them on the Kanha meadow.

The wet season. After originating in the south Indian Ocean, the southwest monsoon surges as a massive current of vapors across the seas, spurred on, so to speak, by the breakdown of the subtropical high pressures over India resulting from the intense heat. After a passage of five thousand miles the monsoon arrives at the west coast and moves north and east, arriving fairly punctually each year in Bombay around June 5, in Calcutta around June 15, and in Delhi around July 1 (Kendrew, 1961).

Clouds often drifted in during the afternoons in early June, and occasional light showers fell. The air grew heavy, enervating, as the humidity rose although temperatures continued to climb above 100°F. On the evening of June 21 the sky blackened, and at last the rains came. Clouds settled on the hills for two weeks, and downpours were frequent. There was a week of relatively little rain during the latter part of July, but in August the sun appeared infrequently. The rains began their retreat in September and terminated during the first half of October. The average annual rainfall at Bichhia, about 12 miles north of Kanha village, was 73 inches (34–81) during the years 1936–45 (Mehta, n.d.); at Kanha 63 inches fell during 1964 (Table 4). June to September receives about 95 percent of the total annual rainfall, with July and August sharing some 70 percent of it. With the clouds providing shade from the sun, the temperatures drop suddenly (Table 4), averaging 20°F lower than during the preceding months. Relative humidity is high, usually 75 percent and above (Fig. 4).

With the first heavy rains and the release from the oppressive heat, all life bursts forth as if it has been waiting for the moment. Frogs (*Rana tigrina, R. cyanophlyctis, R. breviceps, R. limnocharis*) suddenly appear in number and mate; large red mites (*Dinothrombium tinctorium*) emerge from the soil by the thousands, court, then disappear again; winged termites (*Odontotermes* sp.) swarm from their subterranean chambers and funnel into the night sky. Biting insects, particularly tabanid flies on the meadows and mosquitoes in the forest, become somewhat bothersome for the only time of the year. The color of the vegetation changes within a period of two weeks from predominantly grey and yellow to an intense green as the leaves on the deciduous trees unfold and the grasses sprout. By the middle of July the grasses are two feet high, and numerous forbs, especially monocots and creepers, cover the forest floor, which was bare only a month before. The small species of grasses and sedges bloom from late July to mid-August, but the tall ones, such as *Themeda*, flower in September. In October the grasses are in seed, and by the end of the month those on the meadows have turned slightly yellow. Villagers begin to cut the vegetation that has grown up on all the forest roads. Minor streams, which for brief periods were torrents, cease to flow, and the large ones confine themselves to their beds. The monsoon is at an end.

PART II

THE HOOFED ANIMALS

Of the ten wild species of hoofed animals in Kanha Park, only the chital, sambar, and gaur were fairly abundant. The barasingha and blackbuck, though conspicuous, were rare in actual number. This part of the report is devoted to a description of the behavior of these five species.

An additional five species were rare to uncommon in the study area and so elusive that very little information was obtained on them. A nilgai male was once seen in the northern corner of the park, and the four-horned antelope, a solitary species, was encountered three times. The tiny mouse deer was observed twice, but its habit of scurrying away through the grass often made identification uncertain. Barking deer were tallied on twenty-three occasions, usually solitary but sometimes in a group of two. Herds of wild pigs, numbering nine to fourteen animals each, were seen three times and lone boars twice. Since these species played a rather minor role in the ecology of the area during 1964, they are not discussed in detail.

CHAPTER 3

THE CHITAL

The lithe grace and lovely spotted coat of the chital or axis deer (*Axis axis*) have made it a favored inhabitant of zoological gardens and parks for centuries. Because of its wide distribution and abundance, it has also been the most persistently hunted deer for meat and sport in its native India, Nepal, and Ceylon, acquiring in certain respects a position similar to the *Odocoileus* deer in North America There have been detailed studies of the life history of these North American deer (W. Taylor, 1956), but very little data about deer in their subtropical environments are available for comparison. Such knowledge is particularly urgent in the case of the chital because the species has declined drastically throughout its range in India, and is now only locally abundant in some sanctuaries and forest tracts. The remaining populations are highly vulnerable to poaching, habitat destruction, and other forms of decimation; in Madhya Pradesh, for example, all wildlife in forest areas of ten square miles and less which are surrounded by cultivation are being slated for extermination because of supposed damage to crops (Mehta, n.d.). Yet the chital, perhaps more than any other Indian ungulate, would lend itself well to management practices, and with a little effort the species could once again become a conspicuous and economically valuable member of the forest fauna.

The deer belonging to the genus *Axis*, the chital and hog deer, are considered by Flerov (1960) to be among the most primitive of the true cervids, having been present during the Pliocene and Pleistocene in Europe and Asia (Matthes, 1962). Lydekker (1913–16) regarded *Axis* as a subgenus of *Cervus*, but Simpson (1945) raised *Axis* to generic rank, a classification followed by Ellerman and Morrison-

Scott (1951). The last-mentioned authors also recognized two sub-species, one from Ceylon (*A. axis ceylonensis*) and the other from India (*A. a. axis*).

Description

The chital is a medium-sized deer standing about 35 to 38 inches high at the shoulders. Its coat is rufous brown and covered with white spots that persist throughout the life of the animal. A dark stripe runs down the back from the nape to the tip of the tail. The abdomen, rump, throat, and the insides of the legs, tail, and ears are white. A black band circles the muzzle (Plate 3). Adult bucks have a dark brown, swollen neck during the rut, yearling bucks lack the prominently enlarged neck although its color is sometimes a darker shade than that of does. There is no seasonal difference in the color of the coat, except that during the cool season it is somewhat glossier, darker, and thicker than during the hot and wet seasons. One adult buck weighed 145 pounds (Hornaday, 1885), and Brander (1923) stated that large bucks may reach 190 pounds in weight. One spike buck at Kanha weighed 101 pounds, and two adult does weighed 123 and 124 pounds, respectively.

The first set of antlers in yearlings consists of simple spikes, usually less than 5 inches long. Adults carry three-tined antlers, each composed of a beam forked at the summit and a brow tine that grows at right angles with the beam. Large bucks sometimes grow one or two small projections in the angle made by the beam and the brow tine. Lydekker (1898) and Anthony (1929) illustrate the size of antlers in a stag for a number of consecutive years. Record antler length, measured on the outside curve, is 39 inches (Dollman and Burlace, 1935).

Geographical and Ecological Distribution

To determine the precise distribution of the chital throughout India was a task beyond the scope of my work, but an attempt was made to delineate its general range, particularly at the periphery, in order to assess its ecological requirements and the factors that limit its distribution.

The eastern boundary of the chital's range lies in western Assam along the Bhutan border in the districts of Goalpara and Kamrup as far east as the Dhunsiri River in Darrang District (Gee, 1964) and in Bhutan itself along some of the forested valleys below an altitude of 3,000 feet (Gee, pers. comm.). In northern Bengal, chital occur in the forests along the Kurseong-Nilpara railroad line, the Sukna and Mahanadi forest reserves, in some of the valleys near Darjeeling (Biswas, pers. comm.), and in neighboring Sikkim at the junction of the Tista, Rangpo, and Ranghit rivers (G. Hyde, pers. comm.). The species also persists in the Sunderbans of East Pakistan and West Bengal.

The northern boundary of chital distribution runs along the foothills of the Himalayas from western Assam through West Bengal, Nepal, and Uttar Pradesh to but not including the Punjab (Russell, 1900), following in general the range of the sal tree. According to R. Willan (pers. comm.), chital occur in Nepal throughout the Siwalik Hills and adjoining plains where patches of forest survive, but the animals have failed to penetrate the Mahabharat Range, which borders the Siwaliks to the north. Similarly the chital in Uttar Pradesh are found in and around the Siwalik Hills but not in the outer range of the Himalayas above an altitude of about 3,500 feet.

The western boundary of the chital's range lies in Gujarat, in the northeastern part of the state and in the Gir Forest, and in eastern Rajasthan, particularly in the forest tracts around Kota, along the Chambal River, and in a number of reserves like the Sariska Sanctuary near Alwar and the Keoladeo Ghana Sanctuary near Bharatpur (Sankhala, 1964).

Chital occur sporadically throughout the peninsular plateau in the forested areas of Bihar, Madhya Pradesh, Orissa, Andhra Pradesh, Maharashtra, Mysore, and Madras. In Kerala they are found in forests of low rainfall (K. Mathew, pers. comm.) below an altitude of 3,000 feet (Fletcher, 1911).

The present distribution of the chital has, of course, been greatly affected by the elimination of its habitat for agricultural purposes, but even so the species displays a number of preferences for certain conditions which in the past undoubtedly also influenced its dispersion. A brief comparison of the geographical distribution of the chital with the forest types in Figure 2 (p. 21) shows that the animal is generally found in moist deciduous and dry deciduous forests and that it has occupied the evergreen and thorn forests only peripherally. Four factors appear to have limited the chital to these vegetation types: (1) the need for water, (2) the need for shade, (3) the avoidance of high, rugged terrain, and (4) the preference for grass as forage. The need for water and shade probably influences the distribution of the species greatly in areas with an average annual rainfall of less than 30 inches. Chital drink at least once a day and usually twice a day during the hot season, a trait which under semi-desert conditions would tend to localize the animals around the widely scattered water sources and hinder their emigration into new areas. Chital seem to have relatively little tolerance for direct sun, in contrast to the barasingha and blackbuck, and this may also have deterred them from extensively colonizing such open habitats as the thorn forests. The animals fail for unknown reasons to ascend the Himalayas and Western Ghats above an altitude of 3,500 feet although physical barriers are absent and forage, shade, and water are available. In Ceylon they are said to remain below an altitude of 1,500 feet (Storey, 1907). Even in the Kanha and Shivpuri parks the chital rarely leave the shady valleys to visit the dry deciduous forests in the surrounding low hills; in Corbett Park most chital crowd into the valleys at a time of year when the ridges also provide their necessities for life.

The fact that the animals have failed to penetrate the evergreen forests very far is at first surprising because shade and water are abundant and the terrain is not rugged. That the chital are not deterred by a wet environment is shown by their occurrence in the mangrove swamps of the Sunderbans, and that they can thrive in evergreen forests under certain conditions is illustrated by the success of their introduction in the Andaman Islands, where they have become an agricultural pest. Their absence from the evergreen forests may originally have been based on a lack of grass, which under the continuous canopy of primary forest is usually sparse or absent. Chital are essentially inhabitants of secondary forests or of open forests, broken here and there by glades, with a good understory of grasses, forbs, and tender shoots, and they tend to avoid the interior of extensive tall forests, a habitat preference similar to that of the North American *Odocoileus* deer. The forests of Assam remained relatively undisturbed until cut over by agriculturalists within historic times (Milroy, 1953), and it is possible that the chital have not yet had the time and opportunity to colonize the favorable habitat opened to them as a result of man's activity.

Population Dynamics

Various data pertaining to the size, growth, maintenance, and mortality of the chital population in my study area are presented in this section and information from other areas is included for comparison whenever pertinent. The term "population" applies to all chital in a localized area; a "herd" indicates any aggregation of two or more animals within a population. The prolonged fawning season makes precise age classification of fawns and yearlings difficult. For convenience January 1 was used as the dividing line in separating the two age classes: fawns born during the first half of the year were recorded as yearlings, but those born between July and December were considered still to be fawns and were added to the fawn crop of the current year. The age of fawns was estimated on the basis of comparative size and the known ages of animals in the Calcutta Zoological Garden.

Pedicels become visible as two small bumps on the frontal bones of yearling bucks by the age of about twelve months and then grow into spikes, which are shed at the age of about twenty to twenty-two months. Any buck which had lost his spikes was considered to be an adult. The adult bucks were segregated into several classes based on estimated antler length. Although Severinghaus and Cheatum (1956) showed that antler size is a poor criterion for determining age in deer, the length does give a rough idea of the age of bucks until their fifth year. Ditmars (1919) found that the antlers in one captive male showed a steady increase in size to the seventh year, a leveling in the eighth and ninth years, followed by a gradual decline. At Kanha the majority of bucks with antlers 11 to 20 inches long appeared to be about two to three years old, most bucks with antlers 21 to 30 inches long were probably three to four years old, with some perhaps five years and over, and those with antlers over 31 inches long were at least four to five years old.

POPULATION SIZE AND DENSITY

The chital in Kanha Park were concentrated into two populations, one around Kanha village, the other around Kisli village. The mixed forest in the hills was generally avoided, and even much of the sal forest contained few animals. The forest department censused both populations in June, 1964, and derived a figure of 143 animals for the Kisli area and 480 for Kanha, a total of 623. My estimate for Kisli, based on frequent visits, was about 200–250 chital. On August 8, when a track census along the forest roads around Kanha showed that almost all chital were concentrated in a few large herds on or along the periphery of the meadow, I counted 525 animals there. A few small herds were undoubtedly overlooked, which would raise the total to about 600 animals, a figure that was rechecked on subsequent days. The total park population comprised an estimated 900–1,000 chital, considerably fewer animals than tallied by the forest department during their annual censuses between 1958 and 1963 (Table 2, p. 16). The forest department census in June, 1965, gave a figure of 873 animals for Kanha and 273 for Kisli, a total of 1,146. Assuming that my 1964 estimate of 600 chital around Kanha was accurate, the supposed increase during the year was 29 percent, about three times the actual amount (see Mortality, p. 54).

The population density of the chital in 1964 was about 7 to 8 deer per square mile in the park as a whole. However, the Kanha population actually occupied only about twelve square miles of terrain, giving a density of 60 animals per square mile; the figure for the Kisli population was about 17 per square mile. For comparison, there were about 375–400 chital in the Keoladeo Ghana Sanctuary (Schaller and Spillett, 1966). These animals occupied about eight square miles of habitat, or 45 per square mile. Several large areas in Kanha Park are suitable for chital yet contain few or no animals, suggesting that with proper management, particularly with protection from poaching, the range could support many more deer than it does now. The competition from livestock for forage in the Keoladeo Ghana Sanctuary is so heavy that the chital population there is probably approaching its highest possible level.

SEX AND AGE COMPOSITION

Sex and age ratios denote the status of the population, giving an idea whether it is increasing, decreasing, or remaining stable. Herd composition counts were taken almost daily, but since most of these were made around the Kanha meadow, the data are typical of this sample area alone and not necessarily of the population as a whole. The sampling technique and the time of year during which counts are made have a striking effect on the ratio of bucks to does (Table 5). Bucks traveled widely and concentrated on the Kanha meadow primarily during the peak of the rut and immediately afterward. Movements were also influenced by the food supply, with the result that, for example, fewer bucks came to the meadow in January, 1964, than a year later when ample green grass was available (Table 5). Bucks tended to congregate at certain times of the year, and the count of even one large buck herd was sufficient to skew the population figures of a monthly sample. This occurred in Corbett Park, for instance, during early February when I tallied one herd consisting of 43 bucks, 3 does, and one fawn.

TABLE 5

AGE AND SEX RATIOS OF CHITAL AT MONTHLY INTERVALS
AROUND THE KANHA MEADOW

Month	Total Number Classified	Bucks	:	100 Does	:	Fawns
January, 1964 . . .	1,467	45.4		100		15.6
February	3,185	43.5		100		27.6
March	2,258	66.6		100		47.1
April	1,901	63.2		100		51.9
May	2,203	71.6		100		66.8
June	2,911	67.6		100		65.3
July	2,049	72.4		100		67.5
August	1,567	62.5		100		68.5
September.	732	53.5		100		64.2
October.	852	65.6		100		68.4
November.	403	42.0		100		64.6
December	567	52.5		100		66.4
January, 1965 . . .	681	77.2		100		22.8
March	1,386	57.7		100		45.8

The bucks associated closely with the does during and following the peak of the rut from May to July, and the average buck to doe ratio during this time was 70.5:100 (Table 5). Composition counts in other areas (Table 6) showed ratios quite similar to the one at Kanha, females outnumbering males by 20 to 30 percent in each locality. The ratio of bucks to does in an introduced chital population in Hawaii was 77:100 in 1959 (Nichols, 1960). Selective hunting is probably not a major factor in the disproportion of the sexes in most areas since poachers snare and shoot more or less indiscriminately and the legal kill of adult bucks is insignificant. For example, only 88 bucks were shot on license in the state of Uttar Pradesh during the fiscal year 1961–62 (Hingorani, 1962), and 104 the following year (Misra, pers. comm.); the legal kill in West Bengal in 1958–59 was 3 bucks (Rao, 1961). Selective predation has a possible effect

TABLE 6

AGE AND SEX RATIOS OF CHITAL IN SEVERAL LOCALITIES

Date	Location	Number Classified	Bucks	:	100 Does	:	Fawns
January 23–31. .	Corbett National Park	484	69.6		100		17.1
February 11–22 .	Keoladeo Ghana Sanctuary	460	70.8		100		35.4
February 25–March 5 . . .	West Kheri Forest	125	78.6		100		26.2
March 8–10 . .	Vanbihar Sanctuary	217	72.9		100		53.1
April 1–11 . . .	West Bastar District	29	69.2		100		53.8

on the adult sex ratio, but, as shown in Table 57 (p. 323), proportionally fewer males than females appear to be taken. The disproportion of adults may be due either to an unequal sex ratio at birth, a higher mortality of male fawns, or both. The sexes of fawns could not be determined in the wild. Of 25 newborn young in the Calcutta Zoological Garden, 10 were male and 13 were female, but figures from such a small sample have little relevance. The sex ratios of North American deer at or before birth usually favor the males. Severinghaus and Cheatum (1956) found a fetal sex ratio of 117 males per 100 females in the white-tailed deer in New York; in four of the five studies on the mule and white-tailed deer summarized by Dahlberg and Guettinger (1956), the fetal sex ratio favored the males. An unbalanced sex ratio in favor of females is said to indicate poor range conditions (Taber and Dasmann, 1954). This might be a pertinent factor in evaluating the dynamics in the Rajasthan sanctuaries but probably not in my study area and in central Corbett Park. Differential fawn mortality, with more males than females being lost through starvation and other causes, was found in the black-tailed deer of California (Taber and Dasmann, 1954) and of southeastern Alaska (Klein and Olson, 1960). Selective predation on fawns is a possibility at Kanha, but no data were obtained on this point.

Most fawns at Kanha are born between January and May, and the ratio of fawns to does increases steadily during these months, finally reaching 67:100 (Table 5). From May until the end of the year, the ratio remains almost constant. This does not imply lack of mortality but indicates that deaths are largely offset by births. Sample ratios from other areas (Table 6) are roughly similar to those from Kanha. In the Hawaiian chital population in the fall of 1959, there were 70 fawns to 100 does (Nichols, 1960).

The age and sex composition of the population, expressed as percent of the total and averaged for the months of May, June, and July, was as follows: adult bucks, 19 percent; yearling bucks, 10 percent; does (adult and yearling), 42 percent; and fawns, 29 percent. Yearling does could not always be classified accurately because of the difficulty in distinguishing old yearlings from adults. According to my counts only 9 to 10 percent of the population consisted of yearling does, a figure which undoubtedly is too low. Robinette *et al.* (1957) found that mortality of yearling buck mule deer is much higher than that of yearling does, but this does not seem to be the case in the chital at Kanha. The disparate sex ratio characteristic of adults was probably present in the yearlings, too, and if this assumption is correct, the percent of yearling does was on the order of 14. The total yearling figure, taken at a time when the majority of animals were fifteen to eighteen months old, was thus about 24 percent. The population as a whole was vigorous, with half of it less than 2 years old. The total yearling figure at Keoladeo Ghana was 22 percent, at Vanbihar Sanctuary 18 percent, and at Corbett Park 23 percent.

The Rutting Season

Few aspects of the chital's life history have created as much confusion in the minds of hunters and naturalists as the time of the year when mating occurs. In southern India the rut is from October to April according to Fletcher (1911), but Krishnan (1959) found no definite mating season. In other parts of India rutting is said to take place in the winter (Prater, 1934), in December and January (Hodgson, 1847), in April and May (Brander, 1923), and throughout the year (Inverarity, 1895). Several lines of evidence were used to determine the period of rut at Kanha and elsewhere: the annual cycle of antler development, the frequency of sexual behavior, and the time of fawning.

Data from Kanha. Adult bucks shed their antlers yearly; no evidence from captivity or from the wild was obtained to support the suggestion by Inverarity (1895) that some animals retain their antlers for more than one year. The antlers are dropped at intervals of roughly ten to twelve months. One buck at the Calcutta Zoological Garden shed one set between November 12 and 14, 1963, and the following set on September 27, 1964; a second buck lost his antlers on September 23, 1963, and on September 14, 1964. Both antlers are usually shed on the same or on consecutive days. For example, one antler of a buck fell off at 0715 hours while he was grazing. He merely shook his head once and continued to forage. At 0730 hours the following day he was walking along when the other antler toppled forward over his muzzle. He jerked to a halt, looked down at the antler briefly, then moved on. Occasionally, the second antler is not cast until two to three days after the first one. At Kanha a buck was seen with one antler on February 24, and when encountered again two days later, it had still not dropped the antler. The new set of antlers begins to grow immediately after the old one is shed.

Studies on various species of deer (W. Taylor, 1956) have shown that the antlers are lost after the rut and that the new growth is completed to coincide with the onset of the next rutting period. Assuming that the annual cycle of antler replacement in the chital follows a

TABLE 7

PERCENT OF CHITAL BUCKS WITH HARD ANTLERS
AT MONTHLY INTERVALS IN KANHA PARK

MONTH	ADULT		YEARLING	
	Total Number Classified	Percent Hard	Total Number Classified	Percent Hard
January, 1964. . .	358	32	60	8
February	648	47	149	14
March	500	63	204	13
April	363	85	196	17
May	427	96	238	28
June	565	98	280	48
July	383	93	235	73
August	261	70	163	83
September	89	56	91	72
October	127	40	112	67
November	53	25	29	68
December	92	22	44	50
January, 1965. . .	175	33	36	33
March	291	61	103	14

TABLE 8

THE PERCENT OF CHITAL BUCKS IN HARD ANTLER IN TWO ANTLER-SIZE
CLASSES AT VARIOUS TIMES OF THE YEAR

MONTH	ANTLER-SIZE CLASS	
	11 to 20 Inches	31 Inches +
October	11	3
November	13	4
December	9	3
January	18	6
February	20	12
March	26	17
April	30	31
May-July (average)	34	34

similar pattern, we should be able to define the rut by the percentage
of animals in hard antler at various times of the year. The presence
or absence of velvet on the antlers was recorded for all bucks; animals
that had just lost their antlers were classified as being in velvet. Because yearlings differ in their antler development from adults, the
two age classes are treated separately. Adult bucks in hard antler
were present in the population during every month of the year (Table
7), but their number increased steadily from 22 percent in December
to 96 and 98 percent in May and June, respectively. About half of
the bucks in hard antler during December had not yet dropped their
old sets, and the other half had recently rubbed the velvet off their
new ones (Schaller and De, 1964). To my knowledge only four bucks

shed their antlers in the Kanha population between mid-February and mid-June. A few bucks lost their antlers in July, but most did so between August and October, observations which in general agree with those made by Brander (1923). Bucks with large antlers tend to shed them earlier in the year than those with small ones. For example, the percent of bucks in the population in both the largest antler-size class (31 inches +) and the smallest class (11–20 inches) was 35. By October, 31 of the 35 percent of the large bucks had shed their antlers, but only 23 percent of the small-antlered males had done so (Table 8). As would be expected, large antlers need more time to reach their full length than small antlers. The time required for antlers to grow from the day of shedding the old set until most of the velvet has been rubbed off the new one is illustrated in Figure 5 for eleven selected bucks in the Calcutta Zoological Garden. Large antlers require, in some instances, twice as long to grow as small ones, but since the former tend to be shed earlier in the year, most bucks of both size classes finish their growth in April just before the peak of the rut (Table 8).

Yearling bucks have a schedule of antler development somewhat

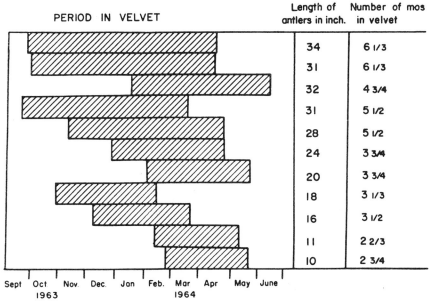

FIG. 5.—The time required for antlers to grow from the day of shedding the old ones to the loss of velvet from the new ones in eleven chital bucks, Calcutta Zoological Garden.

different from that of adults. The velvet is not shed from the spikes until the animal is sixteen to seventeen months old, an age which the majority of bucks reach in July and August (Table 7). Although yearlings are about three months slower in their antler growth than the adults, both age classes finish shedding substantially at the same time, by the end of the year. This enables the yearlings to grow their first set of adult antlers in time to participate in the main rut.

Rutting bucks emit hoarse bellows; every instance of this vocalization was recorded between 0500 to 0900 and 1500 to 1900 hours (Fig. 6). Field conditions naturally could not be standardized to make each month directly comparable, but the relative amount of bellowing is roughly representative. The calls were infrequent from November to January, and they were common from March to June, with the remaining months intermediate. Various other behavior pat-

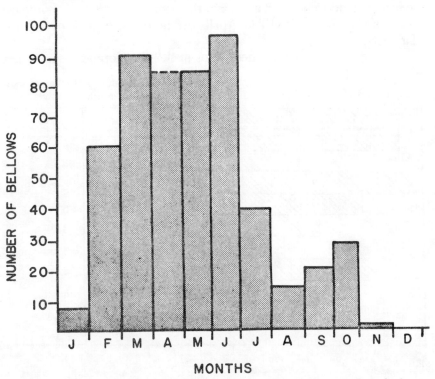

FIG. 6.—The total number of bellows by rutting chital bucks heard daily between 0500–0900 and 1500–1900 hours. (The bellows on five days in April were not recorded.)

terns associated with the rut (see Sexual behavior, p. 81) were also most prevalent between March and June. For example, 81 percent of all courting occurred during these months, with 33 percent in May alone.

Newborn fawns were seen during every month of the year, but over two-thirds of them were born during the first half. Fawns were dropped with increasing frequency during December, and a peak was reached between mid-January and early March. The monthly increase of fawns per one hundred does shown in Table 5 gives only a rough idea of the number of young born in any one month because females keep their newborn young hidden for varying lengths of time before joining a herd with them. From the peak fawning period, it may be determined that most conceptions occurred the previous May (see Gestation Period, p. 52).

TABLE 9

ANTLER DEVELOPMENT OF ADULT CHITAL BUCKS IN DIFFERENT LOCALITIES AT APPROXIMATELY THE SAME TIME OF YEAR

Location	Date	Sample Size	Percent in Hard Antler	Percent 0–5 Inches Long in Velvet
Corbett National Park . .	January 23–February 8, 1965	231	10	48
Keoladeo Ghana Sanctuary	February 11–22, 1965	120	17	18
West Kheri Forest . . .	February 25–March 5, 1965	47	3	38
Vanbihar Sanctuary . . .	March 8–10, 1965	53	77	2
Kanha National Park . .	February, 1964	648	47	11
	March, 1964	500	63	3

All evidence indicates that the rut of the chital at Kanha continues throughout the year but that the activity increases greatly from March to June, with a peak in May.

Data from other areas. In order to determine if the time of rut at Kanha was typical of the species as a whole, observations were also made in several other areas. In addition to recording the percent of bucks in hard antler, the percent with antlers in velvet less than five inches long was also noted (Table 9). Zoo observations indicated that chital require about two months to grow antlers to a length of five inches; thus the figures give an idea of the percent of animals which had shed their antlers during the previous two months or so. The chital at the Vanbihar Sanctuary, Rajasthan, were at a similar stage of antler development and fawning as those at Kanha (Table 9); several bucks were rutting vigorously and bellowing was common. The chital in the Keoladeo Ghana Sanctuary, however, which

is only about fifty miles north of the ecologically similar Vanbihar
Sanctuary, appeared to be somewhat slower in their antler development, only 17 percent being in hard antler as compared with 47 percent at Kanha during a comparable period. Slight differences in
the rate of antler growth do not necessarily imply a difference in the
time of rut (Leopold *et al.*, 1951), but the fact that I heard no bellowing and saw no sexual activity in February suggests that the onset
of the rut was somewhat later there than at Kanha. On the other
hand, the presence of a large number of small fawns indicated that
the peak conception period was similar in the two areas. Thus, it
can be inferred that the main period of rut at Keoladeo Ghana was
of briefer duration than the one at Kanha.

The data from Corbett Park and the Kheri forest areas are strikingly
different from the Rajasthan and Madhya Pradesh data. At Corbett
only 10 percent of the adult bucks were in hard antler as compared
with over 40 percent at Kanha during the same period (Table 9). Almost half of the Corbett bucks had lost their antlers after the middle
of November, a stage reached at Kanha about two months earlier.
Similarly, many females at Corbett were heavily pregnant in late
January, but few had given birth, approximating the stage reached
at Kanha in early December. There appeared to be a difference of
nearly two months in the onset of the main rut between the two areas,
but the peaks were similar, judging by the age of the fawns. The
main difference lay in a much shorter time span of fawning and antler-
shedding at Corbett than at Kanha. This conclusion was strength-
ened by my observations that a far greater proportion of the females
at Corbett were heavily pregnant than at Kanha and that at no time
were as many as 90 percent of the bucks in velvet in the latter area.

To pinpoint the ecological factors responsible for the difference in
the onset of the rut between the chital at Kanha and those along
the foothills of the Himalayas is exceedingly difficult because the two
regions are in many respects very similar. The terrain in both areas
is flat to hilly; the main habitats consist of sal forest and large
meadows; the annual precipitation at Ramnagar near Corbett Park
averages 66 inches (44–111), whereas at Bichhia near Kanha the
average is 73 inches (34–81); temperatures range from a light frost
to 110°F; the altitudes are similar, with those at Corbett starting at
about 800 feet and ranging upward to 3,000 feet and above in the
foothills; the monsoon begins about mid-June; and the general seasonal patterns are alike. The water supply at Corbett is perennial in
the Ramganga River in contrast to Kanha where during the hot

season it exists only in isolated pools. The difference in latitude between the two sites is only about seven degrees, the amount of daylight being little affected by this distance.

The kinds of meadow grasses and the seasons at which they dry
out and can be burned are one of the main ecological differences
between the two areas. Whereas at Kanha the majority of the dominant grasses are six feet or less high and are sufficiently dry to be
burned in December, the coarse grasses at Corbett and Kheri (*An-
thisteria gigantea, Vetiveria zizanioides, Saccharum spontaneum*)
reach a height of twelve feet and grow in moist conditions that usually prevent their being burned until February and March. It is possible that the onset of the rut has been influenced to some extent
by the availability of open areas on which to concentrate and court
and by the presence of nutritious green grass on which to forage.

I was not able to visit southern India, but from the little data
available, it appears that the chital shed their antlers there somewhat later than at Kanha. Of thirty-one yearling and adult bucks
classified by J. Spillett (pers. comm.) in the Bandipur Sanctuary in
southern Mysore in early September, 1965, all were in hard antler;
in the nearby Mudumalai Sanctuary of Madras, he tallied twenty-
five bucks, of which several had very recently shed their antlers.
No chital with antlers in velvet was seen, although Krishnan (1959)
noted that a few occur during every month of the year. In southern
Ceylon, 75 percent of the antlers are shed in April and May (Phil-
lips [1927–28], quoted in Asdell, 1964).

In Hawaii the main mating season of the introduced free-living
chital runs from April to August, and the major birth season from
November to March, although some mating and fawning occur during all months (Nichols, 1960).

These data illustrate that differences in the onset of the main rut
and perhaps the peak of the rut exist from area to area, but a great
deal more precise information on local climatic conditions, on plant
phenology, and on other ecological factors is needed before these
variations can be explained. Differences in the timing of reproduction have also been reported for the impala antelope in Africa, a
species in which the peak of fawning varies from September through
January, depending on the locality (Dasmann and Mossman, 1962).

Data from zoos. The chital bucks in the Calcutta Zoological Gar-
den generally shed their antlers between September and February
(Fig. 5, p. 47), on the average somewhat later than at Kanha. On
September 15, 1964, 92 percent of twenty-seven adults were in hard

antler as compared with 56 percent at Kanha during that month. Fawns were born throughout the year, but of twenty-five births recorded from September, 1963, to August, 1964, 76 percent occurred between January and April. Behavior associated with the rut, such as chasing and mounting, showed a sharp seasonal peak in the ten bucks of the study herd. From January to April most of the animals were in velvet and sexually almost inactive. Of 169 instances of sexual activity recorded, 81 percent occurred between May and August. On January 20, 1965, 28 percent of forty-three adult bucks in the Lucknow zoo, Uttar Pradesh, were in hard antler, a figure very similar to the one at Kanha. The chital in these two Indian zoos seemed to maintain an annual reproductive cycle comparable to the free-living animals.

On the estate of the Duke of Bedford, England, chital rut at any time of the year (Bedford and Marshall, 1942), but the gamekeeper Talbot (pers. comm.) noted that the majority of fawns are born from January to March. In the London zoo, 124 young were born in all months, with a slight (60 percent) concentration in the first six (Jarvis and Morris, 1962); in the New York Zoological Park 225 fawns were born throughout the year, with the lowest number in December and January (Crandall, 1964).

Gestation Period

Hodgson (1847), Prater (1934), and Shull (1962) state that the gestation period of the chital is 6 months; Brown (1936) found it to be 7¼ months, Asdell (1946) 7 to 7½ months, and Sclater (1863) and Stebbing (1911) 8 months. The peak of rutting activity at Kanha occurs in May and the peak of fawning in late January and February, indicating a gestation period of 8 to 8½ months. For comparison, the *Odocoileus* deer, which are similar to the chital in size, have an average gestation period of 6½ months, the caribou 7 to 8 months, and the wapiti 8½ months (Mosby, 1963).

Rate of Reproduction

Confusion exists in the literature as to how many fawns a doe bears at a time. Brander (1923) stated that one to three is usual, with twins being common, figures also quoted by Prater (1948). There were no twins in the 25 births at the Calcutta zoo, nor were there any in 97 births at the Bombay zoo (J. Bombay Nat. Hist. Soc., 1960). The 225 births at the New York Zoological Park included one set of twins. At Kanha, and in all other areas studied, single fawns were the rule, although on two occasions I saw a doe accompanied by two small fawns which appeared to be twins. The chital thus differ from the *Odocoileus* deer, in which twinning is common (W. Taylor, 1956).

If only adults, about two years old and older, bear young, the fawn to doe ratio should not exceed 66:100 (or 100 fawns:100 adult does), as only a single young is born at a time and about 14 of the 42 percent does in the population are yearlings. It was estimated that 46 fawns:100 does died during 1964 (see Mortality, p. 54) and that 49 fawns:100 does survived to become yearlings (seven to twelve months old) on January 1, 1965. The total fawn production was, therefore, 95 fawns:100 does (or 136 fawns:100 adult does). These figures indicate either (1) that some fawns conceive and give birth as yearlings or (2) that some does have young twice in one year. Fawns of the white-tailed deer conceive occasionally at six to eight months of age, but the majority do so as yearlings eighteen months old (Severinghaus and Cheatum, 1956). Many chital are born between January and March and appear to conceive the following year between March and June when fourteen to seventeen months old. It is probable that a few are bred at an earlier age, but how often this occurs could not be determined. One chital doe in Corbett Park whose milk premolars were just being replaced by permanent ones and whose age was estimated to be twenty-three to twenty-four months carried a full-term fetus when killed by a tiger. Nichols (1960) found that one doe in Hawaii was pregnant when killed at an estimated age of eight to ten months.

Captive chital does have a continuous series of diestrous cycles lasting about three weeks throughout the year (Asdell, 1946). The animals are therefore able to conceive during any month since bucks in rutting condition are also present at all times. It seems probable that does which have lost their small fawns through predation or other means come into estrus again soon afterward, with the result that some of them give birth twice within ten to eleven months. In contrast, the black-tailed deer increases its productivity not by having young twice in one year but by giving birth to twins at a ratio of about 1.4 fawns per doe (Cowan, 1956). This deer comes into estrus only from October to early March, which precludes conception for much of the year, an adaptive mechanism that prevents the birth of fawns during the winter. The potential annual production of live fawns by a black-tailed doe is thus two, whereas the figure for a chital doe cannot exceed one.

MORTALITY

Data on annual mortality provide the basis for determining the rate of increase or decrease in a population. Initial fawn production remains rather stable, except in unusual circumstances, but mortality may vary considerably from year to year. The fact that the chital at mid-year consisted of 53 percent fawns and yearlings points to a high rate of turnover in the population. It was difficult to determine the extent of fawn mortality accurately because young were born throughout the year. The fawn to doe ratio during early January, 1965, was 72:100. Of these, 49:100 were estimated to have been born between January and June, 1964, and 23:100 between July and December, 1964. Table 5 shows that the ratio of fawns to does remained relatively stable at about 66:100 from July to December, suggesting that the number of births during this period equalled the number of deaths — about 23 fawns per 100 does. If this figure is projected to the first half of the year, the total fawn mortality in 1964 was on the order of 46 fawns per 100 does, or 48 percent of the annual fawn crop, based on a production estimate of 95 fawns to 100 does. This figure rests on the assumptions that the mortality rate of adult does and fawns was constant throughout the year, that my age estimates of young and yearlings were accurate, and that the seasonal differences of adult doe recruitment into the population did not have an effect on the doe to fawn ratio. Although these and perhaps other factors may have influenced the accuracy of the estimate, the general magnitude of mortality is probably representative.

The fawn to doe count in January, 1964, was only 16:100 as compared with 23:100 the following year. Whether this low figure resulted from a high mortality of small fawns late in the year, a minor fluctuation in the season of birth, a sampling error, or a lower mortality of fawns early in 1963 than in 1964 could not be determined, but the difference in the number of yearling bucks in the population between the two years indicated that the last of these possible reasons contributed to the discrepancy. In March, 1964, 11.5 percent of 1,760 yearling and adult chital sampled were yearling bucks; in March, 1965, 9.5 percent of 1,074 yearlings and adults were yearling bucks. The seemingly higher death rate of fawns in 1964 may have been associated with an increase in the number of tigers in the area.

The percentage of fawns surviving to the yearling age class is an important index for measuring the rate of population increase. Theoretically, the number of yearlings entering a stable population approximately equals the adults leaving it. The 1963 and 1965 censuses were unfortunately not sufficiently accurate to establish the size of the population with precision; but if the fluctuations in size were only slight, it may be inferred from the fact that the yearling age class in mid-1964 comprised 24 percent of the population that adult mortality was also on the order of 24 percent.

An increase in the population requires a fawn survival greater than the total loss of animals in all other age classes. The population estimate in mid-1964 was 600 chital, of which about 252 were does. The number of young produced during the year, then, was around 239 (95 fawns:100 does), of which 48 percent, or 115, died and 52 percent, or 124, survived. The estimated mortality of the older age classes was 24 percent, or 102 animals. The number of surviving fawns exceeded the number of deaths in the older age classes by 22 animals, limiting the potential increase of the population to 3 percent. These calculations are of course based on the assumption that 24 percent of the adult age class was actually removed from the population. It is likely that this was not the case, and the surplus, added to the percent of new yearlings, probably raised the total increment to about 7 to 10 percent. Although fawn survival in 1963 may have been greater than in 1964, excessive adult mortality in the former year apparently prevented the population from increasing in size.

Possible causes of mortality include accidents, disease, and predation. Accidents were rare and had no significant effect on the population. Only two injured animals were seen: a limping fawn and a doe without a tail. Brander (1923) stated that bucks occasionally kill each other when fighting.

Chital are susceptible to rinderpest, as Gupta and Verma (1949) have shown, and this disease, which is very prevalent in livestock all over India, has greatly reduced a number of deer populations in Uttar Pradesh (Singh, 1958; Srivastava, 1957) and elsewhere. Chital are also known to suffer from cattle tuberculosis (Fahimuddin, 1963). Ten chital serum samples from Kanha were tested for hemagglutination-inhibiting antibodies to arboviruses Japanese B. encephalitis, chikungunya, and dengue 1, but all were negative. Tests for antibodies to *Brucella abortus* in precipitin tests were likewise negative. However, neutralizing and hemagglutination-inhibiting antibodies to myxovirus parainfluenza 3 were detected in six out of the ten samples (Shah *et al.*, 1965). This virus is the most important agent causing shipping fever in cattle, and it can be fatal if the animal is placed in a stressful situation.

An autopsy of one adult doe revealed pentastomids (probably *Linguatula serrata* Fröhlich, 1789) in the heart, a nematode (*Oesophagostomum* sp.) in the large intestine, and a trematode (*Paramphistomum cauliorchus* Stiles and Goldberger, 1910) in the rumen. Only the trematode was found in another doe. One out of thirteen chital examined for ectoparasites had ticks (*Boophilus microplus, Hyalomma marginatum isaaci*), and all harbored hippoboscid flies (*Lipoptena indica* Maa, 1965). The tick *Hyalomma brevipunctata* has been reported from chital in Bengal (Kaiser and Hoogstraal, 1964). None of the infestations were heavy, and except for one small fawn with a mangy skin, there was no overt evidence of disease in the Kanha population.

Predation was the major cause of mortality during the study. An unknown number of animals were poached by villagers either by shooting or by placing snares along fences of bamboo, some of which were over a mile long. I watched three villagers shoot a chital doe on the Kanha meadow, and I destroyed snares from about two miles of fencing in the study area. Such poaching probably affects the yearlings and adults more than the fawns. The amount of poaching in the central part of the park was not great in 1964 because of my presence, although I heard sporadic shooting in the hills. All evidence indicates, however, that hunting was heavy in 1963, and the killing resumed around the Kanha meadow soon after my departure according to the forest department staff. Tiger and also leopard preyed extensively on chital in 1964. Chital accounted for 43 percent of a total of 228 predator kills found, and an analysis of 335 tiger feces revealed chital hair in 52 percent of them (see Tables 50 and 51, p. 281, 283), pointing forcefully to the fact that the chital was the most important prey species in the study area.

General Behavior

The chital, like all ungulates, spend a major portion of their life in foraging, resting, and wandering within their range, but the extent of these activities is greatly influenced by the seasons.

DAILY ACTIVITY CYCLE

During the cool season, particularly in December and January, the chital become active at or just before sunup at about 0700 hours, when they appear at the forest's edge and begin to graze. The morning peak of feeding is between 0700 and 0830 hours, and most animals continue to forage for another hour or so before retreating into the forest. Feeding if any is usually cursory between 1000 and 1600 hours, consisting of brief snacks between periods of resting or ambling along slowly. Toward dusk progressively more chital reappear on the meadow, where they graze until about 2100 hours; after that, foraging continues intermittently until past midnight. During the morning hours, between 0300 and sunup, the animals rest in the forest, where it is usually several degrees warmer than on the meadow. The chital in Corbett Park follow a similar pattern of activity.

As the days grow hotter the chital spend most of the daylight hours in the shade. In March some remain in the open until 0830 hours, but by May they go into the forest by 0700 hours, often foraging a little before lying down. Direct sun is avoided when temperatures in the shade reach 80°F. Although a few animals begin to feed again by 1600 hours, the majority do not appear in the open until about 1700 hours, and then only to trudge in a listless manner to a waterhole, drink, and return to the forest. The pattern of activity at night is similar to that of the cool season.

During the monsoon, with its great abundance of forage, the chital spend fewer hours in grazing than at any other time of the year. The morning peak of feeding is over by 0800 hours, but instead of retreating into the forest, the animals sometimes remain in the open all day if the sky is overcast; for example, one herd of fifty chital rested on the meadow from 0800 to 1620 hours. Herds commonly appear at the forest's edge again at 1600 hours but then lie down until 1730 hours or later before beginning to eat.

In general, chital have two major rest periods, one in the hours before dawn and the other from mid-morning to mid-afternoon. Peaks of feeding occur for about two hours after dawn and one hour before and after dusk.

Food Habits and Feeding and Drinking Behavior

Chital eat both grass and browse, with the former providing the bulk of their diet at all seasons. Their favored forage is green grass less than four inches high, but when young shoots are unavailable, the animals readily nip the blade tips and flowering heads off the tall, coarse grasses. A minimum of forty-four species of grasses and grasslike plants, including bamboo, grow more or less commonly

on the meadows and in the forests (Table 10). Although it was sometimes possible to identify the tall grasses when the animals grazed
on them, the small shoots could rarely be determined specifically.
Table 10 lists only sixteen kinds of grasses as being eaten by chital,
but many of the others are undoubtedly taken; at least, no species
are obviously avoided in areas heavily grazed by the animals.

Browse includes the leaves from a number of trees, shrubs, vines,
and forbs, as well as several kinds of fruit. A total of thirty-five
browse species were eaten by chital at Kanha (Table 11), a list undoubtedly incomplete although it does include the major items.
Browse in appreciable amounts is consumed only from October to

TABLE 10

GRASS AND GRASSLIKE PLANTS EATEN AND PROBABLY EATEN
BY WILD UNGULATES IN KANHA PARK

Species	Chital	Barasingha	Sambar	Blackbuck	Gaur
Eaten					
Bothriochloa odorata . .	x			x	
Chloris dolicostachya . .	x				
Chrysopogon fulvus . .				x	
Coix lachrymajobi . . .					x
Cyperus iria	x				
Cyperus pangorei . . .	x				
Dendrocalamus strictus	x		x		x
Digitaria granularis . .	x				
Echinochloa colona . .	x				
Eragrostis gangetica . .	x	x			
Fimbristylis dichotoma .	x				
Heleocharis fistulosa . .		x			
Heteropogon contortus .	x	x	x	x	
Imperata cylindrica . .					x
Oryza latifolia	x				
Panicum miliare . . .	x				
Saccharum spontaneum.	x	x			
Setaria glauca	x				
Themeda triandra . . .	x	x	x	x	x
Thysanolaena maxima .					x
Vetiveria zizanioides . .	x	x		x	x

Present and Probably Eaten

Andropogon brevifolius
Andropogon monticola
Andropogon serratus
Apluda mutica
Arthraxon ciliaris
Arundo donax
Cyperus exaltatus
Cyperus paltestylis
Eragrostis unidoides
Fimbristylis ferruginea
Hemarthria compressa
Isachue albens

Iseilema laxum
Lipocarpha argentea
Manisuris granularis
Oplismenus burmanii
Paspalum scrobiculatum
Pennisetum alopecurus
Pennisetum setosum
Scirpus capillaris
Scleria stocksiana
Spodiopogon rhizophorus
Sporobulus diander

TABLE 11

BROWSE SPECIES EATEN BY WILD UNGULATES IN KANHA PARK

Species	Chital	Barasingha	Sambar	Blackbuck	Gaur
Trees					
Acacia torta	x				
Bauhinea racemosa . .	x		x		x
Bombax malabaricum .	x				
Bridelia squamosa . .	f	x			x
Casearia graveolens . .					x
Cassia fistula	x,f				f
Combretum flagrocarpum			x		
Cordia myxa	f				x
Diospyros malanoxylon .		x			
Ehretia laevis					x
Emblica officinalis . . .	x,f				f
Eugenia vulgaris . . .			x		
Ficus glomerata	f				
Ficus gobosa	x				
Gardenia latifolia . . .					x
Gmelina arborea					x
Grewia abutilifolia . . .					x
Miliusa tomentosa . . .	x				
Miliusa velutina. . . .					x
Mallotus philippinensis					x
Odina wodier					x
Shorea robusta	x		x		x
Stereospermum chelonoides			x		
Syzygium cuminii . . .	x,f				x
Terminalia alata . . .	x				x
Terminalia arjuna. . .	x				
Terminalia chebula . .	x				
Terminalia tomentosa .			x		x
Xeromphis uliginosa . .					x
Ziziphus xylophorus . .			x		x
Shrubs					
Dalbergia rubiginosa . .			x		
Diospyros tomentosa . .	x				
Embelia tseriamcottam .	x,f	x	x	x	x
Kydia calycina					x
Moghania stricta. . . .	x,f	x			x
Ougeinia oojenensis . .	x				x
Pavetta indica.			x		
Phoenix humilis. . . .	x	x			x
Schrebera swientenioides					x
Sterculia foetida. . . .					x
Wrightia tinctoria . . .	x				
Ziziphus jujuba. . . .	x	x			
Vines					
Asparagus racemosus .					x
Bauhinea vahlii			x,f		x
Cryptolepis buchanani .	x				
Dioscorea bulbifera . .	x				
Smilax zeylanica. . . .			x		x
Forbs					
Barringtonia acutangula	x				
Blumea fistulosa. . . .	x				
Blumea glomerata . . .	x				

TABLE 11 (Continued)

Species	Chital	Barasingha	Sambar	Blackbuck	Gaur
Blumea virens					x
Crotalaria sericea . . .	x				
Curcuma ferruginea . .					x
Elephantopus scaber . .	x				
Laggera flava	x				
Lepidagathis fasciculata	x				
Leucas mollissima . . .					x
Naias sp.		x			
Pimpinella heyneana . .	x				
Plectranthus incanus .	x				
Pogostemon plectranthoides	x				
Triumfetta rhomboidea .	x				
Vernonia divergens . .					x

x = leaf eaten.
f = fruit eaten

January, when most grasses are fully grown and dry. At that time chital frequently meander up the stream beds eating the forbs that grow in the moist niches. Sometimes an animal stands on its hind-legs and nibbles on a leafy branch. A major browse species at this period is the shrub *Moghania*, of which both the leaves and seed pods are eaten. In 1964 browsing was also prevalent during the second half of March and in April when green grass was scarce but newly sprouted leaves of sal, *Phoenix*, and *Moghania* were abundant. The leaves from the thorny shrub *Zizyphus* were rarely taken except from mid-April to early June. Chital also consume fruits in season, including *Ficus* from January to May, *Cordia myxa* in May and June, *Syzygium cumini* in June and July, and *Zizyphus jujuba* in December and January.

A total of twelve rumen samples were collected from animals killed by predators in January, April, May, June, September, and November. The average percent of grass by volume was 96, followed by browse and fruits in equal amounts (Table 12), which attests to the importance of grass in the animal's diet.

Chital in the Sunderbans apparently eat small red crabs of an unidentified species, the remains of which have been found in the rumen (Stanford, 1951).

The movements of chital within their range were influenced considerably by the availability of young green grass. The concentration of animals on the Kanha meadow in late January and February, 1964, appeared to be due to the presence of new grass, for by late March, when the shoots had either been grazed off or had withered in the heat, many chital spread out in the forest again. In

TABLE 12

PLANT COMPOSITION OF TWELVE CHITAL RUMEN SAMPLES BY VOLUME
(IN PERCENT)

MONTH	PLANT TYPE		
	Sedge Grass	Browse	Fruit
January	91	4	5 (*Ficus*)
April.	91	4	5 (*Bauhinea*)
May	99	1	
May	95	5	Trace (*Ficus*)
May	97	1	2 (*Cordia*)
May	94	3	3 (*Cordia*)
May	98	2	Trace (*Cordia*)
June	90	2	8 (*Syzygium*)
September.	100		
September.	100	Trace	
September.	100	Trace	
November.	100	Trace	

March, 1965, however, green grass sprouted abundantly on the meadow after several heavy showers, and the chital were twice as abundant there as a year earlier. The large concentration of chital on the meadow during the monsoon persisted until early October when the grass began to dry out.

Natural salt licks were located along the banks of several streams, and at these, chital and other deer scraped at the soil with their incisors, at times leaving holes over one foot deep. Two samples of the soil were collected and analyzed and the results compared with two samples of typical soil, one collected in sal forest, the other on the Kanha meadow (Table 13). Of the five constituents tested, the phosphate (P_2O_5) and calcium were appreciably higher in the salt lick samples than in the others.

A foraging chital herd moves as a unit, each animal cropping

TABLE 13

CONSTITUENTS OF FOUR SOIL SAMPLES FROM KANHA PARK

Collecting Site	pH	CONSTITUENTS IN POUNDS PER ACRE				
		Magnesium	Phosphate	Potash	Manganese	Calcium
Typical sal forest . . .	5.5	331*	50	264*	84	1,900*
Kanha meadow	5.5	67	17	64	10	150
Salt lick along stream . .	7.5	497*	242*	113	15	4,480+*
Salt lick along stream . .	7.6	193*	369*	85	10	4,480+*

* High to very high

grass at the rate of about ninety bites per minute. The herd either remains in a small area, sometimes for as long as an hour on a piece of meadow 200 feet in diameter, or travels slowly at the rate of some 500 to 1,500 feet per hour. Its diameter varies considerably, with the animals sometimes staying tightly bunched and at other times spreading over 300 and more feet of terrain. The general direction of movement of all animals tends to be the same, and the pattern of herd formation is either a loose flock, a broad front with the chital moving parallel to each other, or a single file. As the foraging period passes its peak, the animals feed less intensively and seemingly more selectively, with periods of standing and moving interspersed with bursts of eating. In the morning, herds move toward the forest's edge slowly and in a straggling line, and while some chital continue to forage there, others lie down or remain standing. Cud is chewed at irregular intervals, each bolus being masticated some thirty to forty-five times at the rate of three chews in two seconds. The evening period of foraging begins equally slowly and sometimes twenty minutes elapse before the first and last member of a herd rises and starts to eat.

When langurs feed in a tree, chital frequently crowd beneath it and pick up the leaves and fruits dropped by these monkeys, an association also noted by Champion (1927). Langurs eat rather selectively, for example, taking only the petiole of a *Terminalia chebula* leaf or one bite out of a *Cordia myxa* fruit. The other parts are discarded and immediately eaten up by the waiting deer. On one occasion chital hovered around a fig tree until the langurs moved away about ten hours later. Once a langur descended a *Bombax malabaricum* tree carrying a leafy branch. A chital buck began to nibble on the leaves in the monkey's hand, but the monkey jerked the branch aside, then retreated to the top of a termite mound and ate undisturbed.

Water is so widespread for much of the year that it is difficult to determine how often chital drink. They visit the water holes twice a day during the hot season at about sunrise and in the late afternoon. A similar morning and evening trek to water was noted in the Vanbihar and Keoladeo Ghana Sanctuaries.

Chital approach a water hole cautiously, especially when it is obscured by high grass and shrubs or, as is often the case, lies in the bottom of a ravine. A whole herd sometimes lines up on the embankment, and each animal peers with stretched neck into the stream bed for five or more minutes before one of them finally descends. The chital drink rapidly, muzzle lowered into the water, and afterward spread out to graze. One buck drank for ninety seconds without interruption.

RANGE AND MOVEMENTS

The total area occupied by the Kanha chital population was about twelve square miles. The great majority of the animals spent the whole year, and probably their entire life, within that range, the exceptions being perhaps a few bucks that drifted over a wider area. The Kanha meadow was the focal point of this population, and the animals concentrated or scattered from there depending on the availability of forage and the time of the rut. For at least six months of the year, including much of the hot season and the monsoon, most of the chital were found in an area of four square miles on and around the Kanha meadow. The ranges of individuals tended to be fairly small during that time. I recognized several bucks by their antler patterns and plotted their location on a map whenever they were encountered. One buck was seen 42 times between March and August within an area of about 1,200 acres; a second buck was noted 29 times between March and June within an area of 1,500 acres; a third buck was spotted 23 times between March and August within an area of 1,350 acres; and a fourth buck was seen 35 times between March and June in an area of 400 acres. One doe observed 11 times over a period of seven months was always found within a 450 acre part of the meadow. Sometimes an animal remained for a week or two in a particular locality, resting in the same patch of forest during the day and using the same well-beaten trail to move to a water hole in the evening, before suddenly shifting its activity to another area. The actual distance traveled by a chital in the course of a day probably averaged no more than two to three miles of meanderings within a tract of a few hundred acres. Bucks in rut, however, wandered considerably; for example, one buck seen in the evening was one and a half miles away the following morning. These observations are similar to those made by Dasmann and Taber (1956) on the black-tailed deer. Home ranges in these deer were on the order of one and a half miles in diameter, and movements within them were influenced by daily and seasonal changes in the "quantity and quality of life's requirements," with rutting bucks roaming more widely than does.

INTERACTIONS WITH OTHER ANIMALS

Chital associate peacefully with most other animals in the park, particularly with other ungulates. Mixed herds of chital, barasingha,
and blackbuck were common on the Kanha meadow; chital also
mingled freely with sambar, and, in other areas, with hog deer,
nilgai, and wild pig. Gaur and chital were not seen to forage side
by side, although the two were often near each other, once within
twenty feet. In one instance domestic cattle grazed fifteen feet from
several chital, which watched them alertly. Langur monkeys and
chital were frequent associates, as described earlier. Mynah birds
readily perched on the backs of chital and appeared to search for
ectoparasites; black drongos sat on their heads and snagged insects
flushed by their hooves; and jungle crows pulled strips of velvet
from the antlers of bucks. One chital ignored a peacock which was
courting it in full display (Schaller, 1964). Overt interactions between the species were infrequent. Sometimes chital accepted a member of another species as leader (see Leadership, p. 70), and blackbuck males occasionally courted and attempted to mount chital does
(see Blackbuck, Sexual behavior, p. 168). Once a chital buck assumed the head-down display in front of a barasingha stag, but
when the latter, responding correctly, gave the head-up display,
the chital walked away. Two barasingha hinds jumped aside when
a chital buck jerked his antlers in their direction. A blackbuck male
and a yearling chital buck once faced each other with lowered heads,
and when the latter lunged forward, the blackbuck fled, chasing
two chital does aside as he ran.

Although chital pay seemingly little attention to the animals
around them, any sudden change in behavior such as the flushing
of a jungle fowl, the screeching of jungle babblers and red-wattled
lapwings, the calling of a langur, or sudden running by a member
of the herd is immediately investigated. This recognition of and response to the alarm signals of other species is undoubtedly of great
survival value to the chital in an environment where the chance of
encountering a predator is great. On several occasions a herd became aware of the proximity of a tiger only after having responded
to the sharp ka-kao-ka of an alarmed langur, and the incessant
screeching of lapwings at the sight of man alerted chital to my presence on numerous occasions. The chital, whose senses of smell and
hearing are excellent but whose sight is often not sufficiently acute
to distinguish motionless forms, has extended and complemented its

PLATE 1.—A herd of barasingha and a few chital graze on the Kanha meadow (January 26, 1964).

PLATE 2.—Sal forest near the Kanha meadow (April 2, 1964).

PLATE 3.–A herd of seven chital bucks; one animal has antlers in velvet (March 13, 1964).

PLATE 4.—A rutting adult chital buck follows a herd consisting of two adult does, one yearling doe, and two fawns (March 14, 1964).

PLATE 5.—A chital buck rubs his antlers against a *Butea* sapling (May 10, 1964).

perceptual world considerably by relying in part on other animals. In addition, the chital possess a complex and effective system of visual, auditory, and olfactory signals of their own which serve to warn other members of the species of potential danger.

An alert chital stands or walks with body erect, neck stretched vertically, and ears cocked as it faces the source of the disturbance. This posture alone alerts the other animals in the vicinity, and they then behave similarly. In a situation of somewhat higher intensity, the animal raises its tail, exposing the white rump, stamps one forefoot audibly on the ground, and emits a series of loud, high-pitched barks, somewhat resembling those of a small dog. Chital are said to stand up on their hindlegs to scan the horizon when the undergrowth is dense (Hiteshi, 1947), but I did not observe this behavior. The strength of the response varies of course with the situation eliciting it. When a langur called in alarm some seven hundred feet from a resting herd of chital, only a few animals jumped up and faced the direction of the sound for about one minute. But when on another occasion several chital in the distance barked shrilly in intense alarm, the herd I was observing remained alert for six minutes before relaxing its vigilance. On still another occasion, a herd of seven chital were ambling along in single file. Suddenly the lead doe stopped, raised her muzzle as if sniffing the air, then stood with neck craned and tail raised. The others turned back, retracing their steps, followed by the doe. Tracks showed that a tiger had passed by the previous night. In a similar circumstance four chital faced a patch of high grass and stamped their forefeet for over two minutes, having sensed the tigress that passed through it twenty minutes earlier. In one instance five chital winded a tiger cub hiding in some grass 120 feet away; they briefly milled around, then detoured around the area.

The actual sight of a predator elicited the same type of response. When a jackal trotted toward a herd of chital, the animals watched its approach alertly with raised tail, one permitting it to come to within eight feet before startling back. The deer usually barked vigorously at the sight of a tiger, a higher pitched sound with more of a trill than the usual alarm bark. As the tiger moved away, the chital often followed the cat for a short distance with tail raised and forelegs thumping the ground. Only a few members of the herd barked at any one time, and if the tiger was at a distance, they sometimes remained silent. On one occasion a tiger walked noisily through dry leaf litter. Several chital barked, then watched him stroll by 150 feet away. As soon as he moved from sight, they sniffed at his trail, milled around, and followed it for 100 feet. But on another occasion ten chital merely looked at a tigress walk by at a distance of 150 feet. Rodon (1897) described how a herd of barking chital faced a leopard on its kill.

A chital in flight raises its tail exposing the white underside and the white rump much like the *Odocoileus* deer (W. Taylor, 1956). If the animal has been surprised in high grass, it often initiates its retreat with a series of high bounds, between which it thumps its hindlegs loudly on the ground in unison. These thumps undoubtedly act as auditory signals in dense undergrowth, indicating not only the presence of danger but also the direction of flight. Scent is probably deposited by the pedal or interdigital glands, an olfactory signal which may later warn others of danger, as has been described in caribou by Pruitt (1960). "That the secretion from the pedal glands must scent the ground over which the animal passes seems clear, for the pouch is commonly furnished with long hairs projecting from the orifice or the edge of the orifice, and the function of these hairs seems to be to guide the secretion downwards between the hoofs" (Pocock, 1910). It is interesting to note that the hindfeet of the chital, which are thumped during flight, have well developed pedal glands whereas the frontfeet do not (Pocock, 1910). A startled chital often emits one or more high-pitched yips, alarm barks of the highest intensity. A herd fleeing in the open usually runs about one hundred feet in one compact mass and then looks back at the source of the disturbance. When surprised in dense cover, however, the animals characteristically scatter in all directions, behavior which perhaps confuses an attacking predator.

Chital sometimes closely investigate a potentially dangerous site, apparently out of curiosity. For example, when a doe barked and bounded from a patch of high grass, about fifty other chital in the vicinity scattered and dashed 100 feet before stopping. But soon twenty-three does and fawns slowly approached the grass again. One doe was 15 feet ahead of the others and actually penetrated into the thicket in an apparent attempt to spot the source of the disturbance. On another occasion, a lead doe suddenly became alert and, followed by six other chital, cautiously advanced 45 feet to a bush on which a tigress had sprayed scent the previous night. The animals sniffed the leaves for three minutes, then departed. Once I tied a white goat, which the local chital had probably never seen before, out on the meadow. That evening twenty-three of them approached to within 60 feet and stood there barking for several minutes.

Man also elicited the various alarm postures and vocalizations, although if a person was clearly visible and approached slowly the animals rarely barked and they did not investigate and follow man's tracks as they did those of tiger. The deer readily caught my scent and became alert at distances of 300 to 400 feet if a breeze blew in their direction; but if I stood motionless on the open meadow on a windless day, a herd 100 feet away sometimes failed to become aware of me. Their flight distance to man on foot was usually 200 to 400 feet, depending on the circumstances, but occasionally as little as 120 feet if I walked at right angles to them. In a car it was sometimes possible to approach to within 70 to 80 feet of a herd without disturbing it, particularly at night. Moreover, the response of the animals was greatly influenced by the amount of adverse contact with man. Early in 1965, for example, the chital at Kanha were noticeably tamer than at the beginning of the study a year earlier.

Social Behavior

Although chital spend much of their time in social contact with others of their kind, and although each member of a herd tends to pattern its behavior such as feeding, moving, and resting after that of the others, overt interactions between two individuals are relatively uncommon. The most prevalent types of social interactions are agonistic ones between bucks, sexual ones between bucks and does, and relations between females and young.

HERD SIZE AND COMPOSITION

The average size of chital herds at Kanha varied considerably with the seasons. The average for most of the year was between 5 and 10 animals per herd, but as many as 50 to 70 occasionally congregated at a particular site. Inverarity (1895) and Storey (1907) gave similar figures for other areas. During the monsoon months the size of herds increased greatly, and the averages given in Table 14 are actually too low because it was not always possible to obtain accurate composition counts. Herds of 100 to 200 animals were common then, and in one instance two herds comprising a total of about 450 chital were separated by only five hundred feet of meadow. M. Krishnan (pers. comm.) reported a herd of about 240 chital in Madras. Solitary bucks and does were evident throughout the year.

Herd size was to some extent influenced by the availability of food and water. When preferred forage was scarce, as in November and December, the chital were scattered in small herds, but when green shoots of grass appeared locally, as was the case in February, the animals tended to form large herds at such sites. Similarly, when the water supply was reduced to several pools during May, small herds drifted in from all directions, joined, and frequently grazed together. The large herds characteristic of the monsoon period broke up as the grasses reached their full growth, but whether this was

TABLE 14

AVERAGE SIZE OF CHITAL HERDS IN KANHA PARK

Month	Total Number of Herds Tallied	Average Number of Animals per Herd	Largest Herd Tallied
January, 1964	176	7.9	35
February	291	10.5	54
March	218	10.0	109
April	220	8.2	39
May	242	8.9	69
June	210	13.0	152
July	56	32.4	175
August	41	38.1	164
September	30	24.4	125
October	85	9.9	76
November	82	4.7	23
December	117	4.6	20

because of the height of the vegetation, which made it difficult for the animals to remain in contact, or the lack of suitable forage, or both, could not be determined. Social factors also influenced herd size. Adult does withdrew to fawn in seclusion, and rutting bucks disrupted herds. In addition there appeared to be a social attraction between herds. The whole population was divided into several units, each numbering roughly 100 to 200 individuals, and although these units were unstable in composition and their location on the meadow changed constantly, the fact remained that at any given time chital were numerous at two or three sites on the Kanha meadow in contrast to other and equally suitable areas where deer were few in number. For over half of the year almost the whole chital population in the valley was concentrated around the Kanha meadow even though several other meadows with an adequate supply of food and water were available. This again suggests a basic social attraction, perhaps associated in part with the advantage of mutual stimulation during the rut. The gathering at the meadow may also represent "a

living tradition maintained and transmitted by the older individuals
and learned by the young followers," as reported for Stone's sheep
by Geist (1964*b*).

The size of herds in other areas was similar to that at Kanha. After
part of the Dhikala meadow had been burned in Corbett Park in
late January, the average size of eighty-three herds was 5.5 deer
and the largest herd comprised 39. About 500 chital divided into
four population units congregated on the meadow during early February, and herds regularly numbered 50 or more animals each. In

TABLE 15

Composition of Chital Herds Containing the Same Adult Buck

Date in May, 1964	Adult Buck	Yearling Buck	Doe	Fawn	Total
1.	3	0	1	1	5
4.	1	2	6	3	12
5.	2	1	8	4	15
6.	5	4	7	7	23
8.	2	1	1	2	6
10.	2	0	1	0	3
11.	2	0	5	3	10
12.	4	4	9	9	26
14.	2	0	3	2	7
15.	1	0	0	0	1
16.	1	0	2	1	4
21.	6	5	16	13	40

the West Kheri Forest Division, herds were small, mostly 2 to 5 individuals each, with one consisting of 25. In the Keoladeo Ghana
Sanctuary, herds congregated at dusk as they moved to the marsh
to drink, but accurate counts in the thick undergrowth were not
feasible. A similar joining of herds at water occurred in the Vanbihar
Sanctuary, usually between 0730 and 0830 hours and after 1800
hours, when I saw as many as 74 chital together.

Bucks, does, and fawns associated throughout the year. Small
herds frequently consisted of an adult doe, a yearling, and a fawn;
two or three does with their fawns; a buck and a doe; and two or
three bucks. During the rut, small herds numbering 10 to 15 individuals each were often composed of one large buck, several small
bucks, and a number of does and fawns (Plate 4, Table 15). Large
herds contained many members of all age and sex classes, with one
tallied on July 15 consisting of 36 adult bucks, 24 yearling bucks,
70 does, and 45 fawns, a total of 175.

Although the composition of herds is usually mixed, chital have a tendency to form two other kinds of associations: (1) buck herds (Plate 3) and (2) herds consisting of does with small fawns. Two to 5 adult bucks were commonly together, particularly from October to March, when many of them were in velvet. Yearling bucks usually remained with the does. The largest herds composed solely of bucks at Kanha consisted of 12 individuals and at Keoladeo Ghana of 23. Bucks predominated in some herds, with one being composed of 28 bucks, 4 does, and 2 fawns. The proclivity of bucks to congregate was also shown by the composition of two herds seen on the Kanha meadow in the evening of March 6: (*a*) 33 adult bucks, 10 yearling bucks, 52 does, 14 fawns = 109; (*b*) 1 adult buck, 8 yearling bucks, 51 does, 17 fawns = 77. Buck herds have also been reported for a number of other cervids like the caribou (Skoog, 1956), red deer (Darling, 1937), and black-tailed deer (Taber and Dasmann, 1958). Does with fawns less than two months old sometimes formed their own small herds, whereas those with older fawns lacked this tendency to any marked degree. Somewhat similar aggregations have been described in caribou, but the nursing bands, as Pruitt (1960) termed them, persisted longer than in the chital.

The composition of chital herds changes constantly. The only association of a relatively permanent nature is that of a doe with her fawn and sometimes also her young of the previous year. All other social contacts in a large population are transitory, lasting a few minutes to a day, or exceptionally, perhaps several days. Small isolated herds are possibly more permanent. The same adult buck, estimated to be about two and one-half years old, was seen on twelve occasions during May, and the compositions of the herds to which he belonged are given in Table 15. Bucks in particular were unstable members of herds, and during the rut one or more commonly joined a herd, but within a few minutes parted from it again. Mixing of herds occurred frequently. For example, one herd of 61 chital at a water hole consisted of 7 herds which had joined there; and in the course of one and one-half hours a herd of 27 chital split into 3 herds, numbering 4, 8, and 15 animals, each leaving for a different part of the meadow.

LEADERSHIP

The term "leader" in connection with chital merely connotes a number of followers. One member of a foraging herd sometimes ambled off to one side, and the others then swerved in its direction. Two chital walking from a herd in opposite directions occasionally caused a split with several animals joining each leader. On one occasion 38 chital straggled in single file for a distance of four hundred feet, but when the two does last in line turned around and returned to the locality they had just left, the whole herd, except for several bucks, retraced its steps. Chital had the tendency to follow any animal that moved away steadily, a conspicuous habit when at times members of other species were accepted as leaders. In one instance a barasingha stag was followed by 10 chital in single file for over a quarter mile, and on another occasion two barasingha hinds led a herd of 9 chital. Blackbuck and sambar were also seen to lead chital.

The leadership of any chital, regardless of age and sex, is accepted by the others in times of danger. Under normal circumstances, however, fawns and yearlings rarely elicit following, and bucks, with their tendency to roam widely and erratically, are accepted as leaders primarily by other males. Most leaders of herds are adult females, a widespread phenomenon among ungulates. Of 75 large herds tallied as the animals moved along in single file, 84 percent were led by a doe. Leadership was recorded on 547 occasions in the study herd of 10 bucks and 13 does in the Calcutta Zoological Garden. Does led 56 percent of the movements from one side of the enclosure to the other, a figure much lower than that obtained in the wild. One doe led the herd 23 percent of the time, and 7 of the 23 animals accounted for 82 percent of the leadership, indicating that certain chital are more predisposed to break away from the herd and elicit following than others. These males and females ranked in the top 50 percent of their respective hierarchies (see Agonistic behavior and dominance, p. 79). The doe which led most frequently was fifth in the female rank order, and the leading buck was second in the buck rank order.

Agonistic Behavior and Dominance

Bucks in velvet are very passive, but after their antlers have become hard, they display several distinctive behavior patterns, which are either overtly aggressive or are apparently intended primarily to intimidate the opponent directly or indirectly. The overt aggressive actions, in order of increasing intensity, consist of (1) walking directly at the opponent, (2) jerking the head downward or sideways to point the tip of the antlers briefly at him (3) lunging forward with head lowered, and (4) chasing him over a distance of five or more feet, often with antlers pointing forward.

A characteristic display, termed here the head-up display, is common between bucks. One animal approaches stiff-legged with rather jerky steps, neck stretched upward, and muzzle pointing obliquely toward the sky, a position which exposes the white throat patch. The ears are partially laid back, and on rare occasions, the tail is raised vertically. The buck maintains this position, either while facing his opponent or while standing parallel to him, until the latter moves away, displays in similar fashion, or lowers his antlers threateningly. The posture makes the buck look large and impressive, at least to the human observer, and it appears to be a means of asserting dominance, of challenging the other animal, without resorting to direct aggression. For example, a large buck approached a herd consisting of 3 adult bucks, 5 yearling bucks, 2 does, and one fawn. He assumed the head-up display as he entered the herd, and the two largest bucks promptly turned aside and grazed. Then he stepped toward the third adult buck, which behaved similarly.

Another display, the head-down display, occurs commonly between males when herds join. Typically, one buck stands parallel to and faces in the same direction as another buck. His back is humped, the hairs on the shoulders are somewhat erected, and the neck is either S-shaped or arched with the muzzle pointing toward the ground. The ears are laid back, but the one facing the opponent is sometimes flashed back and forth, making the white hairs on the inside of it conspicuous; the tail is held limply horizontal. The head is averted, and the eyes are rolled so that the whites show. The other buck may assume a similar posture, and both then stand or walk stiff-legged some four to twelve feet apart. Occasionally one circles the other, or both stop briefly and thrash a tuft of grass with their antlers or paw the ground with a forefoot, creating a dust cloud if the earth is dry. Usually only two bucks display in this fashion, but on occasion as many as six or eight animals participate, all stalking around and circling each other. Cowan and Geist (1961) have described a display in the black-tailed deer, "the crouch," which resembles the head-down of the chital, and Thomas et al. (1965) observed a white-tailed deer buck "which turned his head and body approximately 30° from his antagonist, head erect and chin tucked in, and took several sidling steps toward his adversary."

The head-down display is undoubtedly designed to intimidate the opponent, but unlike the head-up display, it does not appear to represent a challenge to the other animal's status and thus rarely leads to a sparring match or other form of aggression. (Most interactions are resolved without an obvious decision having been reached.) Consequently, the display is frequently exhibited by yearlings and bucks in velvet, both of which seldom perform the head-up. Of 231 bucks involved in head-down displays, 34 percent were yearlings. About one-third (31 percent) of the adult bucks were in velvet. Adult bucks with large hard antlers, 31 inches long and over, were never seen to display to bucks in velvet, and the frequency with which they did so to other bucks in hard antler varied considerably. Of 30 displays involving a large buck, 16 (53 percent) were directed at an equally large animal and only 2 (7 percent) at a yearling. On 28 occasions one buck walked in head-down past another buck which failed to respond; in 20 (71 percent) of these instances the buck with the smaller antlers displayed. Yearling bucks displayed to does on 4 occasions, and once an animal did so to a fawn; one buck displayed to no one in particular. Does were seen to give the head-down to each other twice.

The bucks responded to a head-down display in a number of ways. Once, for example, two bucks stood parallel and eight feet apart as they pawed the ground and jabbed their antlers into the grass with upward jerks of the head. They then circled each other, going in opposite directions. A third buck walked between them, displaying the head-down first to one buck and then, while retracing his steps, to the other. All three bucks drifted apart without further interaction. On another occasion a large buck pawed the soil while twenty feet from him another buck belabored a *Butea* shrub so violently with his antlers that the leaves flew high into the air. When the first buck approached in the head-down posture, the second and smaller one retreated and left the herd. In yet another instance a buck with medium-sized antlers entered a herd in the head-down without eliciting a response from a large buck in velvet at whom the display was directed. He then approached and circled a large buck in hard antler, which promptly assumed the head-up and remained motionless while the small buck pawed and thrashed grass. When the latter switched to the head-up display, the other buck immediately responded with the head-down. After about four minutes, the intruding buck left the herd.

Two of the behavior patterns associated with the head-down display — pawing and thrashing vegetation with the antlers — also occur before and after sparring, and with seeming spontaneity. A pawing buck stands with head lowered and scrapes the ground with either one forefoot or alternately both, creating a characteristic bare patch with a series of grooves made by the hooves. Bucks frequently rub their antlers against the trunks of *Butea* and other trees, leaving patches of scoured bark, which were particularly common on the Kanha meadow during the hot season (Plate 5), as were tattered sapling and shrubby plants which had been thrashed with the antlers. Bucks begin to rub their antlers against trunks and shrubs when the velvet begins to dry, and they continue to do so until the antlers are shed. Sometimes this rubbing is vigorous, the antlers clanking noisily, but at other times the buck does it gently by wiping his face, forehead, antlers, and neck over the bark. Tufts of grass and other vegetation are thrashed with violent lateral motions of the head or with upward sweeps of the antlers.

A third type of behavior, related to the thrashing of vegetation, is "preaching," a term applied by Brander (1923) to the sambar's habit of rearing up on its hind legs. The buck stands bolt upright and sticks his head into the leaves of a low-hanging branch. He shakes his head back and forth and, while attempting to retain his balance, treads with his hindlegs, churning the soil. After repeated use, a preaching tree has a characteristic bare patch two to three feet in diameter at its base. Several bucks sometimes use a preaching tree in succession. For example, when a herd moved into the forest past a tree at which a buck had preached earlier that morning, a yearling male wiped his face in the leaves at that spot, and three minutes later another passing buck halted abruptly, raised his muzzle as if sniffing the air, and then reared up and preached.

All instances of thrashing, pawing, and preaching observed at Kanha were recorded in connection with the approximate length of the antlers of the buck exhibiting the behavior (Table 16). The results show that the bucks with the longest antlers displayed proportionately more frequently than those with small antlers and with spikes. Does were not seen to thrash, paw, or preach.

None of the behavior patterns described so far involve actual physical contact between the bucks, the majority serving to cow the opponent by visual and olfactory means. The head-up display is a direct assertion of dominance, the head-down display an attempt to intimidate, and the pawing, thrashing of bushes, and scouring of tree trunks appear to be forms of redirected aggression, with the buck expending his energy on objects rather than directly on another buck. The vigorous pawing and thrashing of the vegetation, with dust, leaves, and grass flying into the air, also increase the effectiveness of the head-down and other displays by drawing attention to the animal and probably by making it look impressive, especially afterward when it stalks around with grass and tatters of velvet draped from its tines. Other cervids show similar patterns of behavior. Wapiti and black-tailed deer paw and rub antlers on shrubs and trees (Graf, 1956), as do reindeer (Espmark, 1964a). Males of the latter series also tramp the ground with their hindlegs while urinating on them. Pruitt (1954) observed a white-tailed deer buck as it pawed, grunted, and "reached up and grasped low-hanging oak limbs in his mouth, pulled them down, and, by twisting his head, raked his antler through them."

These activities leave visual and olfactory signals in the environment which become physical extensions, as it were, of the animal

TABLE 16

FREQUENCY OF THRASHING BUSHES, PAWING, AND "PREACHING"
IN THE ANTLER-SIZE CLASSES OF CHITAL BUCKS

Antler-Size Class	Rubbing Antler on Tree or Thrashing Bush	Pawing	Preaching	Bucks in Each Size Class in Population
Total number of observations . .	167	96	28	
31 inches+	38%	34%	36%	23%
21–30 inches . . .	22	32	32	19
11–20 inches . . .	28	23	18	23
Spikes	12%	11%	14%	35%

itself. The paw marks are a prominent feature of the surroundings, and I have several times observed a solitary buck stop and paw at such a site. The scoured tree trunks and the bare patches at the base of preaching trees remain easily visible for several months. Inseparably associated with these visual signals are olfactory ones. When thrashing bushes and preaching, scent from the preorbital glands is probably deposited on the leaves. On several occasions bucks rubbed their preorbital glands on tree trunks, then appeared to spread the scent over their antlers, head, and neck by brushing against the bark, which not only enhanced the odor of their bodies but also left evidence of their presence on the tree. Secretions from the interdigital gland are perhaps added to the soil when pawing. It is possible that these signals have an intimidatory effect on other bucks that see and smell them (Graf, 1956), and thus a large number of such signs in a limited area might tend to space bucks out. On the other hand, the increased number of signals toward the peak of

the rut probably also attracts the animals and through mutual stimulation influences the synchronization of sexual activity.

Sparring, or fighting with the antlers, is one of the most conspicuous behavior patterns of chital and of deer in general. Two bucks
characteristically approach each other, lower their heads abruptly,
and lock antlers gently before twisting them back and forth and,
with hindlegs braced, attempt to push each other backward. Sometimes the animals break apart and, after a cursory head-up display, spar once again. The number of such rounds in a sparring
match may reach five or six before one buck breaks away and departs. A third buck occasionally butts in from the side and then spars
with each of the others in succession. Groans are emitted occasion-

TABLE 17

FREQUENCY OF SPARRING BEHAVIOR IN ADULT CHITAL BUCKS
OF DIFFERENT ANTLER-SIZE CLASSES

Antler-Size Class	Total Number Of Animals Sparring	Percent Sparring	Percent of Bucks in Size Class in Population
31 Inches+	46	9	35
21–31 inches	124	26	30
11–20 inches	320	65	35
Total.	490	100	100

ally by sparring animals. Most matches are brief, one minute or less,
but some exceptional ones last as long as ten minutes. Of 284 sparring matches observed at Kanha, only one was a serious fight with
the bucks obviously attempting to vanquish each other. Although
sometimes carried on with vigor for brief periods, all other matches
consisted for the most part of gentle grappling with the antlers. The
animals gave the impression of trying to reassert themselves or test
their strength rather than determine their position in a rank order.

The antler length of every buck involved in a sparring bout was
recorded. The results of 245 such matches (Table 17) show that the
adults with the shortest antlers sparred seven times as often (65 percent) as those with the longest ones (9 percent), a difference perhaps attributable in part to the fact that the young, growing animals,
in contrast to the large bucks, change constantly in size and hence
test their strength frequently against others of comparable age and
antler length. The difference in antler length of the participants in
227 sparring matches tallied was 5 inches or less in 55 percent of
the cases, 6 to 10 inches in 24 percent of the cases, 11 to 15 inches

in 15 percent of the cases, and 16 or more inches in 6 percent of the cases. Similarly, in 36 matches between spikes and adults, 70 percent of the latter were in the small (11–20 inches) antler-length class.

The majority of matches terminated when one buck turned aside, walked or trotted off, or began to forage. I designated such an animal as the loser. Occasionally no decision was reached, as when the bucks reacted to some disturbance or when interrupted by a third animal. The buck with the larger set of antlers was victorious in 88 percent of 129 matches observed in which the estimated length of the antlers of the participants differed by at least one inch. When two bucks approached each other before a match, I could in most instances designate the winner and loser merely by estimating the length of the antlers. The whole sequence of events, from the initial approach to the termination of the match, was observed 62 times. The ultimate winner initiated 77 percent of the matches. The loser then occasionally sought out another buck of still more subordinate position and challenged him to a sparring bout. These data suggest that in a majority of sparring matches the dominant animal deliberately chooses a subordinate one to assert its position: in other words the match is "fixed" since the outcome is almost predetermined. This does not, of course, exclude the possibility that sparring is also a "matter of mutual enjoyment and probably has the effect of building up their rutting condition," as was suggested by Taber and Dasmann (1958) for the black-tailed deer.

Since it is highly improbable that all bucks in a large population know each other individually, the animals must have some means by which they are able to determine their rank without overt interaction as soon as they meet. I think that dominance among chital bucks is primarily established by a rapid visual assessment of the opponent's physical attributes: body size, swollen neck, and, particularly, antler length. The simple tine pattern of the antler makes such an estimation relatively simple, at least to the human observer. Espmark (1964b), in his study of captive reindeer, also concluded that the size of the antlers influences rank order. If it is assumed that a chital is able to determine its rank in relation to another individual by visual means alone, the problem remains just how the animal is able to compare its own attributes favorably or unfavorably with those of its opponent, especially when the animals are evenly matched as to body size. Possibly each buck learns from experience to correlate size of antler and strength of opponent after having won and lost a number of sparring matches.

Antlers have a number of functions. They are obviously dangerous weapons. Skoog (1956) mentioned that a caribou was seen to hold off two wolves with lowered antlers, and a wild dog could be similarly held at bay by a chital buck. During intraspecific encounters the antlers are rarely put to their full potential use; in fact, a buck was never seen to take advantage of an exposed and vulnerable part of his opponent's body, and the mere presentation of the neck or flank with the head averted prevented further attacks by the other animal. Although antlers are occasionally used for fighting when two bucks have apparently failed to settle their respective positions in the rank order by other means, they seem to function primarily and para-doxically to reduce aggression by providing a prominent visual signal of status that can be assessed at a distance. That is, the antlers of chital serve mainly in display; they are status symbols. A similar conclusion was reached by Darling (1937) for the red deer and by Espmark (1964b) for the reindeer.

Bucks with antlers 31 inches long and over were seen to spar with each other only two times. These large bucks, the most powerful animals in the population, appeared to avoid physical contact and, instead, established and reinforced their status by using displays and various forms of redirected aggression, with, for example, thrashing and pawing being used more commonly by the large bucks than by the other size classes (Table 16), an inverse correlation with the frequency of sparring.

An adult buck in velvet sparred gently with an opponent on several occasions: three times with a small yearling buck, twice with a yearling doe, and once with another buck in velvet.

Aggressive interactions between the other age and sex classes were infrequent. Does nipped the shoulder or rump of another doe or of a yearling buck on several occasions. Threat in does consisted of facing the opponent with neck held vertically, ears laid back, and muzzle horizontal or slightly above it, a display which resembled the head-up of bucks to some extent. Altmann (1956) described a similar posture in the wapiti, as did Geist (1963) in the moose and Lent (1965) in the caribou. The mere laying back of the ears was often a sufficiently threatening gesture to cause another doe to retreat. If the threatened animal failed to respond, or if it assumed a similar posture, the conflict resulted at times in a fight, during which both combatants reared up on their hindlegs and, remaining upright by leaning on each other, flailed wildly with their forelegs. Bucks in velvet were observed to fight in this manner on two occasions, and fawns on four occasions. Yearling does "locked antlers" with a buck in five instances but adult does never did so. Once, when an adult doe bit a yearling doe in the rump, the latter wheeled around and with spread forelegs and lowered head assumed the male fighting stance. A doe sometimes bit her larger fawn when it attempted to suckle or when it crowded her too closely.

Most subordinate animals avoided contact by merely turning aside when threatened, but two other postures also conveyed submission. Bucks occasionally began to graze intensively in agonistic situations, a displacement activity which served to inhibit further action on the part of the aggressor. Submission was also conveyed, predominantly by does, by lowering the neck and stretching it parallel to the ground with muzzle pointed forward and ears laid back. On one occasion a yearling buck gave the head-down display to a doe, and she immediately lowered her neck and trotted off. When two does threatened each other, one frequently would lower her neck suddenly while the other kept her head in a raised position for several more seconds.

Implied in this discussion of aggressive behavior is the existence of a rank order among bucks based not on individual recognition but on an immediate visual assessment of the opponent's physical features, particularly the length of antlers. Since a herd is in a constant state of flux, its hierarchial system is too. This, together with the extremely limited number of overt interactions between animals, made it difficult to confirm the existence of a hierarchy in herds containing many bucks. When only about five males were together, however, a rank order was sometimes clearly evident. For example, on one occasion I observed a herd of seven bucks, three does, and one fawn. The two largest bucks each courted a doe, implying top ranking; the smallest buck, a spike, grazed. Eleven interactions by the four remaining bucks indicated that they had a linear rank order.

A herd of chital containing ten bucks was observed in the Calcutta Zoological Garden for 173 hours between September 18 and November 4, 1963, usually during the early morning when the animals were most active. All overt aggressive interactions — direct approach, a jab with an antler, chasing, and sparring — were tabulated (Table 18). The 580 interactions show that the bucks had a linear hierarchy, except for buck No. 8 which was dominant over buck No. 5. The number of reversals in interactions comprised 1.7 percent of the total, if buck No. 2 is excluded from the computation. Buck No. 2 shed his antlers on October 1 and instantaneously lost his high ranking. He withdrew to the periphery of the herd and became the recipient of butts even from the bucks lowest in rank. Similar behavior was described by Crandall (1964) in the New York Zoological Park: "The only hard-antlered male in the herd was a spike buck that previously had been kept in order by older animals. Released from restraint, his persecution of now defenseless superiors resulted in extensive damage." The fact that the loss of antlers immediately relegates an animal to a low position in the hierarchy was also noted by Hediger (1952) and Espmark (1964*b*). The combined evidence

TABLE 18

DOMINANCE INTERACTIONS IN TEN CHITAL BUCKS,
SEPTEMBER 18–NOVEMBER 4, 1963, CALCUTTA ZOOLOGICAL GARDEN

Dominant Buck	Subordinate Buck										Total Number of Interactions	Length of Longest Antler in Inches	Comments
	I	II	III	IV	V	VI	VII	VIII	IX	X			
I . . .		21	31	32	35	38	39	36	39	38	309	17	Antler tips broken
II . . .			2	5	5	3		1	2	2	20	28	Antlers shed October 1
III . . .	6	16		14	15	9	9		6	5	80	17	
IV . . .	3				10	17	8	21	4	2	65	22	
V . . .	4	1				10	8		4	3	30	18	
VI . . .	1	2					16	2	3	1	25	14	
VII . . .	6			1				4	5	6	22	12	
VIII . . .	11			4		1			6	4	26	15	One antler deformed, 3″ long
IX . . .	2									1	3	Spike	
X . . .											0	Spike	
											580		Total

from the wild and from captivity indicates that the hierarchy of chital bucks is in a continuous state of flux, not only as a result of the fluid social structure of the herd, but also because of seasonal changes in the physical appearance of the animal itself. The cyclical nature of antler development is largely mediated by the amount of testosterone in the blood (Wislocki, 1943; Wislocki *et al.*, 1947), the shedding of the velvet being precipitated by the increase of the hormone. Since a raise in the testosterone level also increases aggressiveness in vertebrates (Collias, 1944), it is apparent that the physiological state of the animal also has a profound influence on its position in the social order (Allee, 1952).

It was suggested that the length of antlers determines the rank of the animals in the wild to a large extent. The shed antlers of all the bucks in the zoo study herd were measured, and Table 18 shows that, although bucks with large antlers tended to be dominant over those with small ones, there was no complete correlation between antler size and status. This is not surprising, for the captives probably determined their position in the hierarchy not by a brief visual assessment of each other's physical attributes, as was the case in the wild, but by repeated contacts with known individuals. A hierarchy based on and maintained by a relatively stable society in which each member knows the personal idiosyncrasies of every other member can be expected to operate on a somewhat different level than one in which the animals are not known to each other. For example, the dominant buck in the zoo herd was an exceedingly aggressive individual, who in the confines of the enclosure was able to assert his dominance fully in spite of his small antlers. In the wild this animal probably would be at a psychological disadvantage in dealing with bucks whose antlers were larger than his and whose strength and other personal attributes were unknown to him.

In the study herd as a whole, which also included ten adult does, three yearling does, and two fawns, all adult bucks were dominant over all the does, but the status of the yearling bucks was in flux, with some does being dominant over them and others not, approximating conditions in the wild. The does also established a hierarchy, based on biting, as 3,836 interactions recorded intermittently by my assistants Ghosh and Goswami over a period of ten months showed. Reversals were more common (5.4 percent) than among the bucks, and there were four pairs of does who seemingly failed to settle their respective positions in the rank order completely. There was no evidence of a hierarchy among free-living chital does. It is likely that when any group of mammals remains together for a prolonged period, either voluntarily in the wild or without choice in captivity, some form of social organization based on priority rights will become established if competitive situations such as limited food and mates exist. The fact that chital does in captivity have a hierarchy illustrates merely that they have the propensity to form one and does not provide evidence for its occurrence in the wild.

Sexual Behavior

The weight of the testes of white-tailed deer in temperate climates fluctuates seasonally, reaching a maximum during the fall rut and a minimum from late winter to early summer. Similarly, the output of testosterone rises with the shedding of the velvet and remains high for several months, then diminishes before the antlers are dropped (Severinghaus and Cheatum, 1956). It is probable that chital bucks follow a similar hormonal cycle, which, however, is not synchronized in the whole population according to the seasons but follows its own characteristic pattern in each buck. An increased level of testosterone results in more sexual behavior and aggression, two activities often so complementary in deer that separation is sometimes difficult. It is, for example, common to read in the literature such a statement as "the stags fight for hinds" (Brander, 1923), when in fact fighting seems to be related primarily to dominance, a high rank giving in turn priority to estrous females.

One of the most obvious behavior patterns of rutting bucks is bellowing, with the animal emitting a series of 2 to 10 hoarse calls at the rate of about one per second. The number of bellows in a series was counted 459 times. The average number during the peak of the rut from March to June was 4.2 and during the rest of the year 3.7. The majority (96 percent) of the bellows were given by bucks with antlers 31 inches long and over (Table 19). The calls of one buck frequently elicited bellows from one or two others in the vicinity. Most bellowing occurred around dawn and dusk, the time when mating activity in general reached its daily peaks. The bel-

TABLE 19

FREQUENCY OF VARIOUS SEXUAL BEHAVIOR PATTERNS
IN THE ANTLER-SIZE CLASSES OF CHITAL BUCKS

Antler-Size Class	Bellowing	*Flehmen*	Driving, Tending, and/or Chasing	Mounting and/or Attempted Mounting	Copulation	Percent of Bucks in Antler-Size Class in Population
Total number of observations	56	52	135	13	2	
31 inches+ .	96%	67%	58%	46%	100%	23%
21–30 inches .	4	8	27	8	0	19
11–20 inches .	0	7	11	8	0	23
Spikes. . . .	0%	18%	4%	38%	0%	35%

lows appeared to function primarily as auditory complements to the visual and olfactory signals left by the buck in his environment during agonistic displays, and they perhaps also attracted does in estrus.

Rutting bucks are exceedingly restless. They roam widely, often at a fast walk or trot; they lick their lips and occasionally bellow or thrash a bush with their antlers. If they spot a herd they either join it, or if a large buck is already present, they may veer past it and continue their wanderings. One buck observed on February 17 behaved typically. At 0630 hours he walked alone across the meadow. At 0650 hours he joined 3 does, 1 fawn, and a buck in velvet. He left the herd three minutes later after sniffing the vulva of two of the does. At 0930 hours he associated for five minutes with 2 bucks and 2 does before continuing alone again. At 1715 I spotted him once more, this time with 4 does and 1 fawn. Stebbing (1911) and Brander (1923) gave the impression that a chital buck collects a harem of does, and Lydekker (1924) implied that large herds remain under the jurisdiction of one "master bull." Chital bucks make no attempt to collect and retain a number of does, nor do they establish and defend a territory. Instead, bucks join a succession of herds in search of a receptive doe, a pattern of behavior similar to that used by the *Odocoileus* deer (Taber and Dasmann, 1958; W. Taylor, 1956).

When a buck enters a herd, he usually sniffs the anal area of one or more does or pokes them there with his muzzle. This gesture sometimes stimulates the doe to urinate. The buck then either holds his nose in the stream of urine, licking vigorously, or he sniffs the ground, afterward raising his head slightly above the horizontal with an upcurled lip, a gesture termed *flehmen* by Walther (1958), Buechner and Schloeth (1965), and others. The buck is apparently able to determine the doe's state of receptivity by her odor, and if she is in heat or approaching it, he attempts to remain with her. He grazes by her side, usually staying parallel to and within six feet of her, he follows when she walks off, and he lies down when she does. McHugh (1958) referred to such behavior as "tending" in the American bison. When the doe stands still, the buck may poke her with his nose as if to induce her to move, and he chases after her at full speed if she runs. His penis is occasionally unsheathed, and he may emit a hoarse, moaning sound.

When approaching a doe rapidly, the buck sometimes assumes a posture which corresponds roughly to one which Geist (1964a) called the "low-stretch" in the mountain goat. The neck is lowered and held parallel to the ground, but the head is slightly raised with the antlers lying along the back; the ears are held laterally, making the white insides conspicuous when seen from the front. Linsdale and Tomich (1953) noted a similar posture in the mule deer. The stance resembles the submissive posture employed by does except that the raised head resembles the head-up of bucks. It is possible that the low-stretch contains components of both dominance and submission, signifying that, although approach is rapid, attack is not intended.

The head-up display, described earlier in conjunction with dominance behavior, is also given by courting bucks. Whereas in dominance the display is brief and exhibited primarily as the buck faces or approaches another animal, in courtship the actions are more prolonged and intense, and the buck is commonly standing parallel to the doe or following her. With muzzle raised, head slightly averted, neck somewhat s-shaped, and tail held vertically, the buck prances beside or behind the doe, lifting and placing his forelegs in exaggerated fashion. His tongue flicks in and out, and when she ceases to move, he may stand beside her and stamp a forefoot on the ground. The use of the head-up display in both aggressive and sexual situations points to a close relationship of the two patterns, and the response of the doe probably depends on her physiological state: she avoids the buck when not receptive but is attracted to him when in heat. Pruitt (1960) also noted a similarity in the threat and courtship displays of caribou.

The head-up display, sniffing, chasing, and other patterns are given repeatedly in no particular sequence as the buck and doe remain together, usually becoming separated from the herd as they feed and rest at intervals. A receptive doe makes no attempt to escape from the buck, and even though she sometimes bounds away at great speed, she merely circles and returns to him if he has not followed her. At intervals he places his chin on her rump, then mounts. She usually steps ahead, causing him to fall off, but when fully receptive, she stands or walks slowly with her back humped and tail held horizontally. Two copulations were observed in the wild. In each instance the buck thrusted so violently after penetrating the vagina once or twice that the doe was propelled forward several feet. No postcoital display occurred. While the buck licked his genitals, the doe walked off slowly. The courtship may continue for several hours, judging from the behavior of captives, but it was not possible to keep a pair in sight the whole time in the wild. The prolonged sequence of events leading to copulation probably stimulates the animals and synchronizes them physiologically, making the actual coitus very brief. Two detailed examples describe the behavior of rutting bucks around estrous does:

1) 1655 hours. A large buck stands near a herd of 13 animals and thrashes a tuft of grass with his antlers. He joins another herd of about 20 animals some 300 feet away and assumes the head-up display parallel to and 5 feet from a doe. As she walks slowly, he remains beside her; when she stops, he does, too. She urinates, and he sniffs the ground, then curls his lip. Suddenly he leaves the doe and at a trot rejoins the first herd, mingling with it for 10 minutes, his penis unsheathed. He bellows. Once again he walks to the other herd. One doe is lying, and he touches noses with her. He then sniffs her vulva and, after she rises, the ground. Without paying her further attention, he leaves and joins a third herd which has appeared 300 feet away at the forest's edge. After sniffing the rump of one doe, he belabors a tuft of grass with his antlers, both pawing and urinating while doing so. At 1750 hours he follows a grazing doe and keeps in step with her as she moves along. A small fawn tags behind.

2) 0640 hours. A large buck and a doe are 300 feet from a herd of 17 chital. He places his chin on her rump several times, but she either trots ahead or gallops in a circle. When he mounts, she jumps forward, circles, and touches his muzzle with hers. He mounts twice more. A yearling buck trots over from the herd but retreats when the large buck jerks his antlers down at him. He mounts 4 times in succession, then prances beside her in the head-up display; he places his chin on her rump, then bellows 6 times. Again he assumes the head-up, standing beside her as she grazes in cursory fashion. The yearling buck has drifted over again, and the large buck takes a threatening step in his direction before resuming the head-up display. The doe walks to the yearling buck, which has been joined by two adult bucks with antlers in velvet. The large buck threatens the yearling with lowered antlers, ignoring the two other bucks. Another large buck, in size equal to the courting one, appears nearby and approaches to within 60 feet before beginning to graze. The large buck leaves the doe and chases the newcomer for 50 feet at a run. Then he rubs his antlers vigorously on a tree trunk and finally returns to the doe. Both move from sight at 0715 hours.

A buck with antlers in velvet placed his chin on the rump of a doe on two occasions, and a doe mounted another one on four occasions. Fawns, one to six months old, attempted to mount a doe ten times, behavior probably released by the conformation of the female's rump or the odor eminating from her vulva.

In order to determine if all bucks participate equally in the rut, the frequency of occurrence of several sexual behavior patterns in each of the four antler-size classes was noted (Table 19). All observed instances of bellowing and *flehmen* were tallied. Driving and the associated displays are listed only if these patterns were neither preceded nor succeeded by mounting or attempted mounting while the animals were under observation. Table 19 thus gives an indication of the total number of instances of sexual behavior observed and the total number of bucks involved. The largest bucks were sexually at least twice and sometimes almost three times as active as expected: one-fourth of the buck population accounted for over 50 percent of all instances of sexual behavior. Although only two copulations were observed, there is no reason to doubt that these large bucks are also responsible for over half of the conceptions. Yearling bucks rarely chase does or display the head-up to them, but mounting and attempts to do so are frequent. In the white tailed deer, sexual maturity is reached at eighteen months (Severinghaus and Cheatum, 1956), an age which probably corresponds closely with maturity in the chital buck. It is unlikely that yearlings mate successfully very often, especially since most of them come into rutting condition during the monsoon after the peak of the rut. A high rank in the dominance hierarchy is clearly of sexual advantage to the individual, as the close correlation between large antler size and mating activity shows. The genetic selective advantage of being dominant during the rut is therefore great, as Darling (1937) and Allee (1952) have pointed out.

FEMALE-YOUNG RELATIONS

The association between a doe and her fawn persists for about twelve months until she withdraws to give birth again. After the newborn begins to accompany its mother, the fawn of the previous year, now a yearling, often rejoins the doe for another three to eight months. Yearling does sometimes remain with an adult until nearly two years old, whereas yearling bucks have usually become independent by about fifteen months of age.

The doe becomes solitary at least three days before parturition and remains in the vicinity of a patch of dense brush and high grass. The newborn fawn spends most if not all of the first week after birth hidden in the vegetation while the doe remains in the general vicinity. Occasionally I came across a female with a tiny fawn shakily at heel moving from one thicket to another, but usually fawns were not encountered until fully co-ordinated. The young are not found regularly with a herd until at least ten days old, and even then they spend much time lying down while their mother feeds.

Goswami observed one fawn in the Calcutta Zoological Garden immediately after birth. It first attempted to stand up at about thirty-five minutes of age and finally succeeded in doing so when seventy-five minutes old. The doe expelled and ate the placenta two hours after parturition. By then the youngster was able to stand well, and it tried to run. Although still somewhat unsteady on its feet at one day of age, it ran, walked, and jumped playfully on the following day. It rested in a corner of the enclosure for most of the first week of its life while the doe was with the herd, but the age of eleven days it was commonly seen with the other animals.

The doe licks the head, neck, body, and anal area of the newborn fawn frequently and intensively. The fawn observed by Goswami was licked almost continuously for three hours following parturition. Although such licking undoubtedly has sanitary functions, the behavior also appears to play an important role in establishing and strengthening the social bond between female and young, as suggested by several of Ghosh's observations on a fawn one to three days old: (1) The young has a tendency to follow any chital in its vicinity, but when it does so, its mother approaches immediately and begins to lick its body. (2) The doe walks along, closely followed by the fawn. When the young stops and sniffs at other chital, the doe returns and licks it. (3) The doe licks the fawn, then walks ahead with the young following behind. The fawn drifts to one side and stands beneath another doe. Its mother returns, licks it, and again moves away, this time with the young at heel. Pruitt (1960) described a head-bobbing movement by which a caribou female induces a young to follow her. Chital appear to lack such a specialized visual signal and instead rely partly on physical contact in the form of licking. After the fawn reaches the age of about ten days and the social bond with its mother is presumably fully established, the frequency of licking decreases sharply. Of 46 instances of licking observed in the wild, not including bucks licking the vulvas of does, females licked young 32 times, the reverse occurred 7 times, and does licked each other 7 times, indicating that licking is primarily a social gesture between doe and fawn.

Suckling or attempted suckling was observed on 61 occasions in the wild, all young except one being four months old or less. A fawn characteristically ducked between the doe's front legs, butted the udder vigorously once or twice, an action which apparently stimulates the flow of milk (Amoroso and Jewell, 1963), then suckled with tail in a vertical position and one foreleg pawing the air. In 15 percent of the instances, the doe stepped away without permitting the young to feed. The fawn approached from between the front legs 75 percent of the time and from either side or from behind in the remaining instances. The duration of suckling averaged 32 seconds, with a variation of from 5 to 55 seconds. The doe always terminated the activity by walking away. One young, estimated to be two weeks old, nibbled on grass.

Captive fawns suckle frequently, sometimes four or five times in the course of a morning, either on their own mother or on other does. One fawn, born on December 19 and observed by Ghosh for several months, attempted to suckle on a doe other than its mother at the age of five days but was bitten. At the age of eleven days it was seen to suckle on three different females including its mother. After that the youngster commonly suckled on a doe which lacked a fawn

TABLE 20

FREQUENCY AND DURATION OF SUCKLING BY A CAPTIVE MALE CHITAL FAWN, BORN DECEMBER 19, ON ITS MOTHER AND ON A FEMALE NOT ITS MOTHER

DATE	MOTHER		ANOTHER DOE	
	Total Instances of Suckling	Average Duration of Suckling/Sec.	Total Instances of Suckling	Average Duration of Suckling/Sec.
December 19–31	18	65	4	53
January 1–31	51	66	50	57
February 1–29	54	69	97	77
March 1–13	7	44	24	65

of her own, and by the age of two months it spent more time away from than with its mother (Table 20). Although this was an extreme case, six of the ten adult does in the herd accepted suckling from one or more fawns other than their own.

The frequency with which young became separated from their mothers in the wild was striking. Does sometimes wandered alone through the forest looking alertly in all directions, obviously searching for something as they emitted nasal bleats; fawns were encountered in similar circumstances. A single doe was occasionally followed by two, three, and in one instance seven small young of different ages. Fawns became separated by straying from their mothers' sides and by failing to note their departures. Once, for example, a herd left a water hole, then another herd departed, and remaining alone was a fawn standing in the middle of a group of twenty-five langurs. Sometimes doe and fawn found each other by bleating, but in many instances, of which the following was typical, a fawn simply followed any doe that accepted it. A small fawn in a scattered herd gave several high-pitched yips. A doe bleated in answer one hundred fifty feet away. The fawn ran to her, and they touched noses, odor apparently being a means of recognition; but the female was not its mother, for it stood seemingly undecided by her side for a few seconds, then drifted off. When the herd moved into the forest, the fawn remained alone on the meadow. A solitary doe approached. The youngster dashed two hundred feet in her direction, stopped abruptly eighty feet away, then ran back to the spot from which it had come, apparently having noted that the female was not its mother. The doe drank at a nearby water hole, and as she headed back into the forest, the fawn tagged along sixty feet behind her.

Many of the lost fawns probably find their mothers on subsequent days, for the ranges of the animals are small and certain sites like water holes are visited repeatedly. Although some does bite strange fawns, it is likely that most lost ones attach themselves permanently to certain females. In an environment where predation is heavy and orphaned fawns probably fairly common, the general tolerance of does for strange fawns is clearly a useful adaptation.

PLAY

Playful behavior was seen on about thirty occasions, predominantly in fawns. Most play consisted of dashing along, bucking, dodging, and kicking the hindlegs up into the air. Such actions on the part of one animal frequently stimulated others in the vicinity to behave similarly, and even adults sometimes bucked once or twice. The most prevalent forms of mutual play were chasing and follow-the-leader, with as many as seven fawns bounding along in single file, their tails raised. On three occasions two fawns "locked antlers" in typical adult fashion. Once a young chased a mynah bird.

Play was very infrequent during the hot season, but on June 20, with the first heavy rain of the monsoon, the whole chital population behaved exuberantly. One herd of eighty-five chital thundered in a big semicircle at full speed; then individuals bucked and chased each other. Animals which were foraging leisurely suddenly leaped into the air and broke into a brief gallop, soon drawing the whole herd with them as they raced along.

Comparisons with Hog Deer

A brief comparison of the behavior of the hog deer (*Axis porcinus*) with that of the chital is of interest since both species belong to the same genus, they have been known to interbreed in captivity (Pocock, 1910; Crandall, 1964), and their range overlaps extensively.

The hog deer is heavy-set and compact, standing only 27 to 28 inches high at the shoulder (Jerdon, 1874). Its chunky appearance and habit of crashing away through the undergrowth have undoubt-

edly contributed to its popular name. The antlers are about 10 to
15 inches long, three-tined, and set on tall pedicels. The winter coat
is dark brown, the summer one chestnut brown covered with faint
to conspicuous white spots; the fawns are spotted.

The hog deer is or was distributed throughout the basins of the
Indus, Ganges, and Brahmaputra rivers into Burma and Thailand
(Dollman and Burlace, 1935), but the species is not found in central
and southern India. Its preferred habitat is the reed beds and
swampy meadows bordering streams (Finn, 1929; Peacock, 1933),
extensive forests being generally avoided. In Corbett National Park
they were observed occasionally in the valley of the Ramganga
River but not in the surrounding hills; in the West Kheri they were
common on the low-lying marshy meadows bordering the sal forests;
and in the Kaziranga Sanctuary they were abundant in the vast
grass thickets.

The sex ratio of adults was about equal or favored the does only
slightly (Table 21), in contrast to the chital which has a disproportionate sex ratio favoring females. The ratio of fawns to does at a
time of the year when the great majority of young were five to ten
months old was about 42:100 (Table 21); no small fawns were seen
except for two newborn ones in West Kheri. One fawn per doe is
the rule, although Zuckerman (1953) reported the birth of twins
in the London zoo.

According to Prater (1934), Blandford (1888–91), and Lydekker
(1898), the rut of the hog deer occurs during September and Oc-

TABLE 21

AGE AND SEX RATIOS OF HOG DEER IN SEVERAL LOCALITIES

Location	Date	Sample Size	Buck	: 100 Does :	Fawns
Corbett National Park	January 23– February 8	44	90	100	42
West Kheri Forest	February 25– March 5	105	75	100	44
Kaziranga Sanctuary. . .	April 30– May 7	290	103	100	39

tober. After a gestation period of eight months (Brown, 1936; Sclater, 1863; Lydekker, 1898), the fawns are then born in April and
May (Prater, 1948). My observations suggest that the period of mating is more prolonged than indicated by the literature. The newborn
young seen in late February were probably conceived the previous
July. Only 1 out of 11 adult bucks seen at Corbett Park in late January had shed his antlers, but a month later 12 of 30 bucks in the

West Kheri forest had just done so. Observations on 4 bucks in the Calcutta zoo showed that about three months elapse between the shedding of one set of antlers and the completed growth of the new set. Thus a buck which loses his antlers in February is in hard antler again by June. The rut of the hog deer in Uttar Pradesh seemed to run from about June to January, with a peak in September and October. The time of rut in the Kaziranga Sanctuary and in Uttar Pradesh appeared to differ somewhat. Of 100 adult bucks tallied in early May in the former area, 2 were in velvet, 1 was just shedding the velvet, and the rest were in hard antler. The animals were in full rut, indicating that mating commenced there at least one month earlier than at Corbett and Kheri. Hog deer in captivity mate at all seasons (Bedford and Marshall, 1942), and young are born throughout the year, but principally during the first half of it (Crandall, 1964).

The hog deer is said to be unsociable and essentially solitary, collecting at times into groups of 2 to 5 individuals (Prater, 1934; Peacock, 1933) but never into herds (Lydekker, 1898). Seventeen of 44 animals tallied in Corbett Park were solitary, and a doe with fawn was seen on seven occasions. The two largest herds consisted of 1 buck, 2 does, and 1 fawn, and of 4 bucks and 1 doe; but in early February, 1966, Spillett (pers. comm.) saw herds of some 40 hog deer there, which, however, had dispersed by the end of the month. In West Kheri, where the deer were more abundant than at Corbett, they had a similar social structure, except that herds containing 4 and 5 individuals were quite prevalent. One herd consisted of 7 animals — 4 does and 3 fawns — and another of 13, but I was unable to classify them all. The hog deer in the Kaziranga Sanctuary were found principally in the short-grass areas surrounding the scattered ponds. The largest herd seen numbered about 40 individuals, and herds of about 20 were common. The composition of two such herds was 8 bucks, 13 does, and 5 fawns for a total of 26, and 5 bucks, 11 does, and 5 fawns for a total of 21. Such herds never moved or fled as co-ordinated units, and when disturbed, the animals scattered in all directions.

Although hog deer are essentially solitary, they apparently congregate at the time of the rut and at certain feeding sites. The behavior of rutting deer was observed at one locality in the Kaziranga Sanctuary from 0755 to 1615 hours on May 4. From 5 to 15 hog deer were visible throughout the day. Animals appeared single and in pairs at the edge of the high grass and formed a loose aggregation. While the does and young grazed, the bucks roamed around. One sniffed the spot where a doe had urinated, curled his lip, and then chased a nearby buck for 60 feet. One buck assumed the head-up display while standing parallel to a doe—his tail was raised and his muzzle held high as he pranced beside her. When she ran he chased after her, and when she lay down he remained beside her in head-up. Finally both disappeared in the high grass. A buck squirted urine twice on a spot before lying down on it, behavior not observed in the chital. It appears that does and bucks leave the high grass and congregate in the open areas where they can see and display to each other. If a receptive doe is present, the most vigorous and presumably the dominant buck in the herd at that time first courts her, then leaves the area with her. Numerous isolated pairs consisting of a doe followed closely by a buck were seen in the high grass. The sites at which hog deer congregate were thus little more than places where bucks could find and pick up a doe.

Only a few instances of aggressive behavior were observed. One buck stood fifteen feet from his opponent and pawed the ground, his head held low and slightly averted; another buck thrashed a tuft of grass with his antlers; and once two bucks suddenly jerked down their heads and rushed forward, locking their antlers with a crash. One buck in the Calcutta zoo approached another in a head-up display, stiff-legged, muzzle raised, and tail horizontal. Two bucks in Corbett Park gave the head-down display: as one stood still with head lowered and averted, the other slowly circled and at the same time sidled closer, his gait stiff, his ears laid back, and his head lowered. The tails of both animals were raised vertically and tipped slightly toward each other.

Alarmed hog deer raise their necks and tails, occasionally stamp a forefoot, and emit barks which resemble those of the chital but are flatter in tone and more nasal. A fleeing animal displays the white erectile hairs on the rump and the fluffy white underside of the tail and occasionally thumps the hindlegs in unison.

The behavior of the hog deer is in many respects similar to that of the chital, especially in its various aggressive, courtship, and alarm displays. Basic differences lie in the hog deer's solitary nature and in its social organization during the rut. Except for the great discrepancy in size between the chital and hog deer and a preference for somewhat different types of habitat, there seem to be no striking differences between the two species that would prevent them from mating with each other. However, the peak of the rut of the chital in northern India is about May and June, whereas that of the hogdeer is not until September and October.

CHAPTER 4

THE BARASINGHA

Five elephants moved slowly through the yellow marsh grass in a broad front. A mahout sat on the neck of each one, urging the animal on by digging his toes in behind its ears. In all directions spread tall reeds and glistening sloughs and pools. Somewhere to the left was the Sarda River and far to our right stretched the dark line of trees of the Kheri forest. It was silent except for the swishing of grass against the elephants' bodies. Suddenly the water churned and the reeds shook ahead of us, and galloping up onto a slight rise was a herd of over five hundred barasingha. The brown, undulating mass thundered along, one moment crowded together, the next split into several weaving lines as it disappeared over the skyline and back into the cover of the grass. Sitting on the back of a swaying elephant, and looking at the vast number of deer and the wild country around me, I had a glimpse into the past, a vision of India as it was a hundred and more years ago. But this was the last large herd of barasingha in existence.

The barasingha (*Cervus duvauceli*) has declined so drastically in number in recent years that the continued existence of the species in the wild state is not assured under present conditions. To learn as much as possible about the habits of the animal while it still survived, I studied it at Kanha Park and also observed and censused it in other parts of its range.

Ellerman and Morrison-Scott (1951) recognize two subspecies, *C.d. branderi* from central India and *C.d. duvauceli* from northern and eastern India.

93

Description

The barasingha resembles the red deer in size and appearance. It is a large, graceful deer, standing 44 to 46 inches high at the shoulder (Blanford, 1888–91). Published weights of stags include one of 370 pounds (Brander, 1923) and two of 460 and 570 pounds (Cooch Behar, 1908), the latter two being the heaviest of many shot; two captive hinds weighed 305 and 320 pounds (Crandall, 1964).

Barasingha show a marked seasonal change in coat color. The animals in their summer coat are a rich chestnut brown on the back, somewhat lighter brown on the sides and belly, and creamy white on the inside of the legs, rump, and underside of the tail (Plate 6). A dark brown band, bordered by white spots, runs down the length of the spine. The chin and the throat are whitish and so are the insides of the ears. The winter coat of hinds, acquired by November, is of dull to grayish brown. The white spots and the dark band along the back are not discernible or only faintly so in both sexes. Adult stags have a long, coarse, dark brown, almost black, coat, considerably darker than that of hinds and young stags (Plate 7). The hairs on the neck are up to five inches long, giving the animal a prominent ruff. One stag was seen with frost on his back, attesting to the insulating quality of the winter coat. The molt begins in March and by mid-May all animals are in their summer pelage, although a few may retain patches of old hair. The fawns have brown coats without spots.

The first indications of the antlers are small bumps on the frontal bones, which appear at about seven months of age in the fawn. Yearling stags have simple spike antlers. The first set of adult antlers consist usually of a brown tine and a main beam with one or two forks. The antlers of fully adult animals are very characteristic of the species, with the main beam sweeping upward for over half of its length before branching repeatedly in the distal third (Plate 7). The name "barasingha" literally means "twelve-tined." Of 46 adult stags tallied in 1964 and 1965 at Kanha, 28 percent had antlers with 6 to 9 tines, 33 percent had 10 or 11 tines, 30 percent had 12 tines, and 9 percent had 13 or 14 tines. Record antler length is 41 inches (Ward, 1922). Pocock (1912) illustrates five stages of growth in the barasingha antler.

There was a slight regional variation in the appearance of the barasingha. The summer coat of the animals seemed to be of a deeper and richer chestnut color in the Kaziranga Sanctuary than at Kanha; and the winter coat of adult stags appeared to be darker on the average at Kanha than in the Kheri forest. The antlers of the stags in the Kheri area were lighter in color than those at Kanha, presumably as a result of having been rubbed against the tall grass in the marshy habitat.

Distribution and Status

GEOGRAPHICAL AND ECOLOGICAL DISTRIBUTION

In former times the barasingha was distributed in suitable localities throughout the basins of the Indus, Ganges, and Brahmaputra rivers as well as in central India as far south as the Godavari River. Bones probably belonging to barasingha were found in the Langhnaj site of Gujarat dating back about two thousand years (Clutton-Brock, 1965), but the species has disappeared from the western part of its range together with the rhinoceros and elephant (Burton, 1952). Blanford (1888–91) gave the distribution in the past century as "along the base of the Himalayas from Upper Assam, in a few places in the Indo-Gangetic plain from the Eastern Sundarbans to Bahawalpur to Rohri in Upper Sind, and locally throughout the area between the Ganges and Godavari as far east as Mandla."

Near the turn of the twentieth century the species survived primarily in the marshes bordering the Himalayas and along some of the rivers in the Gangetic basin from about 78°E. latitude eastward to West Bengal. It also occurred in the Sunderbans (Prater, 1934) and surrounding areas, with some animals being killed near the town of Midnapore (Jerdon, 1874). In Assam, barasingha were common in the Brahmaputra River valley, where as late as 1934 a good number survived in the Goalpara, Kamrup, Nowgong, Sibanger, and Danang districts (Bhadian, 1934).

In central India, barasingha were found in scattered pockets mostly south of the Narmada River in what is now the state of Madhya Pradesh. Brander (1923) mentioned their presence in the Mandla, Bilaspur, Raipur, Balaghat, and Bastar districts, and one population is also said to have occurred in the Shapure Range near Dindori, north of the Narmada River. According to Finn (1929) one population had existed near Pachmarhi (about 78°30'E., 22°30'N.) but died out. Brander (1923) also recorded the barasingha from eastern Maharashtra state, primarily in the Chanda District.

Today the barasingha exists only in a few isolated pockets (Fig. 7). Its main center of survival is in the West Kheri Forest Division near the Sarda River in Uttar Pradesh and the adjoining area of south-

FIG. 7.—The distribution of barasingha. The black spots indicate areas where barasingha have been reported to exist as late as 1960. (For details see Table 21.)

western Nepal. Scattered small herds also occur in northern Bengal and in Assam. No barasingha have been sighted in the Sunderbans for many years by the Forest Department, and the deer has undoubtedly disappeared from there. The surviving populations in central India are small, and all are on the verge of extinction.

PLATE 6.—A herd of ten barasingha stags rest at mid-morning on the Kanha meadow; all are in their summer coat and all have antlers in velvet (July 29, 1964).

PLATE 7.—A barasingha stag expresses his dominance with the head-up display; the threatened stag has his head averted in submission; all stags are in their winter coats (March 8, 1964).

PLATE 8.—Typical barasingha habitat in northern India at Ghola, West Kheri, Uttar Pradesh, consisting of tall grasses and swampy ground. The elephants were used to census the deer (March 2, 1965).

PLATE 9.—Two barasingha stags spar (March 8, 1964).

PLATE 10.—A barasingha herd rests and grazes at the forest's edge; one hind threatens another with a head-up display (March 16, 1964).

PLATE 11.—A barasingha wallow (February 1, 1964).

The past and present range of the species encompasses a wide variety of forest types, including dry and moist deciduous forest, mangrove forest, and evergreen and semi-evergreen forest. However, the animals once reached their greatest abundance in the grasslands and reed beds bordering the major rivers in the northern part of their range (Champion, 1927; Inglis, 1892; Pollock and Thom, 1900), where, because of periodic inundations, forests grew only in patches or not at all. This type of habitat still exists in the Kaziranga Sanctuary, where the flat alluvial plains are covered with grasses up to fifteen feet high, the expanse broken here and there by small pools and patches of forest on higher, drier ground; it is also found in the western part of the animals' present range in the Kheri Forest Division, where the ground is either swampy as at Ghola (Plate 8) or sandy as along the banks of the Sarda River. But, to repeat, the animals also occur in certain forested areas, particularly in sal forests as Finn (1929) has pointed out. Sal is the principal forest type in and surrounding much of the barasingha's habitat in Uttar Pradesh and Nepal, in northwestern Assam, and in Madhya Pradesh. Dry deciduous forest has not been extensively occupied, although populations once occurred in the West Bastar and Chanda districts where this type predominates.

Within each vegetation type the species is found primarily in areas with the following attributes: (1) open localities consisting either of marshes and grasslands or woodlands with an understory of grasses, (2) water, and (3) flat to moderately hilly terrain. As pointed out below (see Food Habits, p. 111), barasingha subsist almost exclusively on grasses. Grass is not a conspicuous component of forests with a closed canopy, such as primary evergreen forest, and it is possible that the lack of suitable forage was once a major factor in limiting the distribution of the species in eastern India to the vicinity of the major rivers. Although the barasingha are found predominantly in marshy grasslands in northern India, they are almost wholly confined to relatively dry forests in central India. But water for daily drinking and for wallowing during the rut appears to be essential, and even in their forest environment they have a marked tendency to enter pools of water, sometimes up to their necks, while drinking and feeding.

Another factor which has influenced the distribution of the barasingha is their avoidance of extensive steep terrain like the foothills of the Himalayas. The large grass meadows in Corbett Park have been in existence at least since 1840 (Srivastava, 1957), but they have not been colonized, the animals having failed to venture over the one or two ridges that separate their habitat in the plains from that in the foothill valleys. On the other hand, the barasingha readily climb into the low hills at Kanha, and Forsyth (1889) noted that they congregated on the plateaus during the rut.

NUMBERS AND STATUS

Table 22 gives the localities where barasingha still occur or where they have been seen since about 1960. A few small herds may have been overlooked, especially along the Assam-Bhutan border, but otherwise the list is probably complete. The population figures are rough estimates in most instances, but they reflect the precarious position of the animals in the various localities.

E. P. Gee and R. Willan investigated the status of the barasingha in Nepal in 1963. Their population estimates vary from 400 (Gee) to 1,200 (Willan) in southwestern Nepal, with a few also surviving in the Rapti valley of the Chitawan Division, where Gee (pers. comm.) saw five animals in 1959 and G. Hyde (pers. comm.) a few in 1963.

Several small isolated populations still exist in Uttar Pradesh. Although the state government has since 1958 established five sanctuaries for the preservation of the barasingha, and although the animal is strictly protected throughout the state, the deer in three of them have been almost exterminated by poachers. Some survive in the Jaulasal Sanctuary where I heard stags calling in late October, 1963. Forest rangers told me of occasionally seeing herds of up to 20 individuals in the South Kheri Forest Division. Foot transects for two days through the supposed main area of concentration of the species there revealed only a few tracks and fecal droppings. One or two small herds occur also in the grass thickets bordering the Ganges River according to Dang (pers. comm.). The only area in Uttar Pradesh where the barasingha is locally common is between the Sarda River and the Nepal border in the West Kheri Forest Division. There in an area of roughly ten thousand acres of marsh, grassland, and forest near the Neora and Soheli rivers and an adjacent tract called Ghola, some 800 barasingha were tallied, including one herd of about 500–600 animals. The barasingha population of Utter Pradesh probably does not exceed 1,400 to 1,800 animals.

Gee (pers. comm.) saw 3 barasingha in the Jaldapara Sanctuary in the Cooch Behar division of West Bengal, and two additional animals were spotted by the forest department in 1964 in the Chila-

TABLE 22

DISTRIBUTION AND NUMERICAL STATUS OF THE BARASINGHA IN 1965

Location	Estimate of Numbers	Source
Nepal		
Kanchanpur Division . . .	1,000	R. Willan (pers. comm.)
Bardia Division	200	,, ,, ,,
Banke Division.	A few	,, ,, ,,
Chitawan Division	A few	,, ,, ,,
Kanchanpur and Bardia divisions.	400±	E. Gee (pers. comm.)
Uttar Pradesh		
Jaulasal Sanctuary	Fewer than 100	This study
Lalkua Sanctuary.	Very few, if any	D. Misra (pers. comm.)
Maldhan Sanctuary. . . .	Very few, if any	,, ,, ,,
Sonaripur Sanctuary . . .	Fewer than 50	This study
Along Ganges River, west of Bijnor	Probably some	H. Dang (pers. comm.)
Along Ganges River, west of Chandpur.	100±	,, ,, ,,
Between Hardwar and Luksor	1 doe shot in 1963	Source withheld on request
South Kheri Forest Division.	Fewer than 200	This study
Bahdi Tal, 6 miles west of Bellraen.	A few	A. Singh (pers. comm.)
Mirchia, bordering Nepal .	A few	,, ,, ,,
Ghola and surrounding tracts	800–900	This study
West Bengal		
Jaldapara Sanctuary and surrounding forests . . .	A few	Forest Department; Gee (pers. comm.)
Assam		
Manas Sanctuary.	Perhaps a few	E. Gee (pers. comm.)
Darang Division along Bhutan border	A few	S. Thakur (pers. comm.)
Kaziranga Sanctuary . . .	200–250	This study
Madhya Pradesh		
Kanha National Park. . .	50±	This study
Motinala and Karanjia Ranges, Mandla District.	A few seen	Forest ranger (pers. comm.)
Balaghat District between Baihar and Lamba . . .	Several seen in 1960	D. White (pers. comm.)
Near Amarkantak, Bilaspur District	A few	Forest ranger (pers. comm.)
Near Kota, Bilaspur District	1 stag shot in 1960	Source withheld on request
Madhya Pradesh-Orissa border, Raipur District .	100±	H. Ahmedulla (pers. comm.)
West Bastar Division near Tekemeta	4 seen in 1963	S. Thakur (pers. comm.)
West Bastar Division near Kutru in Toynar and Bhairamgarh Range. . .	Rare	D. R. Kochhar, D.F.O. (pers. comm.)

pata Range adjacent to the sanctuary, indicating that a few stragglers persist in the state.

Scattered individuals may perhaps survive in the Manas Sanctuary (Gee, pers. comm.) and the Darang Division (Thakur, pers. comm.) of Assam along the Bhutan border, but the only known concentration of the barasingha occurs in the Kaziranga Sanctuary. There the species appears to have increased considerably in recent years, from perhaps 20 animals in 1950 (Gee, pers. comm.) to a forest department census tally of 522 in 1963. My population estimate in May, 1965, was 200–250 individuals. Once a herd existed in the Kaki Reserve in the Mikir Hills of Assam, but according to Gee (pers. comm.) it died out in about 1930. It is unlikely that more than 500–600 barasingha survive in eastern India.

Kanha National Park has long been considered the last stronghold of the species in central India, but in 1964 fewer than 100 animals survived there. A forest ranger saw several barasingha in the Motinalla Range 20 miles to the east of the park in 1960, and another ranger told me that some also occurred in the Karanjia Range of the Mandla District. D. White, a resident engineer, reported seeing several animals in the Balaghat District, just south of Mandla District, near the town of Baihar in 1960. To the east, in Bilaspur District, one stag was shot in 1960, but when I queried the district forest officer as to the status of the species he replied "not seen or heard of of late" (letter, August 12, 1964). One small population survives along the Orissa-Madhya Pradesh border (M. Ahmedulla, pers. comm.). Barasingha are reported occasionally from the West Bastar Forest Division, most recently in 1963, but after spending ten days in the area, I was unable to obtain any reliable reports of recent sightings. The continued survival of the species in central India is obviously in doubt; if the two small populations and the scattered individuals are taken into account, there are probably no more than a total of 400 to 500 animals there.

The total population estimates for the various regions range between about 2,700 and 4,100 barasingha; but until further censuses clarify the status of the animal in areas which were not visited during this study, an estimate of fewer than 5,000, and more likely 3,000 to 4,000 animals is indicated.

The preferred habitat of the barasingha — the expanses of grasslands along rivers — is coveted by man for agricultural purposes, with the result that the animal has been progressively driven back as the swamps are replaced by rice and sugar cane fields. The surviving populations in northern India are in reserves like the Kaziranga

Sanctuary or in a few small tracts which have so far not been plowed up. In Uttar Pradesh some of these, such as the South Kheri Forest, are under government jurisdiction and presumably secure from destruction, but the main concentrations of deer exist on private farmland. With an increased demand for food production and a recent government decree designed to cut up all large land holdings, it is unlikely that these remaining marshes can survive for more than a few years. In addition, poaching is exceedingly heavy, with some farmers subsisting entirely on wild meat. A. Singh told me that as late as 1950 herds of 500 and more barasingha were still encountered along the Sarda River near his farm, but that in 1965 only one such herd survived — at Ghola, a 3,000 acre marsh in private hands. Unless the remaining herds in Uttar Pradesh are given immediate and rigid local protection in addition to the legal protection the animal already has, it is unlikely that the species will survive in the state.

The decline in the number of barasingha in central India has been due primarily to unrestricted poaching by villagers, although diseases introduced by cattle may have been a contributing factor. In the West Bastar District, for example, the communal hunts by the tribal peoples indiscriminately destroy the wildlife over large areas so completely that even monkeys are rarely seen.

The prognosis for continued existence of the barasingha in the wild is poor under present conditions. The remaining populations are small, widely scattered, and, with the exception of those in the Kaziranga Sanctuary, declining rapidly because of lack of adequate protection. Most of these remnants have or soon will have reached the point of no return, and the main hope for the species in the wild lies in the rigid maintenance of the Kaziranga Sanctuary and the immediate establishment and subsequent control of reserves in Nepal and the West Kheri Forest Division of Uttar Pradesh.

Population Dynamics

The barasingha in Kanha Park were so few in number that in some respects, such as the duration of the rut and the extent of mortality, the population was probably not wholly typical of a large and vigorous one; thus it is important not to apply data collected there uncritically to other herds.

POPULATION SIZE AND COMPOSITION

The tendency of barasingha to assemble on meadows makes it relatively easy to census them, and the figures obtained by the forest department (Table 2) probably reflect the general size of the population. A census in 1938 gave a figure of 3,023 animals, which, even if greatly in error, points to a large number of animals. The 1912 Mandla District gazetteer, quoted by Nath (n.d.), indicated the widespread occurrence of the animal in the park area: "In cold weather the Barasingha lie up in most of the maidans if they have not been disturbed, particularly in the great maidan east of the Kanha and the neighbourhood of Sharwantalao. The best spots perhaps are Kopedabri and Sonph where Sambhar, Barasingha and Cheetal stay

TABLE 23

Age and Sex Ratios of Barasingha in Several Localities

Location	Date	Approximate Size of Population	Number of Animals Tallied	Stags	: 100 Hinds :	Fawns
Kanha National Park	January 1, 1964	82		90	100	15
Kanha National Park	January 1, 1965	55		104	100	16
West Kheri Forest (A. Singh farm)	February 25– March 5	70–80	140	69	100	40
Kaziranga Sanctuary . .	April 30– May 7	200–250	108	88	100	33

out till comparatively late in the day." The species decreased steadily, however, from 577 in 1958 to 173 in 1963. I searched through all areas in the park formerly occupied by barasingha in 1964 but found them only around the Kanha meadow.

Based on the number of stags, all of which could be recognized individually by their antler pattern, and the largest number of hinds and fawns counted at any one time during the hot season, and adding the animals known to have been killed by predators in the months preceding the census, the number of barasingha surviving on January 1, 1964, was 82 and on January 1, 1965, 55. My figure for 1964 compared quite closely with the one derived by the forest department the same year (Table 2, p. 16). In June, 1965, the forest department counted 109 barasingha, an increase over the previous year explained by immigration from the surrounding forest tracts. My census was made in late March, a time of year when barasingha wander very little. Although it is possible that a few hinds and solitary stags failed to come to the Kanha meadow and were thus not included in the census, the probability that an influx in April and May increased the local population by over 100 percent is very low.

Stags and hinds were present in roughly equal numbers in Kanha Park and in the Kaziranga Sanctuary (Table 23). An attempt was made to obtain composition counts of the large herd at Ghola in West Kheri, but the shyness of the animals coupled with the high grass made this difficult. A total of 185 barasingha were classified, giving an obviously biased ratio of 16 stags to 100 hinds. However, the ratio obtained on the farm of A. Singh appeared to be representative of the population there (Table 23).

The age and sex classes of the Kanha population, expressed as percent of the total, consisted on January 1 of the following.

1964: 37 percent, adult stags; 7 percent, yearling stags; 44 percent, adult
hind; 5 percent, yearling hinds; 7 percent, fawns.
1965: 41 percent, adult stags; 6 percent, yearling stags; 40 percent, adult
hinds; 6 percent, yearling hinds; 7 percent, fawn.

The most striking aspect of these figures is the very low proportion of yearlings (12 percent) and fawns (7 percent). Considerably more fawns were present in the other areas (Table 23), comprising 15 to 19 percent of the population at a time when the majority were over five months old.

THE RUTTING SEASON

Most published sources fail to agree as to when the barasingha ruts. My evidence pertaining to the time of rut is presented separately for central, northern, and eastern India.

Central India. The peak of the rut is from mid-December to mid-January, according to Brander (1923), "and the great mass of the fawns are born in the hot weather, shortly before the rains." This implies a gestation period of only five to six months which is clearly erroneous. Brander (1923) further found that the antlers are shed in April and that the new ones are free of velvet by October. Forsyth (1889) noted that in "about the end of the rains, in September and October, the red deer collect in large herds on the tops of the plateaux; and I have been told of assemblages of several hundred head at that season. They are then beginning to rut. . . ."

The onset of the rut is marked by two prominent behavior patterns, wallowing and bugling (see Sexual Behavior, p. 124). The stags were bugling when I arrived on December 20, 1963, and the last bugle of the season was heard on February 14. In 1964 bugling began on December 17. Wallowing and other forms of sexual behavior, however, had begun by December 9. The frequency of all forms of sexual activity declined after mid-February, although a few instances were seen as long as the stags retained their antlers. The peak of the rut was reached in January.

The first set of adult antlers was shed on May 18 and the last set on July 26, the large-sized stags losing theirs before the small-sized ones. Yearlings began to drop their spikes in mid-July, and the last animal lost his on August 7. All stags were in velvet until mid-October. No stags were encountered between October 18 and December 4, and after the latter date all adults were in hard antler, indicating that the velvet was lost in late October and November.

According to Kenneth (1953) the gestation period of the barasingha is 240 to 250 days, and according to Asdell (1946) it is 250 days, or about 8½ months. With most fawns conceived between mid-December and mid-February, births would be expected in September and October. Although no newborn fawns were found, the physical appearance of the pregnant hinds and a later estimation of the age of the young indicated that the births occurred during this period.

Northern India. The rut in northern India is in November and December, and antlers are shed by April (Prater, 1934). Champion (1933) heard bugling during the latter part of the year and stated that the rut is from autumn to Christmas. Stags in hard antler are found from November to February (Anon., 1956). When I visited the Jaulasal Sanctuary on October 28, 1963, I heard barasingha bugling, and A. Singh told me that the animals can occasionally be heard in late September, or two and a half months earlier than at Kanha. Of 51 adult stags tallied in late February and early March in West Kheri, all were in hard antler except two, which had just lost theirs. A hunter also showed me eight recently dropped antlers. The shedding of antlers thus begins in late February, nearly three months earlier than at Kanha and, according to A. Singh, is largely completed by late April.

The majority of fawns were estimated to be six to eight months old, having been born the previous July and August and hence conceived between mid-October and mid-December. A. Singh has seen newborn fawns in May, conceived in early September. I also noted several fawns which were only two to three months old, having been conceived in March or April. Successful matings can thus occur at any time between September and April, a period when at

least some stags are in hard antler, but the peak of the rut is probably in November.

Eastern India. In eastern India the rut is in late October according
to Lydekker (1898) and in April and May according to Prater (1934)
and Bhadian (1934). The last two authors also stated that the antlers
are shed in February and March, somewhat surprising dates, since
the antlers would then be in velvet at the time of the rut. Wright
(1930) and Prater (1945) found that the velvet is shed in April,
but Bhadian (1934) says this stage is not reached until August.

I visited the Kaziranga Sanctuary in early May, the period for
which the statements in the literature are highly contradictory. Of
43 adult stags tallied, all but 3 were in velvet, and of those in velvet,
77 percent had antlers two to fifteen inches long. If the antler
growth rates at Kanha and Kaziranga are similar, the majority of the
animals had shed their antlers between January and March and
few in November and December. The three stags in hard antler
had lost the velvet recently, and they were in full rut with greatly
swollen neck, a condition which most of the other stags would not
reach for nearly three months. The evidence suggests that rut begins
in late April and lasts until about December, with possibly a peak
around August. Two small fawns, one to two months old, were seen
and several hinds were heavily pregnant, indicating conception during the previous monsoon period, but further details are needed before the peak of the rut can be determined with precision.

Captivity. Eight stags on the estate of the Duke of Bedfored in
England were all in velvet on June 18, 1965, and the gamekeeper
informed me that fawns are born in June and July. The barasingha
at the New York Zoological Park shed their antlers in February and
March, and the main rut is from August to October. All of the 109
fawns born at the zoo were dropped between March and November,
with 82 percent of them coming between April and July (Crandall,
1964). Fifteen births at the London zoo occurred between May and
September (Jarvis and Morris, 1962).

The barasingha shows some striking differences in the time of onset of the rut from area to area—in late April at Kaziranga, in early
September at Kheri, and in early December at Kanha (Fig. 8). The
season of rut was prolonged at Kheri and Kaziranga, lasting some
eight months, judging by the age of the fawns. In contrast, the rut
at Kanha was well defined and concentrated in a two-month period,
with only a limited amount of sexual activity at other times. This
may, however, result from the small size of the population, for the

comment by Forsyth (1889) quoted earlier suggests that in the past the rut may have lasted longer. The peak of the rut also differs from locality to locality: in January at Kanha, in about November at Kheri, and during the monsoon period at Kaziranga.

An attempt to explain the regional variation in the annual sexual cycle by relating it to environmental conditions is difficult (Table 24). Climate, phenology, and other factors are fairly similar in the three localities, the main differences being that at Kaziranga the annual range in temperature is not as extreme and the rainless season

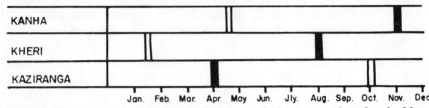

FIG. 8.—The onset of the rut (black bar) and the onset of antler-shedding (white bar) in barasingha in three areas of India.

is shorter and the monsoon longer than in the other areas. As a result Kaziranga remains wet throughout the year, with less fluctuation in the availability of green forage and water than at Kheri and particularly at Kanha. Some 50 to 60 percent of the Kaziranga Sanctuary is inundated during the rainy season, with as much as 99 percent of the area standing under water during the peak floods that occur once every year or two (Gee, pers. comm.).

Changes in the length of day have been known to influence the yearly sexual cycle of mammals in the temperate parts of the world (Amoroso and Marshall, 1956). Since the differences in latitude between study areas are relatively slight, it is unlikely that the amount of daylight has much of an influence on the barasingha. Darling (1937) noted that in the red deer a lowering of the temperature stimulates the rut. The coolest season of the year is from November to February in all three localities, and although at Kanha the animals seemed to respond with an increased level of sexual activity when temperatures suddenly dropped, the Kaziranga population rutted during the monsoon when climatic conditions were relatively constant.

Einarsen (1956) summarized data on fawning, antler-shedding, and mating in the mule deer for various parts of North America; he found that the animals in Alberta, Canada, fawned in the first half of June but that those in Sonora, Mexico, over 20° latitude to the south, fawned in mid-August. The difference was related to the availability of green forage. Some green forage is present at Kaziranga throughout the year; at Kheri most conceptions occur at a time when the grass begins to dry out, and the fawns are born during the monsoon when the food supply is at its peak; at Kanha most mating occurs when the grass is already quite dry, and the young are born at the end of the rainy season. A clear-cut correlation between conception or fawning and the food supply is obviously lacking. Indeed, it may be a mistake to look for one factor that influences the pattern of reproduction in all three areas. Each population is adapted to the environmental conditions in its particular locality, and a factor important in one may be less so in another. Thus it is possible that the seasonal rhythm of the barasingha at Kanha has been influenced

TABLE 24

ENVIRONMENTAL SIMILARITIES AND DIFFERENCES
OF THREE AREAS OCCUPIED BY BARASINGHA

Environmental Factors	Kanha, M.P.	Kheri, U.P.	Kaziranga, Assam
Approximate latitude and longitude . . .	22°45′N.,80°45′E.	28°45′N.,80°30′E.	26°45′N.,93°30′E.
Terrain	Undulating to hilly	Flat to undulating	Flat
Altitude/feet.	1,750–2,900	500	300
Range of temperature. . . .	Light frost to 110°F	Light frost to 110°F	45°–100°F
Average annual precipitation/inches. .	73 (Bichhia)	66 (Ramnagar)	74 (Tezpur)
Main habitat	Sal forest and meadows	Marshy and dry grasslands	Marshy grasslands
Burning of meadows .	December–January	February–March	December–March
Amount of green forage	Scarce during latter part of hot season	Scarce during latter part of hot season	Available in varying amounts throughout year
Monsoon period . . .	Mid-June to early October	Mid-June to early October	Many showers from latter part of April onward with heavy rains from early May to early October
Percent of rain falling during monsoon . .	95	90–95	March–May, 26 June–September, 66
Availability of water.	Scarce March to mid-June	Some permanent streams and marshes present throughout year	Abundant throughout year
Cool season	November– February	November– February	November– February

by the need for short-grass meadows on which to congregate, court, and mate, the presence of a suitable water supply for wallowing, and a high level of nutritious forage during the latter stages of pregnancy in the hinds, a combination of conditions making January the optimum month for mating. Different factors, outweighing those that are important at Kanha, may operate on populations in other areas, making it necessary to study not only the gross environmental differences in each locality but also the fine ones like the nutritional, hormonal, and mineral level of the forage if an explanation for the pattern of a particular sexual cycle is to be found.

RATE OF REPRODUCTION

None of the yearling hinds at Kanha appeared to be pregnant when in August the adults were obviously so. This suggests that the hinds participate actively in their first rut when just over two years old and have their first fawn at the age of about three years, a pattern similar to that found in the red deer (Darling, 1937) and wapiti (Murie, 1951). One fawn is born at a time; there are no records of twins. The barasingha, unlike the chital, is monestrous (Asdell, 1946), and one fawn per year is the rule.

MORTALITY

The drastic decline in the barasingha population in Kanha Park is probably due to both disease and predation. In an autopsy of a part of one animal, I found two species of trematode (*Paramphistomum gotoi* Fukui, 1922, and *Gastrothylax crumenifer* Creplin, 1847) in the rumen. Several animals had reddish hairless patches near the neck during the hot season (Plate 9), seemingly a skin infection, but these disappeared with the molt. Mehta (n.d.) stated that a virulent epidemic of rinderpest occurred in the area in 1925 and 1926, during which many barasingha died. Circumstantial evidence points to the fact that the Kanha population is at present suffering from brucellosis, a bacterial infection caused by *Brucella*, or some similar disease causing spontaneous abortion of the fetus. Brucellosis is common in the cattle of the area, according to the livestock officer at Mandla. Studies in North America have shown that white-tailed deer and other wild hoofed animals are readily infected with the disease (Hayes *et al.*, 1960). I tallied a total of 31 barasingha hinds on July 23, and all except 3 yearlings were heavily pregnant. Yet of 22 adult hinds seen the following March, only 4 were accompanied by fawns. The fawn crop the previous year was similarly poor. This indicates a very high mortality prior to or soon after birth. Although predation undoubtedly accounts for a few of the fawns, the magnitude of the loss suggests a disease like brucellosis, which affects the fetus primarily in the later stages of its development. No blood samples from barasingha were obtained to confirm the presence of the disease, and the other wild ungulates in the area showed no evidence of it. However, if a population is small and relatively concentrated, the infection of even one animal through contact with the expelled fetal matter of a domestic cow, for example, is sufficient to transmit the disease to the other members of the species. Transmission can occur by simple contact through abrasions and inhalation, as well as through milk from hind to fawn and during copulation from stag to hind (Bang, pers. comm.).

During 1964 the known number of barasingha in the park declined from 82 to 55, a loss of 27 animals, or 33 percent of the population. Of the 6 fawns present in 1964, all survived to become yearlings in 1965. Two out of 6 yearling stags were killed by tigers, and one other did not reappear in 1965. Of 4 yearling hinds alive on January 1, 1964, three were seen the following year, one presumably having died. The yearling age class thus declined from 10 to 6 animals, or 40 percent, in one year. I cannot be certain that the same animals were involved in the two censuses, but there is some evidence that they were; for example, three of the fawns present in 1964 were male and three were female, and in 1965 the yearling count showed the same number and proportion of animals. The other deaths were in the adult age class. The remains of barasingha killed by predators were collected throughout the study, and a total of 39 were found. Some of these dated back to 1963 and a few had died in 1965, but at least 16 were killed during 1964, the majority of them by tigers. A few barasingha were probably also shot and snared by villagers when the animals left the vicinity of the Kanha meadow during the latter part of the year, but it was not possible to determine the number killed in this manner.

The decline of the barasingha population was due to low fawn production, probably caused by the disease brucellosis, coupled with heavy predation by man and tiger on the adult segment of the population. The annual increment was only 7 percent for two consecutive years, which was clearly not enough to sustain the population existing under natural predator pressure, much less under the added pressure of poaching by man.

General Behavior

The barasingha remain on or at the periphery of the Kanha meadow from January to August, making observation relatively easy during these months. From September to December, however, most of them scatter widely through the forest, and I was not able to obtain much information for the rest of the year.

DAILY ACTIVITY CYCLE

During the cool season the barasingha graze actively from about 0600 to 0800 hours and then continue to feed in a more cursory fashion until around 0900 hours, when they either move into the shade or rest in the open. From about 1000 to 1630 or 1700 hours most of the animals stand around or lie down, although a herd sometimes grazes intermittently throughout the day. A resting herd is often scattered, with the animals lying here and there, some chewing cud and others seemingly dozing with their chins on the ground and eyes closed. Herds resting at the edge of the forest on hot days

TABLE 25

AMOUNT OF TIME SPENT BY THREE BARASINGHA STAGS
IN VARIOUS FORMS OF ACTIVITY, 0610 TO 1840 HOURS, FEBRUARY, 21, 1964
(IN MINUTES)

Activity	Stag 1	Stag 2	Stag 3
Lying.	431	448	414
Standing without grazing	39	26	59
Walking without grazing	28	18	13
Grazing.	252	258	264
Cud-chewing while lying or standing	25	35	41

are characteristically compact, their diameters being generally 40 to 70 feet or less. On one occasion 37 barasingha all attempted to crowd into a patch of shade 40 feet long that was cast by a solitary tree. They changed positions constantly as those at the periphery tried to push into the center and as those exposed by the movement of the sun sought shade. Yet animals that were in shade one day readily rested in the sun on a following and equally hot day.

Three stags were watched continuously from dawn to dusk on February 21 (Table 25). They grazed until 0756 hours, then rested in the open until 1241 hours, occasionally snacking for five or so minutes, before moving into the shade to continue their siesta until 1550 hours. From 1550 until 1700 hours they stood around, grazed, or rested, then foraged without interruption until 1840 hours. By

2030 hours two of the stags were lying down again. They moved a distance of 650 feet in the course of the day, and at 0725 hours the following morning, they were still within 200 feet of where I had seen them the previous evening. Cud-chewing occurred only between 1230 and 1545 hours. Two of the stags had two cud-chewing sessions each, and one had three. The average number of chews per bolus for one stag was 40 (range 36–47), and the average duration that a bolus was retained in the mouth was 58 seconds (range 50–65). For comparison, the averages for two hinds were 37 chews in 46 seconds and 35 chews in 39 seconds.

One herd of 16 barasingha was watched throughout the night in an area about 600 × 900 feet in size. All animals grazed until 2230 hours, after which a few rested while others fed until 0300 hours. Then all lay down until dawn at 0550 hours. However, two nights later, a herd of 20 barasingha grazed throughout the night within an area 600 × 500 feet, and only a few animals rested at any one time.

The morning activity of the barasingha during the hot season generally ceased by 0700 or 0800 hours, when the animals moved to a shady coppice, and the evening feeding period began at about 1700 hours with a herd filing to a water hole to drink. The schedule of grazing and resting at night remained similar to the one observed during the cool season. With the onset of the rains, the animals were active intermittently throughout the day, without any conspicuous morning and evening peaks of activity.

A prominent behavior pattern of the barasingha was ear-waving, a trait which was displayed only during the hot season of the year. When walking or standing, but particularly when resting in a compact herd, the animals waved their large ears back and forth steadily. There were no bothersome insects, and the behavior was not seen at night. I first noted it in late February when the days grew hot, and it ceased with the beginning of the monsoon. Ear-waving is possibly a cooling mechanism, a fan, so to speak, which circulates the air around the head of the animal.

Food Habits and Feeding and Drinking Behavior

The barasingha are almost exclusively grazers (Tables 10 and 11), although they also eat the leaves of a few shrubs and trees. Many of the grasses eaten by the animals are coarse and dry; in fact, they grazed on dry stalks and leaves of *Eragrostis gangetica*, *Saccharum spontaneum*, and *Vetiveria zizanioides*, among others, in early January when young green shoots were also present. Dry grasses were still being eaten regularly in February, although by then green forage formed the bulk of their diet. This suggests that the animals were attracted to the Kanha meadow in December and January not because green grass was becoming available there but because they were congregating for the rut, as will be discussed below.

Stomach samples were collected from seven animals killed by predators, one in January, four between June and August, and two in September. Six of the seven samples contained 100 percent grass, for the most part coarse blades and stems, with two also showing traces of browsed leaves. One sample collected in September consisted of 90 percent grass and 10 percent dry leaves of an unidentified species.

The animals in a moving herd graze either in a broad front or a loose scattering, most facing in the same general direction (Plate 1). If a herd is stationary, the animals fan out, each foraging with muzzle to the ground, nipping off blades of grass at the rate of about 40 to 50 bites per minute. Frequently an animal grazes while wading in a stream, and on one occasion six barasingha spent over an hour in a small pond submerged to their abdomens and occasionally to their necks while eating a water weed (*Naias*).

Barasingha drink at least twice a day during the hot season, making obvious treks to a water hole soon after daylight and in the late afternoon. Drinking at other seasons is not as regular and perhaps not as frequent.

RANGE AND MOVEMENTS

The annual range of the barasingha could not be determined because most animals are widely scattered through the sal and mixed forests from September to December. Villagers five miles from Kanha told me that barasingha sometimes raid their crops in November, and I have several times seen animals about two miles from the Kanha meadow. The stags in particular roam widely and possibly leave the park for some of the forest tracts to the east; on the other hand, some hinds remain in the vicinity of the Kanha meadow throughout the year.

The barasingha began to congregate on the meadow in December, arriving singly and in pairs, until by early February over three-quarters of the deer in the population were there or had been there but had wandered away again. A few stragglers appeared for the first time in March. About 60 to 65 animals remained around the meadow from April to August. The difference between this figure and the total population estimate of 82 was due mostly to the restlessness of some stags which continued to roam and to the depredation of tigers.

For seven to eight months of the year the majority of the deer frequented an area of about four square miles, of which only about one and a half square miles were used during most of the hot season and the peak of the rut. Herds often confined their meanderings to areas of 100 to 200 acres for several days. In many instances, they moved only 1,000 to 2,000 feet between dawn and dusk and then grazed and rested throughout the night in one corner of the meadow. The movements of the barasingha were not affected much by the availability of green forage, and the animals remained on the meadow during the hot season, eating the coarse grasses which remained in the moist depressions and along ravines.

Response to Predators

The frequent peaceful interactions and other contacts between barasingha, blackbuck, and chital have already been described in conjunction with the last species. The responses of the barasingha to the alarm calls of birds, langurs, and the various ungulates are very similar to those of the chital, as are the postures and gestures used to communicate the existence of possible danger. An alert barasingha holds its neck erect, ears cocked, and faces the disturbance, such as approaching jackal or jungle cat, sometimes sniffing the air with raised muzzle. This posture immediately alerts the other members of the herd, in one instance requiring only five seconds between the time a hind jerked to attention and the last of twenty-eight barasingha behaved similarly. The animal commonly emphasizes the alert posture by raising its tail, which exposes the white rump area, and by audibly stamping a foreleg on the ground. All members of a herd jerked to attention when a stag stamped his foot once in response to my approach. The alarm call of both hinds and stags is a distinctive screaming and roaring bark, repeated many times and interspersed with a few short yips. If danger is imminent, as at the sight of a tiger, the bark rises in pitch, becoming a scream. Under extreme duress, the barasingha emit high-pitched yips. This alarm call was heard only once when a tiger captured a yearling stag, which died after a series of moans. The barking may continue as long as the tiger remains in view. The vocalizations are particularly prolonged if the deer seem to suspect but cannot see a hidden predator. In one such instance several animals barked for forty-five minutes while facing a particular spot.

From late August to October, solitary hinds frequently gave one bark followed by a series of two to ten loud grunts, a vocalization which was not heard at other times of the year. It is possible that the sounds alert newborn fawns to possible danger and stimulate them to hide.

A fleeing deer trots or gallops away, flashing its white rump. If surprised in high grass, it may give a series of high bounds and thump its hindlegs loudly on the ground in unison before proceeding at a more conventional gait. The two forelegs are also thumped occasionally in this manner.

The sight or smell of a tiger appears to arouse the curiosity of the barasingha just as it does the chital. On one occasion a tigress with four cubs rested after a heavy meal in a thicket. Seven stags passed by and scented the tigers, then milled around at the edge of the thicket barking sporadically. One yearling stag entered the undergrowth for a distance of about five feet, as if attempting to obtain a better view in the high grass. On another occasion, thirty-three barasingha barked and craned their necks as they slowly advanced in a compact unit toward the top of a slight rise on which a tigress was hiding behind a boulder. The tigress, apparently feeling herself discovered, walked into the open 120 feet from the deer. Several animals wheeled and dashed 100 feet away, only to advance again at a trot. After watching the cat walk away the herd resumed its grazing. On a third occasion, one hind merely looked at a tigress 100 feet away, while a stag trotted after the retreating predator for about 50 feet. The general tendency, of course, is for the deer to circumvent situations that may lead to an encounter with a tiger. For example, a stag that was walking slowly through the high grass toward a road stopped when 30 feet from it and suddenly bolted 60 feet down his former trail, then trotted off. A tiger had walked down the road earlier that morning, and the stag had picked up the scent.

The barasingha on the Kanha meadow were used to the presence of man. When seeing a person, they rarely barked, and the flight distance of a herd, if approached casually and at an angle, was about 150–200 feet and occasionally as little as 100 feet. In a car it was sometimes possible to drive within 60 to 70 feet of a herd without causing a disturbance among the grazing animals. In general, the barasingha were not as excitable as the chital, and when the two species associated, a chital was usually the first to flee at the approach of danger.

Social Behavior

For about three months of the year at Kanha, from September to December, the barasingha are essentially solitary, with hinds dropping their fawns and with stags wandering around singly and in pairs. However, with the beginning of the rut in December, until the grass has once again grown high just before the retreat of the monsoon, the animals congregate in herds of varying sizes. This section discusses the structure of the herd and the interactions between individuals, particularly as they relate to dominance and the rut. The following types of herds were recognized: (1) mixed herds containing at least one stag and one hind, (2) breeding herds consisting of stags and hinds during the peak of the rut, (3) stag herds of two or more males, and (4) hind herds with a variable number of females and young.

HERD SIZE AND COMPOSITION

The barasingha congregated on the Kanha meadow in December and January and there formed herds of varying sizes. Between January and August, mixed herds averaged 13 to 19 individuals each, except in March just after the rut, when the average was 25 (Table 26). Large herds, numbering 45 and in one instance 61

TABLE 26

BARASINGHA HERD SIZE AND COMPOSITION AND FREQUENCY
OF SOLITARY INDIVIDUALS IN KANHA PARK

DATE	MIXED HERDS			STAG HERDS		NUMBER OF TIMES SOLITARY HIND SEEN	NUMBER OF TIMES SOLITARY STAG SEEN
	Total Number Classified	Average Size of Herd	Stags : 100 Hinds	Total Number Classified	Average Size of Herd		
January, 1964	39	13.0	46 : 100	11	2.3	4	14
February . .	66	12.6	71 : 100	20	2.8	1	5
March . . .	22	25.0	50 : 100	14	5.0	0	1
April	40	19.1	46 : 100	9	6.1	2	1
May	22	16.8	59 : 100	8	8.6	1	0
June	35	14.5	45 : 100	16	6.6	2	2
July	18	18.2	36 : 100	13	9.3	0	0
August . . .	19	14.4	55 : 100	13	6.3	4	2
September. .	5	5.8		2	3.0	9	3
October. . .	1	2.0		0	.0	7	4
November. .	1	2.0		0	.0	6	1
December. .	24	3.2		4	2.0	10	17

individuals, occurred during every month until August. The herds broke up in September, and from then until the end of the year the average size of mixed herds was fewer than 6 animals each (Table 26). Eleven mixed herds were tallied on the farm of A. Singh in West Kheri, and these averaged 8 (range 2–26) individuals each. At nearby Ghola, however, one herd comprised at least 500 animals. Eleven mixed herds in the Kaziranga Sanctuary also averaged 8 (range 3–13) animals each.

The majority of the barasingha associate in mixed herds for the first eight months of the year, with the ratio of hinds to stags being about 2:1 (Table 26). The proportion of stags in the herds was highest in February, at the end of the main rut. Although 2 or 3 stags may be found together during any month of the year, in March, after the rut, many stags leave the hinds and form their own herds, which average 5 to 9 individuals each, with as many as 14 joining together on occasion (Plate 6). Although such stag herds sometimes retain their composition for several days, in most instances males join and depart at intervals, spending their time either alone or with mixed herds. Small herds of hinds and fawns are common, but they rarely persist long, for they either join a mixed herd or are joined by a roaming stag. Solitary animals occur throughout the year. Lone stags in particular become conspicuous during the rut in December and January (Table 26). Some of these males were seen on the Kanha meadow only at that time, apparently spending the other seasons as solitary wanderers. Hinds, on the other hand, were observed alone primarily from September to December, before, during, and after the fawning period.

The only stable social relationship in a herd is between a hind and her fawn and sometimes between a hind and a yearling. All other associations are casual and constantly changing as members of the herd depart and others join, rarely remaining together for as long as one day. One yearling stag accompanied the same hind from the time he was first seen on January 2 until July 10, when he was killed by a tiger at 0100 hours. A sample of fourteen herds in which he and the hind were members gives an indication of the changes in composition that occur (Table 27).

LEADERSHIP

An adult hind characteristically leads mixed herds, which move in a single file, with the stags tending to bring up the rear. Of 17 movements of large herds recorded in March, a hind was in the lead on 16 occasions and a stag once. Any hind may assume leadership, and her position depends solely on having a number of followers. If no members of the herd join her, she either continues alone or returns to the others. On one occasion, a herd of 35 animals walked along in single file led by a hind, but when another hind, last in line, turned around and retraced her steps, all the others did so too. Herds frequently split, with animals following 2 or 3 different leaders.

Leadership in stag herds appears to have no definite relation to dominance, although when only two males travel together the one of higher rank usually leads. In one herd of 3 stags observed several

TABLE 27

Composition of Fourteen Barasingha Herds Containing the Same Yearling Stag and Hind at Various Times of the Year

Date	Adult Stag	Yearling Stag	Hind	Fawn	Total
January 2	0	1	1	0	2
January 11	2	2	5	0	9
January 20	5	2	15	1	23
January 31	10	3	25	2	40
February 9	1	2	8	0	11
February 23	4	1	7	0	12
March 3	3	2	6	1	12
March 25	7	2	23	3	35
April 1	0	1	5	0	6
April 23	0	2	8	2	12
May 18	2	4	24	3	33
June 21	2	1	4	0	7
June 25	0	1	1	0	2
July 8	1	3	11	2	17

times over a period of three days, the smallest stag was consistently in front and the largest one brought up the rear. Once, when all 3 stags were lying down, the largest one rose and threatened the medium-sized one. The latter scrambled to his feet, walked ten feet to the smallest stag, and gave a head-up display. The small stag rose and began to graze, whereupon the large stag threatened him with his antlers, apparently to make him move on, for, as soon as he took the lead, the other two fell behind in their usual positions. This general sequence of events was observed on one other occasion in this herd.

AGONISTIC BEHAVIOR AND DOMINANCE

Most aggressive interactions occur between stags during the rut and the months following it until the antlers are shed. My observations are based primarily on 16 stags which remained around the Kanha meadow in 1964 and on an equal number of animals the following year. Although I recognized each stag individually by his antlers in 1964 and in 1965, it was not possible to determine how many of these animals were present both years because the configuration of the tine pattern changes with each new set.

Overt aggressive interactions between stags are usually brief, consisting in the order of increasing intensity of (1) walking directly at the opponent, (2) jerking the head down and pointing the antler tips at the other animal (3) lunging forward with lowered head and sometimes slashing with a foreleg, and (4) chasing actively.

A head-up display, closely resembling that of the chital, is also exhibited by the barasingha during agonistic encounters. One stag characteristically approaches another with his neck raised, his muzzle stretched skyward to reveal the whitish chin, his ears held erect or laterally, the white insides facing the opponent, and his gait very stiff (Plate 7). Sometimes the displaying stag just stands and faces the other one or slowly circles him and then stands parallel, his head slightly averted. The ear facing the opponent is often flashed back and forth. Occasionally, the threatened stag, instead of turning aside, displays similarly, and then each animal attempts to stretch its muzzle higher than the other. It was my impression that the height of the reach was one factor in determining dominance.

In contrast to the chital, barasingha rarely rub their antlers against tree trunks during aggressive encounters. Stags were seen to scar up trees with their antlers on only three occasions. However, they frequently jab their antlers into the grass and afterwards walk around with tufts of it draped from the tines. No attempt was made to dislodge this adornment; on the contrary, the animals walked with head more erect and steady than usual as if to prevent the grass from falling off. Stags of all ages belabor grass, but the large ones do so most frequently. For example, eighteen instances of this behavior were observed between January 3 and 10 in one herd containing at various times from 5 to 13 stags, with an average of 10. The two largest stags accounted for 50 percent of these instances. The behavior is elicited by a number of different situations. For instance, one small stag, after having lost two sparring matches in succession, began to thrash a *Phoenix* bush. Another stag that thrashed was sexually excited as he followed a hind. He jabbed his antlers into a tuft of grass, attempted to mount the hind three times, and, when she walked away from him, once again belabored the vegetation. Two stags sometimes stand near each other and at the same time jab their antlers vigorously into the grass. The behavior appears to be a form of redirected aggression, which, as in the chital, has acquired the secondary function of intimidation. The stags rarely indulged in this activity after the cessation of the main rut in mid-February.

As the stags poke their antlers into the vegetation, scent from the preorbital glands is undoubtedly deposited. One stag rubbed his neck up and down a sapling, then gently wiped first his antlers and afterward both preorbital glands over the same area. On two occasions stags wiped a preorbital gland up and down on a dry grass stalk.

Wallowing may perhaps also feature directly and indirectly in agonistic encounters, because the visual and olfactory presence of the wallow itself may have an intimidatory effect on other stags. However, since the wallow is primarily associated with the rut, it will be discussed fully in that context.

Direct contact between stags is usually in the form of a sparring match — a light pushing back and forth and a twisting of the head sideways (Plate 9). Bouts are short, lasting a minute or less, although I observed two longer ones of eight and eleven minutes. Of 309 matches recorded, only two were serious fights, with one causing a shift in the existing rank order. None of the other encounters observed resulted in a change in the status of the animal, even though there was usually an obvious winner as one stag turned aside or trotted off. Occasionally, one stag would touch the antlers of another without eliciting a response. In one instance, a stag faced a second stag at a distance of ten feet in a head-up display. He maintained that position for fifteen seconds, then stretched his neck a little higher. The other stag just stood, head slightly averted, seemingly ignoring the gesture. The challenger stepped closer and lowered his antlers. Finally, the threatened male responded first by locking antlers, then by standing flaccidly, almost like an inanimate object, while the other stag attempted to spar. Sixty-two percent of 63 sparring matches were initiated by the animal that was ultimately judged to be the winner, indicating that stags challenged an animal of higher rank almost as readily as one of lower rank. The animals were sparring, it seemed, not to determine rank, but either to reassert themselves or to test their strength against a superior opponent. Large stags with long, many-tined antlers sparred rarely, only one-tenth as often as expected, whereas small stags, two to three years old, fought frequently (Table 28).

The various responses of the animals to each other suggested that a rank order existed among them. The existence of a hierarchy in such captive herds of ungulates as domestic cattle (Schein and Fohrman, 1955; Schloeth, 1961), American bison (McHugh, 1958), and reindeer (Espmark, 1964a) has been well documented, but detailed data on the presence of one in free-living animals, although

TABLE 28

THE EXPECTED VERSUS THE ACTUAL FREQUENCY OF SPARRING
IN TWENTY ADULT BARASINGHA STAGS OF VARIOUS ANTLER-SIZE CLASSES

Antler-Size of Stag	Total Number of Stags	Expected Number of Sparring Interactions	Actual Number of Sparring Interactions*
Large.	4	70	7
Large–medium	3	52	23
Medium.	7	123	130
Small.	6	105	190
Total.	20	350	350

* Based on 175 sparring matches involving 350 animals.

deduced a number of times, as for example, in the wapiti (Altmann, 1956), are lacking. In the red deer, Darling (1937) observed:

When the horns have stopped growing, and even before the rags of velvet are all off them, from late August to October, stags engage one another with their horns, pushing and wrestling against each other, but often in a quite brief and formalized manner. It seems almost certain that before the rut begins in October a male hierarchy is well established: in fact it is quite possible that the segregation of the sexes during the preceding months is primarily an adaptation to facilitate this, without interference with or by the females and calves. As early as August it is easy after a few minutes' observation to pick out which are the dominant stags in a herd.

I recorded the outcome of interactions between a selected number of barasingha stags during two periods, during the 1964 rut and during the 1965 rut. Whenever a stag terminated a sparring match by moving away or when he turned aside after being the recipient of an aggressive display such as the head-up, he was recorded as being subordinate to the other animal. Tables 29 and 30 show that the stags that were in frequent contact with each other on the Kanha meadow had a linear dominance hierarchy. This rank was to a large extent correlated with body size and antler length, the larger animals being dominant over smaller ones. It is possible that in addition to antler length the general complexity of the tine pattern contributes to the effectiveness of the antlers as a status symbol. Of the interactions recorded in Table 29, 6.7 percent were reversals, and in Table 30 3.5 percent were reversals, but these outcomes did not imply a change in status. Occasionally, the dominant animal turned away because he was at a temporary disadvantage during a sparring match or, seemingly, because he lost interest in the proceedings. Yearling stags interacted infrequently with each other or with adult stags. In a series of 182 sparring matches involving 364 animals, for

TABLE 29

DOMINANCE INTERACTIONS BETWEEN ADULT BARASINGHA STAGS
IN KANHA PARK, FEBRUARY 3–18, 1964

Antler-Size of Stag	Dominant Buck	Subordinate Buck											Total Number of Interactions
		I	II	III	IV	V	VI	VII	VIII	IX	X	XI	
Large.	I	7	3	8	6	4	8	4	1	2		4	47
Large.	II		1	3	5	1	1	1	1			5	18
Large–medium.	III			7	7	1	2	4				1	22
Large–medium.	IV				16	1				1	2		20
Medium . . .	V					3			3	3	1	1	11
Medium . . .	VI				1			1	1	1	1	1	6
Medium . . .	VII				1				5	2	5	2	15
Medium . . .	VIII				2	1				3	9	7	22
Small.	IX								1		4	7	12
Small.	X				1	1				3		12	17
Small.	XI									2			2
Total. . .													192

example, only 3 were spikes. Yearlings rank below the smallest adult, but whether they have a hierarchy among themselves could not be determined. A hind and a yearling stag were seen to interact aggressively on two occasions: once the hind asserted her dominance by assuming the head-up, and the other time she slashed the yearling with her hooves.

The frequent changes in the composition of the herds keep the hierarchy in a constant state of flux. As pointed out earlier, however, the barasingha at Kanha are part of a small localized population, and most of the individuals meet each other frequently during the course of the rut. The hierarchy is thus probably based on individual recognition, and when stags meet, each assumes the position he took during previous encounters. Two condensed examples from my field notes illustrate the behavior of stags when meeting:

1) *A herd consisting of 4 adult stags, 3 yearling stags, 12 hinds, and 1 fawn graze at 0650 hours. The 4 adults spar frequently with each other, and the results indicate that they have a linear hierarchy. At 0730 hours 1 stag and 4 hinds appear at the forest's edge. While the hinds join the herd without overt interaction, the new stag grazes for 12 minutes at the periphery before approaching the largest stag in the herd. The newcomer jerks his head down, and both spar briefly. The new stag turns aside, but when the winner gives a head-up display, he once again lowers his antlers and spars. The two fight briefly with the same result, and when afterward the newcomer gives the head-up, the other merely threatens with antlers*

TABLE 30

DOMINANCE INTERACTIONS BETWEEN ADULT BARASINGHA STAGS
IN KANHA PARK, JANUARY 2–10, 1965

Antler-Size of Stag	Dominant Buck	Subordinate Buck									Total Number of Interactions
		I	II	III	IV	V	VI	VII	VIII	IX	
Large.	I		1	3	2	1		2			9
Large.	II			1		1	1	1	1		5
Large–medium. . .	III				1	2	3			1	7
Medium	IV					2	16	1		1	20
Medium	V						5		7	5	17
Medium	VI					3		7	8	22	40
Small.	VII								3	20	23
Small.	VIII									20	20
Small.	IX								2		2
Total.											143

lowered. Further interactions with other stags show that the new stag has assumed the number 3 position in the hierarchy.

0757. Three stags, including the one dominant over the whole meadow, and 3 hinds approach the herd. A hind is in the lead, but the large male passes her at a rapid walk and enters the herd first. He approaches the 5 stags there directly. They have been sparring but suddenly cease and graze assiduously. As soon as the large stag has walked past them and turned his back, so to speak, all look up.

2) *A large stag walks alone across the meadow toward a solitary hind. Coming from the forest nearby is the dominant stag, trailed by a medium-sized one at 100 feet. When 80 feet separates the two large stags, the dominant one gives the head-up display and continues to advance. He stops 30 feet from the other, muzzle still raised. When he steps forward, the other gives the head-up, too, but turns away, then challenges and spars with the medium-sized stag. When the dominant stag steps toward them, both desist; he suddenly turns and walks 400 feet to the hind. He displays the head-up to her, drives her back to the other stags, and as he passes them, gives a final head-up to each one.*

In these interactions, and numerous others of a similar nature, the displays, sparring matches, and other behavior patterns were used by the animal merely to reassert its position; no change in the rank order resulted. It is significant that the only two serious fights observed were between the two most dominant animals on the meadow. In 1964 the dominant stag retained his position; in 1965 he lost it, as described below:

January 7. 0800. A herd of 10 stags, 10 hinds, and 3 fawns graze on the meadow when the dominant stag appears alone from the forest. He rejoins the herd, having left it the previous day, thrashes a Phoenix with his antlers, and then approaches the number 2 stag in the hierarchy, who has been with the herd for two days. The latter stag steps aside very slowly. Both walk side by side to a wallow, and while the dominant stag watches, the other digs his antlers into the sod and throws turf vigorously into the air with upward jerks of his head. Then both toss turf, standing 20 feet apart.

0810. The dominant stag approaches the other in head-up, and they begin to spar. Their antlers meet with a crash, the sod flies from under their churning hooves, and their backs are humped with the effort of trying to force each other backward. Six stags leave the herd 300 feet away at a run, then stand and watch the fight. One stag dodges in twice and pokes a combatant in the rump. The fighting stags, see-sawing back and forth, cross a ravine, crash through a grove of saplings, and almost disappear in some high grass, all with antlers locked. Suddenly at 0821 hours, the dominant animal twists aside and trots 100 feet away, having lost the battle. The other stag follows slowly in head-up. He bugles. The vanquished stag walks 300 feet and stands there alone until 0855 hours. As he walks away, a small stag from the herd follows him.

The winner retained his dominant position for the rest of the season. On the day following the battle, the loser was back with the herd, now second in rank.

It was impossible to determine if the hinds possessed a stable rank order, for they rarely interacted. Most aggressive contacts involved a brief nip on the shoulders or rump. A threatening gesture, somewhat resembling the head-up, consisted of stretching the neck erect while facing the opponent with head held horizontally and ears laid back. One foreleg was sometimes raised, apparently to indicate an intention to rear up and strike with the hooves as described in wapiti by Altmann (1956). If the threatened hind did not retreat, or if she assumed a similar posture, both occasionally stood up on their hindlegs and slashed at each other with their forelegs for several seconds. Stags were not seen to fight in this fashion, although the behavior probably occurred at times after they had lost their antlers, as reported for the wapiti (Murie, 1951). Hinds also employed the head-up display, like the stags, with each animal attempting to push its muzzle higher into the air than her opponent (Plate 10). Some displays of hinds appeared to be intermediate between the head-up and the threat gesture, as judged by the position of the ears and head.

In most instances stags and hinds indicate their submission by moving away, by averting their heads slightly, or by failing to respond when threatened. Stags occasionally begin to graze, apparently a displacement activity, as in the moose (Altmann, 1959), which signals a lack of aggressive intent. A submissive posture, resembling the one described for the chital, is occasionally seen in hinds but rarely in stags. The animal walks away with neck held low and parallel to the ground, muzzle pointing forward, and ears laid back, a position apparently designed to make the animal look inconspicuous, the opposite of the head-up display.

SEXUAL BEHAVIOR

At Kanha the stags begin to rut in early December when their antlers are hard, their necks are swollen, their voices have deepened, and they have molted into their dark winter coat. In contrast, it is interesting to note that the stags at Kaziranga begin to rut after they have molted into their light summer coat, which lacks the long, shaggy hairs on the neck and, in general, is not as impressive in appearance as the winter one.

During the early part of the rut stags and hinds drift from the forest singly and in small groups and congregate on the meadow. Both sexes give the impression of being exceedingly restless as herds split and join, and solitary individuals, particularly stags, roam widely. All patterns of behavior characteristic of the rut — bugling, wallowing, and various aspects of sexual behavior including copulation — are evident, and increase in intensity as more and more animals reach the meadow. Typical behavior of the barasingha during the early phase of the rut is described in the following field observation:

0630 hours. A large stag and a medium-sized one walk along, the former in the lead. At 0720 hours, having traveled 1,000 feet, they approach a herd of 7 hinds and a yearling stag. The large stag raises his muzzle briefly in an incipient head-up display when 70 feet from the hinds, then walks rapidly into the herd with neck held low and parallel to the ground but head slightly raised, the low-stretch display that has been described for the chital. He sniffs the anal area of one hind, another, and then a third. After a brief flehmen, he sniffs a fourth hind, curls his lip once more, and having apparently determined that the herd contains no receptive females, leaves 6 minutes after his arrival. The second stag follows him at a distance of 300 feet. At 0806, some 900 feet farther on, they approach a hind with fawn. She watches as they draw nearer. The large stag sniffs her vulva, follows her as she walks away, and then all 4 graze together and lie down at 0815 hours.

As the rut progresses, the amount of roaming decreases, and the deer establish a breeding herd. The animals formed their breeding herd in the same locality during both rutting seasons observed — a relatively dry open slope with a number of wallowing places in the form of seepage springs. Each morning shortly after dawn, the time when rutting activity reached its daily peak, small herds appeared at this site from all directions and joined. Sometimes most of the animals remained together throughout the day and the following night, reaching a second peak of rutting activity at dusk, but at other times the herd disbanded by mid-morning. The majority of hinds and fawns were part of this one breeding herd during the peak of the rut, as were most or all of the 16 stags around the meadow (Plate 10). During the 1963–64 rut the breeding herd began to form on about January 20 and started to disintegrate on February 3, the animals failing to meet each morning in their usual area. The size of the breeding herd varied from day to day, ranging from 18 to 40 individuals with an average of about 30. Some animals joined the breeding herd daily, whereas others showed up only intermittently. Although the animals remained on the meadow and continued to associate closely, indeed forming the largest herds of the year in March after the rut, the amount of sexual activity and associated behavior decreased sharply and was rarely seen after mid-February. During the 1964–65 rut, the breeding herd was formed on January 2, over two weeks earlier than the previous year. On that date 11 animals congregated, and three days later 25 came together. Although 22 barasingha still actively rutted on January 10, the animals failed to meet the following day, and the breeding herd had not reformed by the time the study was terminated a week later.

Two aspects of the formation and composition of the breeding herd are of particular interest when compared with the behavior of certain other members of the genus *Cervus*: (1) a stag makes no effort to retain a number of hinds under his jurisdiction, and (2) a stag makes no attempt to drive away other stags from the vicinity of the herd. Instead, a number of stags and hinds form a loosely integrated breeding herd, with the males establishing a linear dominance hierarchy, as discussed earlier. The activity of the dominant stag is thus directed not toward the maintenance of the breeding herd but merely toward association with whatever hind is sexually receptive. The highest ranking stag in the herd takes priority over any hind in heat, tending to stay by her side until copulation has been successfully completed. Brander (1923) maintained that "master stags collect a herd of does and fight for possession of their harem in the same way as the European stag" and that large stags "will not tolerate a youngster with them," but these observations do not agree with mine. With stags associating freely and competition for hinds based on an established system of priority rights, the rut of the barasingha takes a more peaceful course than that of such species as the reindeer (Espmark, 1964a), red deer (Darling, 1937), and wapiti (Altmann, 1956; Murie, 1951). In these species one male tries to maintain a harem of females, a task which keeps him constantly active as he tries to keep them together and other males away, as described by Altmann (1956) in the wapiti:

The bull of the group circles the harem and often drives a particular cow. While the cows, yearlings, and calves are grazing, the bull rarely takes time to graze. Bugling, roaring and watching the harem keep him fully occupied. A bugle made by a rival puts the bull into a rage and starts him on a widespread search for the intruder. One bull, seen tramping and sniffing through the underbrush, broke into a group of fir trees and, after discovering a hiding bull, drove his rival away with sharp-sounding blows of his antlers.

The system evolved by the barasingha appears to be more efficient than that of the wapiti in that less energy is expended by the stags in obtaining females with which to mate. A barasingha stag feeds regularly during the rut and at the end of it appears to be in as good physical condition as before, whereas the wapiti has obviously lost much weight (Murie, 1951). However, efficiency can only be measured in terms of survival of the species, and this is partly dependent on the genetic selective advantage of having the prime stags do most of the mating. No data are available for the wapiti on this point, but presumably the large males with harems have the opportunity to mate more often than the others. I observed 8 copulations in the barasingha, all by large-antlered stags. Stags of all size classes show sexual behavior such as chasing and mounting in a breeding herd, but the dominant animal is more active than the others. Thirty-three instances of sexual behavior were observed in the 1965 breeding herd between January 3 and 10, and the dominant male on the meadow was involved in 48 percent of these (Table 31). A total of 54 instances of sexual behavior were tallied between December 9, 1964, and January 17, 1965, in the breeding herd and outside of it, and large-antlered stags accounted for 54 percent of these. These data suggest that the highest ranking stags do most of the mating. In this respect the social organizations of the barasingha and the wap-

TABLE 31

FREQUENCY OF SEXUAL BEHAVIOR PATTERNS IN BARASINGHA STAGS
IN A BREEDING HERD, JANUARY 3–10, 1965*

Antler-Size	Number of Instances of Driving or Chasing	Number of Instances of Attempted Mounting or Mounting	Number of Instances of Copulation	Number of Instances of Bugling
Large-antlered stag (1st in rank) . .	10	5	1	21
Large-antlered stag (2d in rank) . .	4	0	0	2
Large–medium antlered stags . .	6	0	0	0
Medium-antlered stags.	3	1	0	0
Small-antlered stags.	2	0	0	0
Spike-antlered stags.	1	0	0	0
Total.	26	6	1	23

* Herd contained 5 to 13 stags (average 10).

iti, though quite different during the rut, achieve similar results, but adequate hypotheses to account for the evolutionary advantage of one system over the other in the particular species are lacking.

My observations on the formation and social organization of the barasingha breeding herd during the rut are based on a very small population. The behavior of the animals when many hundreds and even thousands occupy a limited area is unknown, but general comments by Baker (1890), Champion (1933), and Lydekker (1893), as well as statements of foresters and hunters with whom I talked, indicate that the large herds break up into smaller units at the time of rut. It is probable that in a place like Ghola many breeding herds are distributed over the area, each in its specific locality, but that there is a certain amount of movement of individuals between herds. The size of these breeding herds is unknown, but they may well be on the order of the one formed at Kanha in 1964. It is significant that both in 1964 and 1965 the number of stags that remained on the meadow was 16, even though in the former year at least 30 stags had been present in the population. Possibly the optimum number of stags in and around a breeding herd is about 15, and with the number of surviving hinds apparently too few in number to form two breeding herds, the excess males left the area. With the numbers of males to females in the populations almost equal (see Table 23), hinds in a breeding herd probably number no more than about 20 to 25 individuals. If the probable number of fawns is added, the total hypothetical breeding herd will comprise about 40 to 60 animals. There may be an optimum number below which mutual stimulation sufficient to maintain the herd is inadequate. The 1964 rut at Kanha was in every respect more vigorous and the breeding herd of longer duration than in 1965, when the number of animals on the meadow in January had dwindled to only about 30 animals.

A number of distinct behavior patterns are associated with the rut, prominent among them bugling, wallowing, and several display postures during courtship.

The bugle of the barasingha consists of a series of distinct two-toned notes — a rather mournful uu-aa, uu-aa, or ring-hon, ring-hon as written by Champion (1933) — repeated some 10 or 25 times with the last notes dropping progressively in pitch until they are almost inaudible. A peculiar resonant drone accompanies the bugle. The number of two-toned notes in a series in 67 bugles averaged 19 (range 9–27). The duration of each note is about .8 seconds, about 16 seconds elapsing during a bugle of 20 notes. Although stags occasionally call during the night, most bugles are heard after dawn and before dusk. Of 74 bugles recorded between dawn and noon, 43 percent were between 0700 and 0800 hours; of 37 bugles noted between noon and dusk, 56 percent occurred between 1700 and 1800 hours. The call of one stag occasionally elicited an answer from one or two others in the vicinity. Only large-antlered stags were seen to bugle, and the dominant male in the area did so more frequently than the others (Table 31). Occasionally, a stag was stimulated to bugle after hearing the alarm bark of a member of his own species. It is probable that the sound attracts stags and hinds to the rutting area, but at the same time it may also serve to space out males by indicating that the locality is already occupied by a large stag. The first bugle during the 1964–65 rut was heard on December 17, and the last one of the 1963–64 season was noted on February 14. Bugling during the 1963–64 rut occurred more or less regularly throughout the season, but the following year it was sporadic until January 5, reaching a high level on that date, which was maintained until January 10, when it ceased abruptly.

The stags wallowed at four places on the Kanha meadow where water had seeped out of a slope and created a swampy area (Plate 11). The same sites were used during both the 1963–64 and 1964–65 rutting seasons. During the 1964–65 rut, a stag wallowed probably for the first time on December 11; the previous season's wallowing had ceased by mid-February, when the sites dried up. The wallows were made and used by the stags, although on two occasions I saw a hind briefly lie down in one. Stags dig out the wallows by jabbing either their brow tine or the tips of their antlers into the sod and then jerking up their heads so vigorously that in some instances the earth flies several feet into the air. These actions, as well as churning the sod with sharp hooves, create a muddy depression with a pool of water in the middle, in which the stags lie down and sometimes continue to dig with their antlers. Similar behavior has been described for the wapiti by Murie (1951). Wallowing is particularly prevalent when stags join or leave the breeding herd, and the activity of one animal frequently stimulates others in the vicinity to behave similarly. In one instance six stags tossed turf and wallowed together. A typical wallowing sequence is described below:

0727 hours. The dominant stag leaves the herd and walks 70 feet to a wallow. He digs his tines into the mud and sod a total of 44 times, throwing pieces of it into the air with sudden upward jerks of the head. A yearling stag approaches to within 20 feet. When the adult jerks his head at him, he trots in a 50 foot circle but returns and watches. The stag lies down in the wallow for 30 seconds and digs his antlers into the earth 4 times with sideways and upward twists. He rises, goes 10 feet to another marshy spot, throws sod 3 times, then returns to the wallow. The yearling walks to the spot just abandoned by the adult and lies down for 15 seconds but gallops away when threatened by the adult. He digs his antlers in another 33 times, now being closely watched by two yearling stags from a distance of 6 feet.

0740. One medium-sized stag and two hinds join the herd. The dominant stag leaves the wallow and stands parallel to and 10 feet from the new stag. The latter walks 120 feet to the wallow where he throws sod 8 times, lies down for 3 minutes, digging his antlers into the earth another 2 times, and at 0745 hours rejoins the herd.

Such jabbing of antlers into the sod appears to be a form of re-directed aggression resembling the thrashing of bushes, although the action of the head is primarily up and down without the lateral movements conspicuous in thrashing. Throwing sod may also occur away from the wallow if the ground is soft. Wallowing itself is usually brief, rarely lasting for more than two to three minutes, and there is no vigorous rolling of the body as, for example, has been de-scribed for the American bison in dust wallows (McHugh, 1958). It is likely that a wallowing stag mixes scent from his tarsal and metatarsal glands with the water and mud, an action which marks both the area and the animal himself with odor in the manner de-scribed for moose by Geist (1963).

When a hind is sexually receptive, the stag displays various pat-terns of behavior. He sniffs her vulva frequently or pokes it with his muzzle, and when she urinates, he either places his nose into the fluid or smells the moist ground. *Flehmen* with curled lip is common afterward. If the hind moves away, he follows her, and if she runs, he chases her, endeavoring to stay by her side. If she stands, he may poke her rump with his muzzle, driving her on. Sometimes, instead of following behind her, he moves parallel to her, 5 to 10 feet away, adjusting his speed of movement to hers. At such times he displays the head-up, emphasizing the posture by walking stiff-legged and thumping a foreleg on the ground with each step. Sometimes he walks ahead of her, tail raised, flashing his white rump. If she stops moving, he may lick her rump and face, the only time licking is a prominent social interaction between adults. When approaching a hind rapidly, a stag occasionally assumes the low-stretch display that has been described for the chital. Driving, chasing, licking, and perhaps a brief halt to thrash some bushes with the antlers may con-tinue for several hours, with the stag forming a so-called tending bond with the hind, as described for the wapiti by Altmann (1960) and the caribou by Lent (1965). If another stag approaches, he may be attacked. On one occasion a stag expended much effort in at-tempting to drive away a yearling stag that persistently followed a hind that was presumably its mother. The youngster remained with the courting pair, however, and the stag later copulated successfully. Usually the stag took the initiative in the sexual advances, but once a hind playfully nipped a stag while he stood in a head-up display, then bounded away 10 feet, returned to his side, and dashed away again, bucking as she ran, this time followed by the stag. If the hind stands still, the stag may mount. Usually she walks out from under him, and in the course of a courtship, numerous mountings are attempted. One stag mounted 27 times in 15 minutes. A fully receptive hind stands with her back humped and her tail held limply horizontal. The stag places his chin on her rump, mounts, thrusts violently once or twice, rearing up on his hindlegs during orgasm, and then leaves the hind without a postcoital display. The prolonged courtship probably helps to synchronize the two animals physiologically, making the copulatory act itself very brief.

Two courtship sequences, the first one within a breeding herd, the other outside it, describe mating behavior in detail:

1) February 2. 1530 hours. A total of 39 barasingha, including 8 adult stags, graze. The dominant stag drives a hind, staying 3 feet behind her. As they pass through the center of the herd, he lunges at the stag second in the rank order. While he is occupied with the other stag, a small stag mounts the hind but jumps off quickly when the dominant stag returns. After driving her briefly, he walks to a tree about 100 feet away and rubs his antlers against it. Meanwhile two stags follow the hind. The larger of the two jerks his antlers at the smaller one, then mounts her. The dominant stag returns, and both stags step aside rapidly when he lowers his antlers at them.

1610 hours. The dominant stag leaves the hind and begins to browse. A spike yearling mounts the hind, but flees when the other stag returns at a trot. At 1613 hours, after driving the female briefly, he mounts her and thrusts once violently, propelling her forward. He jerks his antlers at a spike nearby, rubs his neck on a tree trunk, charges 40 feet at another stag, and finally returns to the hind and stands beside her. He bugles, then licks her rump. Five minutes later he charges at two stags that drift by. When the hind lies down, he licks the top of her head before joining her.

1650 hours. He jumps up and lunges at 3 stags that approach to within 30 feet. He then thrashes grass until his tines become draped with it. The hind rises, and he drives her and stays by her side until 1720, when observations are terminated.

February 3. 0805. A herd of 32 barasingha is in the same place as yesterday. The dominant stag lies beside a hind 100 feet from the others. The number 2 stag in the rank order licks the rump of another hind for about 5 minutes. After she rises, he drives her. When the dominant stag becomes aware of them, he leaves his hind and runs 150 feet to the other one. The stag steps aside while he mounts. She walks ahead but stands still when he mounts a second time. He gives one vigorous thrust, then stands, licks his lips, and curls his upper lip. The hind which the dominant stag had left earlier walks toward the herd and is immediately joined by a small stag, which, however, steps aside to a somewhat larger one. The dominant stag stands nearby and belabors a tuft of grass before rejoining and driving this hind. He briefly chases a stag aside and sniffs the anal area of two other hinds in passing, giving each a light push with the muzzle. After lunging at another stag, which immediately begins to graze, he drives his hind once more briefly and licks her rump before tossing some grass with upward sweeps of his antlers. The whole herd then stands or lies.

0935. Meanwhile the dominant stag has drifted somewhat from the side of the hind, and a spike yearling mounts her but jumps aside when the other returns. When the male second in rank passes by, he runs 10 feet at him and slashes out with a foreleg. He runs at another stag, bugles, jerks his antlers at two stags, and chases a third one; while his attention is occupied, the stag second in the rank order mounts. The dominant stag rushes up, but his attention is again diverted by another stag, and while he displaces that one, the other large stag mounts and thrusts once, completing a successful copulation. The dominant stag returns and rests by the hind until observations are terminated at 1100 hours.

2) 0810 hours. A large stag, a medium stag, and one hind, all of which were unsuccessfully stalked by a tigress 25 minutes earlier, move across the meadow. The large stag walks at first parallel to the hind in a head-up display but then lags slightly behind her, followed at 120 feet by the medium-sized stag. The hind grazes. Suddenly, the stag assumes the low-stretch display, takes several rapid steps, and mounts the hind. She walks out from under him, and he gives the head-up once more; she turns, and he turns with her, walking with thumping forefeet. When he stands still, she swivels her rump toward him, but when he sniffs, she trots ahead. They move 400 feet during the next 15 minutes. As the hind veers off in one direction, he lowers his antlers as if to block her way, but she trots around him and stops after 40 feet. The stag walks rapidly to her in the low-stretch posture, sniffs, puts his chin on her rump, mounts, sniffs again, and mounts again, but she walks ahead. An ejaculate drips from his unsheathed penis. After 50 feet she stands again, and he mounts, giving one violent thrust. While she walks slowly with tail horizontal, he begins to graze at 0840 hours.

The amount of sexual activity decreased rapidly after mid-February. In 1964 a large stag was last seen to mount on February 22, and one small stag attempted to do so on April 5; the following year two such attempts were noted in March.

Hinds mounted hinds on four occasions, all in March and April. One small stag mounted a fawn, and fawns tried to mount hinds on five occasions. One fawn, six months old, attempted to mount a hind three times in succession, then sniffed her leg and curled its lip; finally it gave the head-up display to a yearling stag, which responded by merely flipping his head up quickly.

FEMALE-YOUNG RELATIONSHIPS

The heavily pregnant hinds disappeared from the meadow by late August, except for a few that remained hidden in the high grass, either solitary or accompanied by a large fawn or yearling. In contrast to their usual placid disposition, the animals became very shy, and they barked vigorously on seeing a person on foot, something they had rarely done earlier in the year. Some hinds remained for several days near certain patches of brush, but even though we searched such sites for fawns from late August to October, we never discovered any.

Suckling was observed three times, all in February. The fawns approached the hind either from the side or between the front legs and suckled thirty to forty seconds. When a fawn became separated from its mother, it emitted a plaintive bleat — eeaa or eeau — which the hind either ignored, answered in similar fashion, or responded to directly by approaching the source of the sound. Yearlings occasionally bleated in similar circumstances. Once a hind was accompanied by two fawns, the second young apparently having lost its mother at least temporarily. One of the fawns followed the hind closely and the other tagged 30 feet behind. Whenever the latter attempted to approach, the other fawn jumped at it and chased it off.

CHAPTER 5

THE SAMBAR

The sambar (*Cervus unicolor*), the largest deer in southeast Asia, has an exceedingly wide geographical distribution. Ellerman and Morrison-Scott (1951) summarized the range of the species as follows: "Szechuan, Yunnan, Kwantung, Hainan, Formosa, Ceylon, northwards through Peninsular India to Kumaon and Nepal, Assam, Burma, Indo-China, Siam, Malay States, Sumatra, Java, Borneo, Celebes, the Philippines and many small Malayan islands." Of the four subspecies listed by these authors, *C. u. niger* occurs in India. No Indian ungulate has adapted itself to a wider variety of forest types and environmental conditions than the sambar. It is found in the thorn forests of Gujarat, Rajasthan, and other states, in the dry and moist deciduous forest throughout peninsular India, in the pine and oak forests of the Himalayan foothills up to an altitude of 10,000 to 12,000 feet (Lydekker, 1898; Jerdon, 1874; Baldwin, 1877), and in the evergreen and semi-evergreen forest regions of eastern India. Although I encountered sambar in all my study areas, they were nowhere abundant. In addition, the nocturnal habits of the species, its propensity for remaining under cover, and above all its alertness and shyness made it difficult to locate, much less to observe for prolonged periods. The literature contains little detailed information on the sambar, although useful general accounts are given by, among others, Baker (1890), Lydekker (1898), Blanford (1888–91), Fletcher (1911), Brander (1923), and Thom (1937). My limited observations at Kanha, together with a summary of pertinent published data, are the basis for this brief chapter.

134

Description

The sambar is larger than the barasingha, with stags standing 48 to 56 inches high at the shoulder (Blanford, 1888–91). The length of the body is 6 to 7 feet, and the tail an additional 12 to 13 inches (Jerdon, 1874). Published weights of stags shot in the wild include 562, 682, 707, 717, 743, and 776 pounds (Cooch Behar, 1908; Brander, 1923; Morris, 1937b). But since these weights are from record animals, the average is probably closer to the 410 and 445 pounds obtained for two stags in the New York Zoological Garden (Crandall, 1964); one hind in the same zoo weighed 360 pounds.

The winter coat of the sambar is gray-brown to dark brown, adult stags appearing almost black on occasion. Generally, the molt into the summer coat is completed by May, but patches of the old pelage persist in a few animals until early June. The color of the summer coat is brown to chestnut brown. The molt into the winter coat begins in October and is completed by early December. The rump, the underside of the tail, and the inner side of the legs are light to rusty brown. The tip of the tail is black, and the base of the back of the ears is whitish. Both stags and hinds have a conspicuous unkempt ruff of hair around the neck. The hairs on the swollen neck and on the shoulders of rutting stags are several inches long and tipped with grey. Small fawns have a chestnut brown coat without spots.

The antlers of yearlings consist of simple spikes up to 10 inches long. Adult antlers are massive and resemble those of the chital in that they are three-tined, with a brow tine and a forked main beam. Antlers are generally about 20 to 35 inches long; Ward (1922) lists a record pair measuring 50⅛ inches long.

Population Dynamics

The sambar is distributed sparsely throughout Kanha Park in the mixed forest of the hills as well as in the sal forest. Although most animals leave the high ridges during the hot season and descend to the base of the hills, a few of them stay on the slopes, obtaining their water from seepage springs. There was no marked concentration of sambar around Kanha meadow from March to June, as there was of gaur, chital, and barasingha. This, together with their ability to remain inconspicuous, makes an accurate estimate of numbers difficult, a fact reflected by the fluctuating census figures (Table 2).

Population Size and Composition

The forest department staff tallied 60 sambar in the central part of the park in June, 1964, and 35 one year later. My estimate for the study area, based on the frequency of my encounters with them, was about 50 to 60 sambar. The population density appeared to be similar in the valley to the southwest of Kanha and around Kisli, but it was lower in the other parts of the park. The sambar population in the entire park was probably between 200 and 300 animals.

A total of 363 sambar were classified in Kanha Park; in terms of males and young per 100 females, the ratios were 29.7 males:100 females:33.7 young. The proportion of the various age and sex classes in the population was 14.9 percent adult male, 3.5 percent yearling male, 51.4 percent adult female, 9.8 percent yearling female, and 20.4 percent young. Hinds outnumbered the stags by a ratio of about 3:1, a disparity already apparent in the yearlings (one to two years old). The reason for this great disproportion of the sexes is unknown, but it may be due to selective predation on the males, both as fawns and as adults (see Table 57), and perhaps also to an unequal sex ratio at birth.

The Rutting Season

Published comments are almost unanimous in stating that the time of rut in peninsular India runs from October to December, with Forsyth (1889), Blanford (1888–91), Lydekker (1898), Russell (1900), Comber (1904), and Stockley (1913) limiting it to October and November and Prater (1934) and Brander (1923) to November and December. Comber (1904) and Blanford (1888–91) pointed out further that in the Himalayas the sambar mate in the spring.

As in the other deer, the annual changes in antler development give an indication of the probable state of sexual activity in the animal. Most authors (Stockley, 1928; Russell, 1900; Baldwin, 1877; Brander, 1923; Jerdon, 1874) noted that sambar shed their antlers between late March and mid-May and are in velvet from May to October or November, although in southern India some stags are in hard antler during July and August (Fletcher, 1911) and in Ceylon shedding occurs irregularly throughout the year (Baker, 1890). The picture has been further confused by the insistence of some observers, like Gilbert (1888), Baker (1890), Fletcher (1911), Forsyth (1889), and Lydekker (1924), among others, that stags sometimes retain the same set of antlers for two to four consecutive years. Brander (1923), on the other hand, emphasized that antlers are shed yearly. None of the sambar in the New York Zoological Garden retained their antlers for more than one year (Crandall, 1964). A total of 33 adults were seen at Kanha between November 19 and May 18, and all were in hard antler; of 12 stags encountered between June 10 and November 7 all were in velvet, which indicates that most shedding occurred in late May and June. One stag in the Calcutta Zoological Garden lost his antlers on April 8–9, 1964, and on April 19–20, 1965.

The birth season can also be used to pinpoint the time of rut if the gestation period is known. According to Prater (1934) and Brander (1923), the young are born in late May and early June, and according to Fletcher (1911) primarily in late June and early July. With a gestation period of eight months (Sclater, 1863; Finn, 1929; Asdell, 1946), these fawns were conceived in October and November. Both Fletcher (1911) and Brander (1923) noted, however, that some fawns are born during the hot weather, presumably in April and May, having been conceived in August and September. Age estimates of small fawns at Kanha revealed that births occurred during every month from June to December and perhaps also rarely in April and May.

My findings disagree with most published information in that the rut of the sambar does not appear to be as discrete as has been suggested but rather to be spread over a period of at least seven months of the year. However, the peak of the rut does coincide with other findings — November and December. That this peak may vary somewhat from area to area is suggested by the fact that the sore spot (see Sexual Behavior, p. 144), which is present in rutting sambar at Kanha only from mid-November to mid-December, was seen in three Kaziranga animals in early May.

Forty-one births in the New York Zoological Park were spread over every month, except December and February, and antlers were shed in all seasons (Crandall, 1964), conditions similar to those at Woburn Abbey, England (Bedford and Marshall, 1942). Fawns in the Trivandrum zoo, Kerala, were born in December and January (Simon, 1943a).

RATE OF REPRODUCTION

None of the yearling hinds at Kanha appeared to be pregnant, and it is likely that hinds gave birth to their first fawn when about three years old. Each adult female probably bears young once a year, not once every three years as stated by Brander (1923). A single fawn is the rule, although Crandall (1964) recorded one set of twins in forty-one births at the New York Zoological Park.

MORTALITY

The fact that 20 percent of the sambar population consisted of fawns and 13 percent of yearlings points to a moderately high annual turnover, although a considerably lower one than in the chital, for example, where the comparable figures are 29 percent and 24 percent, respectively. If it is assumed that each adult has one young per year, fawn mortality was apparently heavy, for 3 out of 5 hinds were not accompanied by young. A few of these hinds were two to three years old and therefore had not yet given birth to their first fawn, but the figures nevertheless indicate that about 50 percent of the young died before reaching the age of one year. Since the number of adults leaving a stable population roughly equals the number of yearlings entering it, there was at least a 13 percent annual loss of adults.

Predation was the only known cause of mortality during 1964. Out of a total of 228 predator kills found, 25 percent were sambar, and out of 335 tiger feces checked, 10 percent contained the remains of sambar (see Tables 50 and 51), making this deer numerically the second most important large wild prey species in the park. Sambar were also hunted by villagers; the remnants of one freshly killed animal were found in a poacher's camp near the Kanha meadow.

General Behavior

The sambar is predominantly a forest animal, coming out into the open occasionally at dusk and during the night but seeking the cover of trees within an hour after dawn. Sambar ventured onto the Kanha meadow infrequently, except during the hot season, when small herds would approach the water holes cautiously, usually in the evening, drink, and then retreat back into the forest. From about 0930 to 1600 or 1700 hours, the animals usually rested, often lying on the slope of a hillock partially hidden by grass and quite invisible until flushed. A few deer, however, sometimes fed and moved at mid-day, especially during the monsoon and the main rut in November and December.

FOOD HABITS

The sambar probably subsist on a wider variety of plants than any other ungulate at Kanha, with the possible exception of the gaur.

Although Tables 10 and 11 list only fifteen species as having been eaten by sambar, this merely reflects the difficulty of observing undisturbed animals, not the limits of their diet. According to Brander (1923), the fruits of *Phyllanthus emblica* and the bark of *Adina cordifolia* are also taken. Young green grasses constitute the preferred forage of sambar, and when available, particularly from June to October, the bulk of their diet undoubtedly consists of them. As the grasses reach maturity and until the meadows and forests are burned, the deer readily eat the coarse blades and stems. The green grasses which appear after the burning of the sal forests in about April provide them with much of their food during this season, supplemented most commonly with the new leaves of sal and *Moghania*. On May 5, for example, I watched four sambar for forty minutes as they fed almost exclusively on *Themeda* shoots and sal leaves. Browse becomes an important component of their diet whenever green grass is scarce. I watched one stag on December 8 as he moved 150 feet in ten minutes, nibbling on at least three different species of shrubs and trees, one vine, and one grass. The seasonal changes in the food habits are described well by Forsyth (1889):

The short green grass that clothes the banks of pools and springs, and the tender shoots of young trees and bushes, may be said to be at all times the foundation of their fare. . . . Later on, in late autumn, the young wheat and grain crops of neighboring clearances are made to pay heavy toll; and with the commencement of the hot season comes a great variety of wild fruits. . . . At one time (March and April) it is the luscious flower of the Mhowa tree [*Madhuca latifolia*] which they share with the Gond and the bear and most other animals and birds. The Tendu [*Diospyros melanoxylon*], the Chironji [*Bachanania latifolia*], the Aola [*Emblica officinalis*], the Bher [*Zizyphus jujuba*], and many other trees, also fruit plentifully in spring; and a little later the pods of numerous species of acacia, chiefly Babul (*A. arabica*), Reunja (*A. leucophaea*), Kheir (*A. catechu*), and of the tamarinds which have overgrown many deserted village sites, and the fruit of several species of wild fig (*F. indica, religiosa, guleria*) amply support the sambar through the hot season.

The rumen contents from three sambar were analyzed. One sample, collected on January 24, contained 33 percent grass and 67 percent twigs and leaves, some of the latter being *Moghania*; another sample, obtained on February 24, consisted of 5 percent grass, 25 percent *Emblica officinalis* fruit, and 70 percent finely chewed bark from an unidentified tree; a third sample, that of a fawn collected on February 15, was wholly composed of sedge grass material.

The readiness with which the sambar either grazes or browses has undoubtedly been a major reason for the wide distribution of the species. Whereas the chital and barasingha are largely confined to forest types with a good understory of grasses, the sambar has not been limited in this respect and has occupied the evergreen forests and other primary forest types in which there is little grass but plentiful browse.

RESPONSE TO PREDATORS

The sambar exhibit a number of signals which serve to alert other members of the herd, as well as other ungulate species, to possible danger. Visual and auditory cues appear to predominate, but olfactory ones probably contribute importantly as well. When a sambar stands motionless, neck held stiffly upright, the ruff of hair around the neck erect, and gazes steadily with cocked ears in a certain direction, the position alerts the others in the herd, and all behave in similar fashion. The long tail is usually raised vertically and may remain in that position for several minutes, a very conspicuous gesture (Plate 12). The rump patch of the sambar is a light to rusty brown, not as striking a visual signal as the white rump in the other deer studied. While standing in an alert position, the animal may thump a foreleg on the ground with a hollow thud, the noise carrying at least 300 feet at night. Startled sambar often bound away thumping in unison first the forelegs, then somewhat louder the hindlegs, before continuing at a more conventional gait. This stamping of the feet appears to be an auditory signal, as in the chital, communicating not only the existence of possible danger but also the direction of flight taken by the animal. The alarm bark of the sambar is a loud, ringing call, termed "pooking" or "belling" by hunters because of its resonance, which is audible for at least a half mile in the forest.

The sambar respond to potential danger more readily than the chital and barasingha, frequently raising their tails and even barking after perceiving something which the other species nearby have either failed to detect or simply ignored. The sight or scent of a tiger is a common cause for alarm. Once, for example, a hind pooked three times at 0545 hours when she smelled the spot where a tiger had killed a chital at 1410 hours the previous day. She then walked off with her tail raised, thumping her forelegs alternately on the ground. On another occasion, three hinds and a fawn grazed in a clearing overgrown with sal seedlings. Suddenly, one hind raised her tail and pooked vigorously while looking at a ravine 80 feet away.

The other sambar jerked to attention. A tigress left the ravine and walked off, trailed at a distance of 150 feet by the three hinds. Only the lead hind barked; the fawn remained standing. After following the tigress about 100 feet, the sambar began to forage.

At the sight of a man on foot, sambar either flee immediately or watch the approach alertly from a distance of about 200 to 300 feet before moving away; barking in this context is rare. Two additional behavior patterns not noted in other deer, serve to make the sambar inconspicuous and undoubtedly have contributed to their reputation of being elusive and difficult to hunt. Instead of crashing away and thus drawing attention to itself, an animal often stands motionless; its dark pelage blends so well into the surrounding dark foliage that in several instances I detected its presence only accidentally. After perceiving danger, the deer were also observed to lower their necks, holding them horizontally, and in a semicrouch trot silently into a thicket. On two occasions when I had spotted sambar in the distance, there was no sign of them when I reached the place where they had been.

Social Behavior

The small size of the social groupings precluded a large number of interactions, and except during the main period of rut, the animals were usually encountered as they foraged in the forest, spread over about 100 feet of terrain, or rested within 20 to 30 feet of each other, chewing cud intermittently at the rate of about one chew per second.

Herd Size and Composition

The typical herd is small, numbering fewer than 6 individuals. Average group size is 4 to 5 according to Jerdon (1874) and Prater (1934), 3 to 5 according to Peacock (1933), and 10 to 15 according to Forsyth (1889) and Fletcher (1911). Brander (1923) never saw more than 8 hinds together, and the largest herd observed by Stockley (1928) consisted of 2 stags and 8 hinds. Dang told me of having seen 13 sambar together, and V. Singh (pers. comm.) once counted a herd of 18 in Shivpuri Park. Jerdon (1874) reported herds of up to 20 animals. The largest herd seen at Kanha was composed of 1 stag, 5 hinds, and 3 fawns, a total of 9.

The characteristic social unit at Kanha was one hind and one fawn (Plate 12) or one hind, one yearling, and one fawn, although 2 to 3 adult hinds were also seen together on occasion. Yearling stags usually remained with the hinds. The average size of 73 herds containing 2 or more individuals but not including an adult stag was 2.3. The average size of 26 herds containing one or more adult stags was 3.8. Solitary hinds were encountered 21 times. Adult stags, when not with hinds, were either solitary or in groups of 2. Herd compositions in other areas were similar to those at Kanha (Table 32).

Small herds, consisting of a hind or two with their young, probably retained their composition for weeks and even months, occa-

TABLE 32

COMPOSITION OF SAMBAR HERDS IN SEVERAL LOCALITIES

Locality	Adult Stag	Yearling Stag	Hind	Fawn	Total
Keoladeo Ghana Sanctuary			1	1	2
Keoladeo Ghana Sanctuary			1	1	2
Keoladeo Ghana Sanctuary		1	1	1	3
Keoladeo Ghana Sanctuary	1	1	2	1	5
West Kheri Forest. . . .			1	1	2
West Kheri Forest. . . .	1		1		2
Vanbihar Sanctuary . . .		1	5	1	7
Kaziranga Sanctuary. . .	2		1	1	4

sionally joining with other herds at a water hole and being visited by transient stags. One herd of 3 distinctive hinds and 1 fawn was seen seven times between March and August in the same general locality, attesting to the animals' fidelity to each other and to their range.

LEADERSHIP

When walking along a trail or across a meadow, sambar progress in single file with an adult hind characteristically in the lead. On one occasion, 2 stags, 3 hinds, and a fawn were at a salt lick. The larger of the two stags walked 150 feet to the edge of the forest and stood there for 20 minutes until the other members of the herd joined him. He led the movement back into the forest, but soon a hind took over his position.

AGONISTIC BEHAVIOR

Agonistic behavior was rarely observed. One hind nipped another one in the rump. In one herd, consisting of 2 adult stags, 3 hinds, and a fawn, the smaller of the two stags tended to remain at the periphery;

but on one occasion he entered stiff-legged with muzzle raised in a
head-up display. When the other stag stepped toward him, he retreated and 40 minutes later left the herd. Hinds fight by rearing
up and slashing with their hooves (Brander, 1923), as do stags when
their antlers are in velvet (P. Singh, 1959) and hard (Thom, 1937).
Sparring is apparently common during the rut, but I failed to see it.
Two published accounts describe the behavior:

The two stags, although in full view and well aware of each other's presence, approach each other stealthily, having been brought together by repeated challenges. At this stage their heads are stretched out, and their
tails cocked up in the air and with all the hair along their back and their
mane bristling, they present a most formidable appearance. . . . When
close together the stags lower their head[s] and close in: it then becomes a
shoving match [Brander, 1923].

At this period the stags fight fiercely for the favour of the hinds. Many a
time I have sat and watched these contests which can best be described as
pushing matches, though often severe wounds are inflicted by the brow
antler. The combatants would push and strain for a few minutes, then separate, and frequently begin to graze. After an interval the fight would be
resumed by mutual consent, and these bouts would go on till one party
acknowledged defeat by retreating [Fletcher, 1911].

Sambar stags also direct their aggression at bushes and saplings,
which they thrash with their antlers until at times only tattered stalks
remain. This behavior was observed twice (see Sexual Behavior, p.
144), and each time the stag also pawed the soil with a foreleg.
Occasionally stags stand up on their hindlegs in an attitude called
"preaching" by hunters. Fletcher (1911), for example, had a captive
stag which "pawed up the ground, turning slowly round at the same
time, then stood straight up on his hind-legs like a goat." And
Brander (1923) observed that stags, after issuing their rutting call,
frequently paw hollows at the base of a tree and "stand right up on
their hindlegs and remain preaching some time." I saw preaching
twice, once after a stag had wallowed and on another occasion when
2 stags, 3 hinds, and a fawn were at a salt lick. In the latter instance,
the larger of the two stags approached a tree in the head-up display
twice within a period of two minutes, then stood on his hindlegs
about six seconds while wiping his face back and forth in a leafy
branch. It is likely that the sambar, like the chital, mark the over-
hanging leaves with scent from their prominent preorbital glands.
Further evidence for this activity was the churned and trampled

areas beneath some trees. One such spot, found on January 26, was 5 × 3 feet in size.

"Sambar have regular 'stamping grounds.' In open grounds as well as in the jungle, one often comes across these circular bare patches, devoid of all vegetation, which have been stamped bare by the hooves of sambar. These stamping grounds may be anything from 10 to 40 feet in diameter" (Thom, 1937). Fletcher (1911) and Morris (1938) reported stamping grounds in southern India, and I found two of them on a ridge top at Kanha on March 4, both 25 feet in diameter. When subsequently checked on July 11 and October 12, neither spot was in use. Thom (1937) observed the behavior of 2 stags at a stamping ground while 8 to 10 hinds and young stags stood nearby:

The particular stamping ground was right out in the open on the top of a watershed in the Yomah hills at an elevation of about 4,200 feet. There was no jungle anywhere within 200 yards. . . . Two stags of the herd were engaged pounding away at each other with their horns and hooves, frequently standing upon their hind leg[s] as goats do when they fight. The clash of their horns as they met in mid air could be heard some way off. The stamping ground on which this encounter took place had a diameter of 30 feet.

The stamping grounds appear to complement the preaching trees and wallows functionally, all being sign posts communicating the stags' presence to other stags and to hinds.

Sexual Behavior

During the first week of November, the sambar suddenly began to wander widely, even at mid-day, becoming highly conspicuous in sharp contrast to their usual elusiveness. Solitary stags, hinds, and sometimes yearlings walked rapidly through the forest, appearing nervous, as if looking for something. Such wanderers were encountered throughout November but less commonly during December. Apparently, the behavior represented the first stage of the rut, a period when the old social groupings broke up and new ones were formed.

One of the manifestations of the early part of the rut is the "sore neck" (J. Bombay Nat. Hist. Soc., 1921; Morris, 1938) or "sore spot." On the ventral surface of the neck is a line of hair, somewhat darker and less sleek than the surrounding pelage, which runs down the mid-line from the throat to the lower part of the neck. At the beginning of the rut, the hair falls out at the terminus of this line, and the skin seems to slough off, forming a circular area about one to two inches in diameter which is bloody in appearance and exudes a serous fluid, "a kind of whitish looking oily or watery substance" (Thom, 1937). The area around the sore spot is sometimes swollen, and Kemp (1914 [quoted in J. Bombay Nat. Hist. Soc., 1921]) observed that hair is occasionally rubbed off over an area as large as eight inches long and six inches wide. I noted the first sore spot on November 15 and the last one on December 15. Many sore spots began to heal during the first half of December, and by January the only evidence of them was an area of pinkish skin lightly overgrown with hair. Sore spots were not seen at other times of the year at Kanha, but in the Kaziranga Sanctuary two stags and a hind all had them on May 3. In Mysore, Morris (1948) shot a stag with a sore spot in May. Between mid-November and early December, every adult and yearling sambar checked at Kanha had a sore spot; two large fawns, about eleven to twelve months old, also had them, but five others of similar age did not. In Thailand, according to Kemp (1914 [quoted in J. Bombay Nat. Hist. Soc., 1921]), "animals of all ages and both sexes suffered from this sore."

Several suggestions have been advanced to explain the cause of the sore spot. Thom (1937) thought that the wound resulted from irritation by plants and ticks, Evans (1912) felt that it was caused by an infection, Kemp (1914 [quoted in J. Bombay Nat. Hist. Soc., 1921]) hypothesized that the mineral water which the deer drank in Thailand was the causative agent, and Davar (1938) suggested that the sore was an "atavistic degeneracy," the site of a former gill attachment. The limited period of the year during which the sore appears and its widespread occurrence among the animals suggest that it is a gland; the fact that the sore becomes noticeable at the beginning of the rut when the sambar wander widely and form new social groupings suggests that the two phenomena are related. Morris (1938) noted that "the cause [of the sore spot] is probably glandular"; and S. Rippon (quoted in Thom, 1937) thought that "the sore might be some secretory gland which functions only at times of sexual activity."

A possible function of the sore spot is one of scent marking, for it is located at the base of the neck in such a way that a walking deer automatically wipes the exuding liquid against the vegetation. The scent may help the sambar to track and find each other in their forest environment. A histological examination of the sambar's neck would disclose the nature of the sore spot, but I was unable to obtain a specimen for this purpose.

There were various other indications that the stags were rutting in November. They appeared with greatly swollen necks, and saplings with shredded bark surrounded by paw marks were found at scattered locations in the forest. Brander (1923) and Lydekker (1924), among others, stated that stags emit a loud "metallic bellow," to which hinds reply with a grunting low, but I never heard these calls.

Wallowing was a prominent activity of stags from November to January (and also during February in Corbett Park), a time when the animals often had coats heavily caked with mud. Although Brander (1923) reported that sambar wallow at all times of the year, the wallows at Kanha were dried up from February to the break of the monsoon, and they were not in use during the rains. I watched at a wallow in a small clearing on December 5. The wallow was about 15 feet long and 8 feet wide, with a small pool of water at one end, the rest of the area consisting of soft mud. At 1650 hours a large stag approached alone, there being no sign of the three hinds and one fawn with which he had associated in the same area seven days earlier. He lay down in the muddy portion of the wallow, dug the tip of his right antler into the soil, and jerked up his head, repeating this ten times in thirty seconds. He then rose and walked slowly to the edge of the forest fifty feet away, where he thrashed a *Phoenix* palm with his antlers and pawed with his left foreleg. When this wallow and another one dried up within a month, a third wallow was made in a moist depression at the other end of the same clearing. On another occasion, a solitary stag approached a large wallow, measuring about 30×12 feet, in a wet hollow surrounded by tall grass. It was 0655 hours and quite cold, with frost on the meadow and steam rising from the water. The stag reclined in the wallow and repeatedly jabbed his antlers sideways and downward into the earth. Four minutes later he walked toward the forest's edge. Thirty feet from the nearest sal tree he suddenly assumed the head-up display and advanced with a stiff gait. He preached for eight seconds, wiping his face in a leafy branch eight feet above ground. He then belabored a tuft of grass with his antlers for ten seconds, shook himself, and disappeared among the trees.

Sexual behavior was rarely observed. A stag followed a hind closely on November 15 and sniffed her vulva; another male licked the vulva of a hind on December 4. A third stag assumed the low-stretch display, with neck held parallel to the ground and sub-orbital glands everted, as he trotted after a hind on December 28. Lydekker (1898) noted that "in the pairing-season the stags stalk about with tail erected, the muzzle stretched out, and the eyepits . . . completely everted. . . ."

Large stags establish a territory during the rut, which they defend against the intrusion of other stags (Prater, 1934). "Included with the possession of the valley are the hinds which frequent it, and these are attracted to the stag by his call and the powerful odour emitted by his facial glands" (Brander, 1923). Forsyth (1889) appeared to contradict the concept of a defended territory during the rut when he wrote: "More than one herd and a few solitary stags will not usually be found in the same tract of country; but in the rutting season they collect together in much larger numbers on the tops of the

TABLE 33

PERCENT OF SAMBAR HINDS ACCOMPANIED BY ADULT STAGS
AT VARIOUS TIMES OF THE YEAR

Month	Number of Times One or More Hinds Seen	Percent of Hinds Accompanied by One or More Adult Stgas
November–January.	34	29.5
February–May.	48	8.3
June–July.	15	37.0
August–October	7	.0

high plateaux. . . ." The localized wallows, stamping grounds, and preaching trees suggested that a stag confined himself for prolonged periods to a limited area, but I was unable to determine if more than one stag used these sites. However, a number of different adult stags were seen in the same general locality near the Kanha meadow. On one occasion two large stags were with a herd of three hinds, but the smaller and clearly subordinate animal soon left the herd and was encountered nearby with a yearling hind two weeks later. It appears likely that, after roaming fairly widely during the initial phases of the rut, most adult stags concentrate their activity in a certain area which overlaps partly to wholly with that of other stags, each of them delineating his range by marking it with scent and by leaving visual signals such as wallows and trees stripped of bark in it. The aggressive behavior of the stag and the accumulation of his signals in a limited part of his range probably tend to space males out in the forest, but I found no evidence of territorial exclusiveness.

The hinds seem to move widely, probably entering the ranges of and being joined by a number of different stags, before remaining with one of them for several days and perhaps longer. One stag stayed with the same herd of hinds for at least four days. The fact that adult stags were solitary for much of the year, and consequently, that only a small percentage of the hinds were accompanied by stags at any one time, attested to the fluid social organization of the animals (Table 33). The high frequency of stags with hinds from November to January corresponds to the main period of rut, but I have no explanation for the large percentage in June and July, the early part of the monsoon, just after the stags shed their antlers. The highly unequal sex ratio of adults which favored the females 3:1, together with the fact that average herd size does not increase appreciably during the rut, makes a loose social organization in which stags are only transient members of herds almost necessary if all hinds are to be bred. Although these comments fit the observed facts at Kanha, my data are meager, and interpretation must remain speculative until more detailed work on the sambar clarifies their social structure in this and other areas.

CHAPTER 6

THE BLACKBUCK

The blackbuck is considered by many to be the most beautiful of all antelopes because of the male's striking black and white pelage and his long spiral horns. The species once roamed in huge herds throughout the open woodlands and cultivated tracts of India, making it one of the most conspicuous and most hunted members of the country's fauna. These large herds are now gone, and the animal clings to the last vestige of its former range in small scattered groups. The behavior of captive blackbuck has been studied by Taibel (1937), Etkin (1954), Walther (1958), and Backhaus (1958), but few details are available concerning their habits in the wild. This chapter describes primarily the behavior of a small herd in Kanha Park.

The blackbuck (*Antilope cervicapra*) is the sole representative of the genus *Antilope* and, together with the Indian gazelle, represents the subfamily Antilopinae in the country. The other two antelopes of peninsular India — the four-horned antelope and the nilgai — are placed into the subfamily Bovinae. Ellerman and Morrison-Scott (1951) recognize four subspecies of blackbuck, of which *A.c. centralis* occurs in central India, *A.c. rajputanae* in Rajasthan and Punjab, *A.c. rupricapra* from Uttar Pradesh eastward, and *A.c. cervicapra* in southern India.

Description

The blackbuck are medium-sized, slender antelopes. The bucks stand about 29 to 33 inches high at the shoulder, and their total length is 49 to 58 inches (Blanford, 1888–91). Twenty-one bucks shot by Meinertzhagen (1939) in Rajasthan ranged from 74 to 94 pounds in weight, and two does weighed 71 and 85 pounds, respectively. It was my impression that the animals in northern India were on the average somewhat larger than those at Kanha Park. The blackbuck is one of the few antelopes in which the coat color of bucks and does differs strikingly. In adult bucks the back, sides, neck, part of the face, and outside of the legs are black. The chest, abdomen, rump, and inside of the legs, ears, and tail are white. A white ring surrounds each eye, and there are patches of white on the nose and chin. The nape is rusty. The horns are marked with rings and make three to four complete spirals in adults. Record horn length is 28⅝ inches (Ward, 1922). Young bucks are light brown in color, but by about three years of age their pelage has turned quite black (Baker, 1890; Taibel, 1937; Prater, 1934). The does and fawns are light brown in those parts of the body where adult bucks are black, and white in the remaining portions (Plate 13).

Adult bucks undergo a conspicuous change of pelage color during the molt, a fact noted by Lydekker (1913–16) and Pocock (1910) but not confirmed by Crandall (1964) in the New York Zoological Park. The sole black buck at Kanha began to lose his dark color in January and had become quite brown by late March. By early July his neck and shoulders had blackened, and in August he had his full black pelage once more.

Distribution and Status

The blackbuck is typically Indian in distribution, having once occurred from what is now West Pakistan along the foot of the Himalayas from Punjab through Uttar Pradesh and Nepal to West Bengal and East Pakistan, as well as throughout peninsular India, but not in Ceylon (Lydekker, 1924). It is an animal of open, flat to slightly undulating terrain, reaching its greatest abundance in areas covered with thorn and dry deciduous forests. With the destruction of the forest cover, the animals readily adapted to wastelands and cultivation. The species has also penetrated the moist deciduous forests in Orissa, Madhya Pradesh, and other states apparently by following the slash-and-burn cultivators and occupying the ephemeral field and village sites opened up by them. The blackbuck in Kanha Park probably colonized the area in this fashion.

Although the blackbuck probably was once the most abundant wild hoofed animal in India, its preference for open habitats made it highly vulnerable to shooting. As it came into increasing conflict with agriculturalists, it was rapidly exterminated over much of its range. At present no sanctuary harbors a large blackbuck population, although a few animals are preserved to some extent in the Keoladeo Ghana Sanctuary, the Kodiakadu Forest in Madras, and a few other minor areas, including private enclosures maintained by maharajas. It was impossible to conduct a detailed survey of the status and distribution of the blackbuck in the time available because the small populations are widely scattered and are located for the most part on private farmlands and wastelands. However, my limited observations and comments by long-time residents, as well as published sources, give a general idea of the precarious position of the species.

The states of Assam, West Bengal, and Kerala contain no blackbuck. In Orissa the species is confined to about 75 square miles of sand dunes on a spit of land that separates Chilka Lake from the sea and to an area around Konarak, some 30 miles north of the lake. De tallied 82 animals in these areas, and it is doubtful if more than 200 to 300 survive in the state as a whole. A population was once found just west of Chilka Lake, but it was killed off by rinderpest in the early 1940's, according to M. Ahmedulla (pers. comm.). The blackbuck in Bihar have "almost become extinct," according to Shahi (letter, May 5, 1965). In Madras the species is rare, apparently confined to the Guindy Deer Park near Madras city, to the Kodiakadu Forest in Tanjore District, and to a few other localities (letter from M. Badshah, May 14, 1964).

Uttar Pradesh was once famous for the number of its blackbuck, particularly in the western part of the state around the cities of Agra and Aligarh and along the Yamuna and Ganges rivers. On a piece of wasteland in the West Kheri Forest Division, I counted 5 bucks, 3 does, and 1 fawn, the only blackbuck seen in over 1,000 miles of travel in the state. P. Jay, who in 1964 and 1965 drove about 10,000 miles through all parts of Uttar Pradesh while censusing rhesus monkeys, saw 1 blackbuck in Philibhit District in the northern part of the state and a total of 5 bucks and 2 does in Chandraprabha Park in the southern part. Dang (1964c) reported surviving herds near Hastinapur, around Saharanpur, and in the vicinity of Lucknow. These few sightings, together with reports from foresters and others, indicate that the species is on the verge of extinction in Uttar Pradesh.

In several states the blackbuck are said to occur over a fairly wide area in a number of small populations. A wildlife map published in 1963 by Andhra Pradesh shows the animals as occurring in most districts of the state. In Mysore the species is found predominantly in the central and eastern part, from near the city of Bijapur in the north to Bangalore in the south, but a local informant told Spillett (pers. comm.) that in areas where herds of several hundred were regularly seen in about 1960 only scattered groups now remain. The animals in Maharashtra are confined largely to the southern and eastern areas of the state. Madhya Pradesh had a few blackbuck in Kanha Park and in Shivpuri Park, and I was told that a few small herds occur near the towns of Sagor, Damoh, Seoni, and Gwalior and also along the banks of the Narmada and Chambal rivers. Indicative of the status of the blackbuck in this state is my failure in 1965 to find any animals in areas where Brander (1953), on a train trip from Bombay to Allahabad in the early years of this cen-

TABLE 34

The Composition of the Kanha Blackbuck
Population in 1964 and 1965

Date	Male	Adult Female	Yearling Female	Young			Total
				Male	Female	Unsexed	
January 1, 1964 .	5	5	2	0	0	1	13
July 1, 1964 . . .	5	5	2	0	4	0	16
June 3, 1965. . .	5	7	4	0	0	4	20

tury, reported he was almost continuously within sight of them. In the Punjab and the adjoining Delhi area, where Jerdon (1874), Lydekker (1893), and others once counted herds numbering several thousand individuals, only a few survivors exist, primarily in the southern half of the state (letter from G. Singh, May 19, 1964) and also in the western part near Ferozepore (Dang, 1964c). Some of these are locally protected by religious sentiment, but others continue to be illegally hunted by the villagers as well as by European and other residents from New Delhi. Blackbuck are found in various parts of Gujarat, especially between the Gulf of Cambay and Gulf of Kutch. Dharmakumarsinhji told me that in 1945 an estimated 25,000 to 30,000 animals roamed in his princely state of Bavnagar but that now a few hundred at most survive there.

A main stronghold of the blackbuck in India appears to be in western Rajasthan, where, according to K. Sankhala (pers. comm.) and Prakash (1960), they are still found sporadically in the isolated semidesert parts of the Jodhpur, Bikaner, Jaisalmer, Jhalore, and other districts, especially where protected by maharajas or by local villagers. In the heavily populated eastern part of the state, the species has been almost wiped out, with only a few small herds surviving; the 70 animals in the Keoladeo Ghana Sanctuary may well be the largest of these.

Population Dynamics

POPULATION SIZE AND COMPOSITION

The blackbuck population in Kanha Park has probably never exceeded 200 individuals. Brander (1953) after a visit to the area in 1928 reported "two good herds," and a census in 1938 gave a count of 168 animals. Since 1955, when 88 were tallied, the population has declined quite steadily, with only 30 reported in June, 1963

TABLE 35

AGE AND SEX RATIOS OF BLACKBUCK IN SEVERAL LOCALITIES

Location	Date	Size of Population	Bucks :	100 Does :	Fawns
Kanha National Park	July 1, 1964	16	71	100	57
Kanha National Park	June 3, 1965	20	45	100	36
Sikandra	February 11, 1965	126	84	100	33
Keoladeo Ghana Sanctuary. . .	Mid-February, 1965	70±	56	100	31
Chilka Lake. . .	November 8–15, 1964	82+	60	100	36

(Table 2), all on the Kanha meadow. By January, 1964, the herd had dwindled to 12 individuals, but from then on it increased, reaching 20 or possibly 21 by June, 1965.

Table 34 presents the composition of the Kanha blackbuck population in 1964 and 1965. On the 5 bucks present in January, 1964, 1 was fully adult with a black coat, 2 were in transition from brown to black pelage (an estimated two and a half years old), and 2 were still brown (perhaps one and a half and two years old, respectively). No males were born in 1964, with the result that the ratio of bucks to 100 does dropped from 71:100 to 45:100 when the female fawns became yearlings on January 1, 1965 (Table 35). An uneven sex ratio favoring the females was also found in other localities studied, at Chilka Lake and at Keoladeo Ghana, but at Sikandra the captive herd showed a higher proportion of bucks (84:100) than the free-living populations. The unequal sex ratio was already apparent in yearlings judged to be nine to thirteen months old. Yearling does in this age group comprised 13 percent of the population at Keoladeo Ghana and bucks 6 percent; at Sikandra the figures were 14 and 11 percent, respectively. Counts to determine the ratio of fawns to does (Table 35) should ideally be made twice a year after the peak fawning seasons. The censuses at Sikandra and Keoladeo Ghana were made just before the main birth peak and thus fail to give an accurate idea of the number of young present somewhat later.

THE RUTTING SEASON

According to Lydekker (1924), Prater (1948), and Asdell (1946) mating occurs primarily in February and March; Baldwin (1877) noted that the rut begins in January and February; and Sterndale (1884) found that though most mating is in the spring some young are born throughout the year. Brander (1923) also emphasized that fawns can be seen at all seasons, but he stated that the "chief rut is about March, and most of the fawns are born shortly before the rains." This statement implies a gestation period of just three months, when, in fact, it is about six months (Brown, 1936; Taibel, 1937; Asdell, 1946).

No copulations were observed at Kanha, but behavior related to sexual behavior, such as chasing and mounting, gave a good indication of the state of the rut. Although the bucks were sexually active during every month of the year, they showed two definite peaks: one in April and the other from mid-August to mid-October. The April rut was less intense than the August-October one, and in this connection it should be noted that the one male in the population was quite brown during the April peak whereas he had molted into his full black pelage in time for the second peak. The males at Keoladeo Ghana were just entering a period of rut in the latter part of February.

Of the fawns present at Kanha in December, 1963, 3 were born between February and April and 1 in about September. Four births occurred in 1964: March 22–24, April 4–5, May 7–9, and May 11–14. Two fawns were born in late February, 1965, and three adult does were heavily pregnant, due to give birth within the next month or two. Thus out of a total of 13 young born or soon to be born between 1963 and mid-1965, all but 1 were conceived between mid-August and mid-November.

There were a total of 19 young aged six months or less at Sikandra on February 11. Sixteen of these had been born between August and October and hence conceived between February and April.

Three fawns had just been born, having been conceived in August, and the numerous pregnant does indicated that a birth peak was approaching. The age distribution of the young at Keoladeo Ghana also pointed to two birth peaks.

The data indicate that blackbuck rut throughout the year, with peaks in March-April and August-October. During the first peak, which is the only one recognized in the literature, a smaller proportion of females conceive than during the second one. The 125 blackbuck born in the London zoo (Jarvis and Morris, 1962) and the 97 in the New York Zoological Park (Crandall, 1964) show no birth peaks.

RATE OF REPRODUCTION

Brander (1923) and Lydekker (1924) stated that one to two fawns are born at a time. I did not see any twins, nor did Crandall (1964) report any in 97 births at the New York Zoological Garden.

The four does that gave birth at Kanha in 1964 did so again in 1965. One doe lost her small fawn in January, 1964, but did not conceive until the October rut, bypassing the one in April. One fawn per year appears to be the rule. Taibel (1937), however, found that one captive doe gave birth to 6 single fawns between June, 1931, and May, 1935, and another to 5 fawns between October, 1933, and February, 1937, less than a year elapsing between some births.

Two yearling does, born early in 1963, failed to give birth in 1964 and were not obviously pregnant in March, 1965, when two years old, which suggests that these females possibly did not bear their first young until two and a half to three years old. Taibel (1937) stated that captive does reach sexual maturity at six months of age; one female born on March 28, 1933, had her first young on May 18, 1934, when not quite fourteen months old.

MORTALITY

One fawn, about four months old, disappeared from the Kanha herd in January, 1964, apparently having been taken by a predator. From then until March, 1965, a period of fourteen months, there were no further deaths, perhaps indicating that the predators find it difficult to stalk the animals successfully on the meadow. The steady decline in the population prior to 1964 was probably due largely to poaching.

General Behavior

The blackbuck is adapted to life on the plains. Except when the temperature in the shade passes the 90°F mark, the animals rarely seek the cover of a tree, remaining instead on the open meadow at all times of the day. They not only tolerate direct sun much more readily than the other wild ungulates in the area, but they also are more diurnal in their grazing and other activities.

DAILY ACTIVITY CYCLE

The blackbuck's daily routine of grazing and resting changes somewhat with the seasons. During the cool weather the animals rise with the first pale light at about 0600 hours and then graze intermittently throughout the day, resting only for brief periods usually between 1000 and 1400 hours, as shown by Figure 9, which is based on 1,082 activity observations. One herd, which was observed during the night of February 26–27, grazed until about 2100 hours and again from 0105 to 0345 hours, lying down for the remainder of the night in the open.

During the hot weather the animals rise at about 0500 hours and

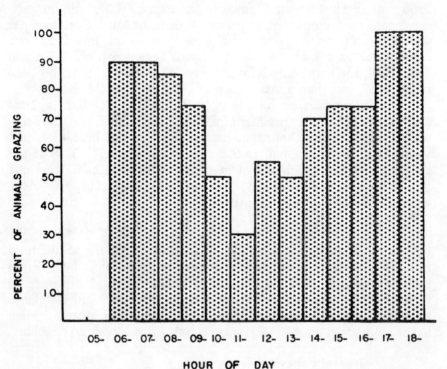

FIG. 9.—Percent of blackbuck grazing at hourly intervals, 0500–1900 hours, November to February.

feed until around 0730 hours, when they often withdraw into the shade until late afternoon, spending much less time foraging during daylight than in the previous season. During the monsoon, with its abundant forage, the blackbuck stand around and walk a great deal but seem to feed little. For example, almost 90 percent of the animals grazed between 0600 and 0900 hours in the cool season, whereas during the rains this figure dropped to 50 percent and there was no afternoon peak of feeding.

Food Habits and Feeding and Drinking Behavior

Blackbuck are almost exclusively grazers (Table 10), although they also take the leaves of one shrub (Table 11). They generally are found in areas with such low-growing grasses as *Andropogon brevifolius* and *Echinochloa colona*, avoiding *Themeda* and other tall grasses, but this is a reflection of their preference for an open habitat rather than their choice of certain grasses as forage. After the burning of the meadow, the animals appeared to eat whatever green shoots became available.

A herd forages either widely scattered or as a compact unit, each animal moving along slowly at the rate of 400 to 600 feet per hour or sometimes remaining for several hours in an area as small as 100 feet in diameter. In contrast to grazing deer, which commonly keep

TABLE 36

DURATION OF ALTERNATE GRAZING AND ALERT PERIODS
BY FORAGING BLACKBUCK

Animal Observed	Number of Consecutive Periods Timed	Average Duration of Grazing in Seconds	Average Duration of Raised Head in Seconds
Buck.	17	71	10
Buck.	24	69	5
Doe	21	80	5

their muzzles lowered to the ground for ten or more minutes at a time if undisturbed, the blackbuck usually raise their heads and look around briefly for no apparent reason every minute or two (Table 36). This behavior appears to be an adaptation for spotting potentially dangerous situations on the open plains by sight rather than smell.

I have never seen blackbuck drink, and even during the hottest months of the year, the animals failed to make the obvious trek to water at dawn and dusk like the chital and barasingha. It is likely that the animals persisted for days and even weeks without drinking.

Blanford (1888–91) also noted that blackbuck rarely drink, and as Lydekker (1924) pointed out, the antelope along the Orissa coast have no fresh water available to them during the dry season (although they do now, in the irrigation ditches of some casuarina plantations). Livingston *et al.* (1962) have shown that various species of hoofed animals living in arid environments on forage of low food value can recycle the nitrogen in their bodies rather than excrete it in the urine. This enables the animal to subsist on food with a low protein content, and it is also an adaptation for conserving water. Blackbuck may possibly have a similar mechanism.

RESPONSE TO PREDATORS

Blackbuck rely more on sight than sound in transmitting information to other members of the herd in a potentially dangerous situation. The alert posture, which as in deer consists of standing erect with the neck held almost vertically, is the most frequently employed visual signal in response to an alarm call of, for example, a chital or to the sight or a predator. A foreleg may be stamped and the short, narrow tail raised. I have not heard blackbuck vocalize when alarmed, but Brander (1923) noted that they hiss, and Dharmakumarsinhji told me that he has heard them snort on seeing a cheetah.

Approach by man or tiger causes the animals first to crowd together and then to flee. The flight distance varies; in response to one person approaching slowly on foot, it is commonly between 150 and 200 feet. Several blackbuck at West Kheri, however, where they are hunted, fled from the elephant on which I was riding at 450 feet and ran for over one mile before halting. Budden (1921) clocked a running buck at thirty-three miles per hour. One herd watched a jackal trot by at 100 feet without fleeing, and another herd behaved similarly toward a tigress 250 feet away.

Blackbuck appear to have a good sense of smell. On one occasion a herd passed me at a distance of 100 feet as I stood hidden by some brush. The lead doe suddenly stopped, sniffed the air, stamped a foreleg as she faced in my direction, walked back over her trail, and tested the air some more; finally all moved off.

Blackbuck in flight usually trot or gallop, but occasionally they assume a means of progression which Brooks (1961) for the Thomson gazelle called stotting or spronking. The animal bounds along stiff-legged, hitting the ground with all four feet in unison, a gait characteristic of gazelles (Walther, 1964) and nilgai, among other animals. Such behavior on the part of one animal usually elicits a similar gait in the others, and all spronk along in single file. Spronking is also employed when moving through high grass. A herd was several times observed to approach an isolated patch of tall grass at a walk, spronk through it, and then continue in its former manner. Fawns spronk in play when only a few days old, and one bright moonlight night I watched several adults spronk around in a large circle. Spronking has several possible functions: (1) the noise of the thudding hooves may be an auditory signal to others nearby, indicating danger; (2) the high leaps, which are accompanied by white flashes from the abdomen and rump, make the animal visible at a great distance, a visual signal like the jumps of the springbuck described by Wynne-Edwards (1962); (3) the leaps may help the animal keep the source of a disturbance in view and spot a lurking enemy ahead in the high grass; and (4) scent may be deposited from the interdigital glands present in all feet (Pocock, 1910), leaving an olfactory signal for others passing by later.

Social Behavior

The social structure of the blackbuck population changes with the seasons. For convenience, I refer to (1) mixed herds, consisting of a loose aggregation of bucks and does, (2) breeding herds, consisting of a buck and several does confined to a territory at the time of rut, and (3) buck herds, consisting solely of bucks. Although there were few blackbuck at Kanha, the social organization of these animals appeared to be typical of blackbuck in general, as judged by the literature and from observations in the Keoladeo Ghana Sanctuary.

SOCIAL ORGANIZATION

The 13 blackbuck at Kanha were divided as follows on December 20, 1963: buck IV (the number denotes his position in the dominance hierarchy) and 4 does were in the northern part of the meadow, 3 does and 1 fawn ranged over the rice fields by the village, and the remaining 4 bucks wandered around together. The last group joined buck IV with his does on December 26, and all remained together until January 1, 1964, when the females separated from the bucks and moved to the other end of the meadow, followed one day later by 3 of the bucks. Buck V went off alone, and buck I stayed in the area until January 9, when he, too, joined the does at their new site. Earlier, on January 3, all females and young had come together, and on January 13, the 13 blackbuck were in one mixed herd for the first and only time during the study. Four of the bucks left the herd the following day but rejoined it at irregular intervals singly or together. On January 14, buck I and two does moved back to the other side of the meadow, where, by January 24, 3 more does had joined them. One fawn disappeared between 0950 and 1315 hours on January 19, presumably taken by a predator. December and January appeared to be a time of general reorganization of the population, with mixed herds splitting up into breeding herds. In the resulting groups, buck I acquired 5 does, buck II acquired 2 does, and 3 bucks remained bachelors. This population structure remained basically unchanged throughout the year, and to my knowledge bucks I and II had no contact with each other for over twelve months even though only about a mile of terrain separated their respective territories.

Buck I and his 5 does remained in a limited area without change in herd composition through April, except for 2 does which became peripheral to the herd while they fawned. A third doe left to fawn on May 8 and was joined by buck III, the two staying together until May 14. The breeding herd lost some of its cohesiveness in early June as the buck sometimes drifted off by himself for several hours. On June 21 he joined 2 other bucks nearby, and then all 3 came back to the herd; on June 25, he abandoned the herd with 3 other bucks for two days, the first time he had left the does unattended for a prolonged period since January. One doe had departed from the breeding herd with her fawn the previous day and joined buck II, but she was back with her former herd 4 days later. The composition then remained constant until mid-October. The bachelor bucks, singly or together, were frequently around the periphery during this period. Although the breeding herd retained its basic structure from late October to mid-January, 1965, it was often split as its members roamed more widely than during the previous months. From October 27 to 29, for example, buck III was with 3 does and 2 fawns nearly half a mile from buck I and the rest of his herd; from November 12 to 15, buck III was accompanied by 3 does and 3 fawns; and on December 4 and 5, buck I was alone in his territory, his herd rejoining him there the next day. At this time of year the attachment of the animals seemed to be more to the territory than to each other, with buck I not making an effort to keep either the does in the territory or the other bucks out of it. When Kanha was revisited in

PLATE 12.—A sambar hind with fawn; the deer have their tails raised, a typical gesture of alarm. (May 11, 1964).

PLATE 13.—Blackbuck at Sikandra, showing the black pelage of adult bucks and the brown one of young bucks and does (February 11, 1965).

PLATE 14.—A nilgai bull in the thorn forest of the Keoladeo Ghana Sanctuary (February 14, 1965).

PLATE 15.—A female gaur with a small calf followed by an adult bull; the dorsal ridge and the dewlaps of the bull are conspicuous (March 29, 1964).

March, 1965, the herd was still in its usual place; it had retained its composition except for the birth of 2 fawns.

The 3 bachelor bucks remained in the vicinity of and sometimes with buck II and his 2 does — an adult and a yearling — from mid-January to mid-March. Once the herd split for two days, the yearling doe going off with buck III. The herd remained stable from April to mid-June except for one birth. A doe with fawn from the herd of buck I joined it briefly on June 24. On August 23, the 2 does and fawn left the buck alone in his territory and moved half a mile away, rejoining him four days later. From then until mid-January, 1965, no further changes in composition occurred, and, in contrast to the other breeding herd, the animals retained their cohesiveness. Twice in December the whole herd moved for a day or two to the rice fields near the village over half a mile away, the only times buck II abandoned his territory that year. The same 4 animals were still together in March, 1965.

In contrast to the breeding herds, which largely confined their movements to a limited territory, the 3 bachelor bucks roamed widely over the whole meadow. The bucks were singly or together at or near the periphery of one of the breeding herds for much of the year; only in April and May were they rarely seen with them. The composition of the buck herd changed from day to day, the animals being alone as often as in groups of 2 or 3.

The social organization of the blackbuck appears to undergo two major changes in the course of the year. From about February to November the population is divided into small breeding herds, consisting of one or more bucks and a variable number of does and fawns, which largely limit their activity to restricted areas or territories. The breeding herds break up during December and January, the social structure disintegrating as the animals congregate into mixed herds of varying sizes. Then in about February, new breeding herds are again formed. A number of excess bucks, which neither establish territories nor acquire does, occur throughout the year either in buck herds or peripherally to breeding herds.

Breeding herd sizes and compositions in other areas were similar to those at Kanha. Brander (1923) found that average herd size was 10 to 20 animals, with as many as 40 on occasion; Lydekker (1924) gave a figure of 10 to 30 and up to 50 does with one adult buck; Prater (1934) and Baker (1890) placed herd size at 20 to 30. In Mysore "an average herd of antelope consists of from 10 to 15 animals, including, as a rule, only one black buck and one or two young males as light in colour as the does" (Russell, 1900). On November 6, 1963, the composition of two breeding herds at Keoladeo Ghana was 4 black bucks, 2 brown bucks, and 15 does and fawns, a total of 21; and 2 black bucks, 3 brown bucks, and 10 does and fawns, a total of 15. De tallied 10 herds, varying in size from 2 to 8, at Chilka Lake in November, 1964. Average group composition was 1.1 bucks (range 1–2), 3.5 does (range 1–7), and .6 fawns (range 0–3). All bucks except one were fully adult. In addition, he saw two aggregations which probably represented breeding herds with a number of peripheral bucks. One of these consisted of 5 black bucks, 1 brown buck, 4 does, and 3 fawns, a total of 13; and the other, 2 black bucks, 5 brown bucks, 3 does, and 1 fawn, a total of 11. Some of the large aggregations reported in the literature probably were divided into breeding herds except when disturbed by hunters. Baker (1890), for example, noted that "many hundreds may be scattered in small groups over the area of a few square miles."

In general breeding herds appear to break up during the cool season. When I visited the Keoladeo Ghana Sanctuary on November 6, 1963, the breeding herds were well established, but on February 12, 1965, almost all animals in the sanctuary were in one mixed herd. By February 20, however, several bucks had begun to establish territories. Similarly, the blackbuck at Chilka Lake were for the most part still in breeding herds in early November, although De reported seeing does and fawns not accompanied by a buck on three occasions, which suggests that some of the herds had begun to disintegrate. Dang told me that in the past blackbuck congregated into large herds around Delhi only during the cool season. The huge herds mentioned by several authors probably refer to the same time of the year. Forsyth (1889), for instance, wrote: "I have seen herds in the Sagar country, immediately after the Mutiny of 1857, when they were little molested, which must have numbered a thousand or more individuals." And Jerdon (1874) observed "larger herds in the neighbourhood of Jalna in the Deccan than anywhere else — occasionally some thousands together." Such large mixed herds appear to have been characteristic of areas with vast uncultivated tracts like Rajasthan, whereas herds of more than 100 to 300 were seldom seen in the heavily populated Gangetic plain (Baldwin, 1877; "Silver Hackle," 1929).

The tendency for males to congregate was evident at Keoladeo Ghana and even in the captive herd at Sikandra, where several bucks frequently split off from the main herd and moved away together. "Silver Hackle" (1929) once saw a herd of 35 bucks, and Sankhala (pers. comm.) noted one of about 60 bucks in Rajasthan in May, 1964.

According to Dang (1964*a*), "With the arrival of the monsoons, the large herds of the 'khadars' of the great rivers would move in masses to the dry ground higher up," movements which in Uttar Pradesh often covered a distance of five or more miles. What effect such travel had on the composition of breeding herds is not known.

When the blackbuck population in an area reaches as low a level as at Kanha, variations in the pattern of social organization may occur. The breeding herds there, for example, probably retained their composition for a longer period than would be possible if a number of bucks held contiguous territories and constantly competed for does. And during the cool season of 1964–65, the two breeding herds failed to split up and mix as in the previous year. However, since the blackbuck have dwindled in number to such an extent throughout India, the social pattern described for Kanha probably has become fairly typical of the species as a whole.

THE ESTABLISHMENT AND MAINTENANCE OF THE TERRITORY

Four bucks joined the herd consisting of buck IV and 4 does on December 26 and remained in a limited area until early January; by January 2 all except buck I had drifted off to another part of the meadow. Buck I stayed behind alone until January 9, often standing motionless on the open slope, easily visible for a long distance. After leaving the area for five days, he returned to it with 2 does, and 3 additional does joined him there later. He remained within his chosen territory for at least twelve months. Buck II settled over a mile away; the boundaries between the two territories were not contiguous.

A herd of about 65 blackbuck in Keoladeo Ghana Sanctuary frequently broke up into small groups by mid-February. The 3 largest bucks occasionally separated from the herd, and each remained alone for several hours to one day in an area usually no more than one hundred feet in diameter. Any intruding buck was vigorously chased for a short distance, but does were displayed to and followed. This behavior undoubtedly represented the intial stages of territory formation, with bucks attempting to retain does in a limited area and to drive other bucks out of it. Dharmakumarsinhji told me that, in the former princely state of Bavnagar in Gujarat, bucks set up adjacent territories and that does were chased by each territorial male in turn as they traveled through the area.

The size of the home range of the blackbuck at Kanha was about equal in size to the main meadow — somewhat over two square miles. Two of the bucks established territories within this range, each territory consisting of a central area of about 20 acres in which the animal spent most of its time and a surrounding terrain which was frequented only occasionally. The total acreage used by buck I was about 350 and by buck II about 200. For comparison, the territory of the Grant gazelle in the Ngorongoro Crater of Tanzania is about 900×900 feet and is surrounded by the overlapping home ranges of bachelor bucks, 1 to 2 square kilometers in size (Walther, 1965). Waterbuck males "have living and breeding territories of quarter to one square mile" in Kenya (Kiley-Worthington, 1965).

Each buck marks his territory with a number of visual and olfactory signs which undoubtedly serve to delineate the boundaries. The most conspicuous territorial marker is, of course, the buck himself, with his striking black and white pelage and long horns, standing, as he often does, in a prominent place. Bucks also tend to deposit their feces at a specific location, but as Brander (1923) has pointed out, they are not consistent in this habit. Buck I had a total of six defecation sites within the boundary of his territory. Counts of five pellet groups indicated that a buck deposits about 235 (153–288) pellets at a time; none of the dung piles contained more than about fifteen relatively fresh deposits. Buck I often dropped his feces away from these spots; on the other hand, he sometimes left the herd and walked as far as 500 feet to a particular dung pile before defecating. Does and visiting bucks also used these sites on occasion. The bucks at Keoladeo Ghana commonly defecated on dung piles established by nilgai.

A buck defecating at a dung pile displays a definite sequence of actions that do not accompany defecation at other places as prominently. He approaches, perhaps sniffs the pile and paws once or twice with a foreleg, and then stands with his forequarters very stiff and erect, the head raised and horns lying almost parallel to the neck; the hindlegs are stretched far back. He urinates in this manner, then squats low and defecates. In contrast, vicuñas in Peru defecate first and then urinate at a dung pile (Koford, 1957). The nilgai and Indian gazelle also squat at dung piles in contrast to species such as chital, barasingha, and gaur, which do not assume a special posture while defecating. It is possible that body position becomes exaggerated in species in which the feces have acquired social significance, the animal itself thus having signal functions.

Blackbuck have prominent preorbital glands used to mark grass and bushes with scent (Dharmakumarsinhji, 1959). When chasing an intruding buck or when driving a doe, the territorial buck often halts briefly and thrashes a tuft of grass with upward and sideways sweeps of the head. On one occasion, after the buck had been deserted in his territory by the does for several days, he spotted two of them approaching as they rounded a coppice two hundred feet away. His tail went up and his ears folded backward and downward; he bounded toward them with muzzle raised, circled them, and then stopped and wiped his face in the grass. Although the belaboring of the vegetation is presumably a form of redirected aggression, the actions apparently also serve to wipe scent from the glands onto the grass, leaves, and head of the animal. Occasionally a buck wiped one preorbital gland gently up and down a grass stalk. I poked my finger into the everted gland of a displaying buck at a zoo. The odor of the scent was musky and faintly like acetic acid. The bachelor bucks without territories also marked the vegetation with scent. The accumulation of olfactory and visual signals in a limited space, therefore, rather than marking in general, characterized a territory in the blackbuck, a conclusion similar to one arrived at by Walther (1964) for the Thomson gazelle.

All aggressive interactions were recorded when the 5 bucks were seen together for the first time on December 26, and the results showed that the animals had a linear dominance hierarchy (Table 37). Rank was based on size and age, the most dominant buck having the largest body and longest horns and the most subordinate having the smallest body and horns. The rank order remained constant

TABLE 37

NUMBER OF DOMINANCE INTERACTIONS OBSERVED IN THE FIVE BLACKBUCK MALES AT KANHA PARK, DECEMBER 26, 1963, BETWEEN 0820 AND 0930 HOURS

DOMINANT BUCK	SUBORDINATE BUCK					TOTAL
	I	II	III	IV	V	
I		1	1	9	4	15
II			1	3	2	6
III				2	1	3
IV					5	5
V						0
Total						29

throughout the period of study and had probably been established before my arrival. Etkin (1954) noted in a study of five captive males that "No. 1 excluded No. 2 male from association with the group by persistent chasing but other males were not so excluded even though occasionally chased. This condition remained constant despite considerable advance toward maturity of some of the males during this period. No evidence of dominance hierarchy among the other males was noted."

Dominance in blackbuck is most commonly asserted with the head-up display, as pictured in the Ajanta Caves, which date from the sixth to seventh century (Rowland, 1963), and as described by Taibel (1937), Finn (1929), and Walther (1958). The buck raises his muzzle so high that the horns lie almost alongside the neck; the ears are folded back, lowered, and held somewhat laterally, exposing the white insides; and the stubby tail is raised and curved up over the buck, making the white patch on the rump conspicuous. The preorbital glands are everted. The buck approaches his opponent at a prancing walk in this posture, sometimes bobbing the head up and down, flashing his white chin. Occasionally he bounds forward in a stiff-legged gallop, uttering a series of harsh grunts and jerking up his head with each sound. The threatened buck usually turns aside, but if he does not, the other buck passes in front of him at a distance of about five feet, showing his broadside, head somewhat averted. In the Grant gazelle, a species belonging to the same subfamily as the blackbuck, this part of the display is highly ritualized. Two bucks approach each other, heads turned slightly to the side and "when the forequarters of each are opposite the tail of his opponent, they stop and lift their heads on high. Then they abruptly and synchronously turn their noses toward one another and show each other the white throat patch" (Walther, 1965).

A direct threat consists of lowering the head until the muzzle almost touches the ground and pointing the tip of the horns at the opponent. This posture may be merely intimated by a rapid downward jerk of the head, a gesture usually sufficient to cause the other animal to retreat. When asserting his dominance vigorously, a buck may chase another for fifty to eighty or more feet with horns lowered. Of the 29 interactions recorded in Table 37, 26 consisted of brief chases, 2 of head-up displays, and 1 of a sparring match. The chased animal trots, gallops, or spronks away, rarely farther than one hundred fifty feet, often circling back to the periphery of the herd.

Sparring was infrequent during encounters except between the three bachelor bucks. Two bucks usually faced each other, jerked their heads down, locked horns sometimes with a crash, and then pushed and twisted their heads until one turned aside. The victor often followed the other animal in the head-up display for a short distance. Occasionally all three bucks sparred, switching partners frequently. Most matches were brief, a minute or less, but with some lasting five to ten minutes. If one animal desisted and presented his flank, the other never pressed his advantage but waited until his opponent either walked away to terminate the interaction or once again faced him in a challenging posture. On five occasions one buck mounted another one after a sparring match; in four of these instances the dominant animal mounted the subordinate one. Once a buck faced a chital doe at a distance of four feet and jerked his head down in threat. The chital, interpreting the gesture correctly, responded similarly, and the buck turned aside. Although the horns are dangerous weapons, they are rarely brought into use, appearing to function mainly as status symbols.

All these patterns of aggressive behavior were shown by territorial bucks when displacing other bucks from the vicinity of the breeding herd. When one or more bucks approached the herd, the resident male usually assumed the head-up display and advanced at a fast walk, which changed into a run if the intruders failed to leave. Pursuit rarely exceeded a distance of two hundred feet, however. While one buck was being driven away, another often joined the does, and after he had been expelled, the first intruder may have circled back to the herd. Nevertheless, the resident male was never seen to make a violent attempt to force the bucks from his territory; rather, he persistently followed them and drove them away from the does again and again, occasionally grunting while threatening them, until they either left the area or hovered around the periphery. The most vigorous defense of the territory occurred during the peak of the rut from mid-August to October, followed by a period of seeming disinterest during the cool season when intruding bucks were tolerated and even permitted to mount the females.

The does remained in the territory of the buck largely of their own accord. The buck sometimes drove a straying doe back to the herd by cutting in front of her in the head-up display or even by nudging her shoulder with the base of his neck, then following her back by zigzagging back and forth over her trail as if to prevent her from veering off to one side. If, however, a doe left the territory, the buck did not pursue her. During the peak of the rut, the buck attempted to herd not only the does of his own species but also those of chital. On one occasion, a chital doe and 3 fawns crossed the meadow. The buck left the herd, circled the chital in the head-up display, and then followed them for a distance of three hundred feet before stopping, wiping his preorbital gland on some grass, and returning to his does.

Movements within the territory were characteristically led by an adult doe, the buck bringing up the rear. Although the male rarely led, he sometimes determined the direction of movement either by walking alone one hundred to two hundred feet away, where he was then joined by the others, or by actively driving the does to another part of the territory.

According to Walther (1960), the does in the captive herd studied by him had a dominance hierarchy, but no data are given. I never saw an overt interaction between adult does and noted no evidence of rank.

Sexual Behavior

The display postures used by the buck in dominance and in courtship are very similar. After sniffing the anal area or the fresh urine of a doe, the buck frequently exhibits *flehmen* with curled lip and then prances with short, quick steps behind her, preorbital glands everted and muzzle raised in a typical head-up display. If she runs, he chases after her, sometimes using a stiff-legged gallop and uttering harsh grunts. Grunting was heard, with one exception, only from August to October. A chased doe circles back to the herd, where the buck continues to follow her or for brief periods stands parallel to her in the head-up display. He shows his intention to mount by placing his chin on her rump, a gesture which causes her to walk or trot ahead if she is not fully receptive. Mounting was observed on several occasions — one buck mounted four does in succession — but no successful copulations were seen. Apparently the animals sometimes copulate while walking or trotting (Backhaus, 1958). The bachelor bucks mounted chital does on three occasions during August, and they displayed to others and attempted to drive them. Etkin (1954, pers. comm.) observed that captive bucks, after driving an estrous female away from the herd prior to mounting, lean forward on their forelegs, raise their muzzles high, and make pushing movements with the neck, a posture which he termed neck-stretching. This display was not seen in the wild, although the head-bobbing of bucks during head-up appeared to be a less intense manifestation of it.

The precoital mating ceremonies of the blackbuck and of other antelopes show certain similarities and differences. Bucks of the Grant gazelle (Walther, 1965) and Uganda kob (Buechner and Schloeth, 1965) also prance after the doe with muzzle raised, but their tails are held horizontally rather than vertically, as in the blackbuck. Bucks of the waterbuck (Kiley-Worthington, 1965), Grant gazelle, Thomson gazelle (Walther, 1958), and Uganda kob touch the underparts of the doe with a stiff foreleg, an action termed *laufschlag* by Walther (1964), and the last two species whirl tightly around one another when courting, behavior patterns which were not observed in the blackbuck.

FEMALE-YOUNG RELATIONS

The doe withdraws from the breeding herd a few days before parturition and has her young in a secluded spot either within the territory or outside of it. One doe was last seen with the herd on March 21 and, when encountered again on March 25, had given birth. Although she returned intermittently to the herd from March 26 onward, the young did not accompany her until April 2. A second doe withdrew from the herd on May 8, apparently had her fawn three to six days later, and yet remained isolated until May 22, when she rejoined the others with her young. A third doe first began to spend several hours or more away from the herd on April 26. Her fawn was born sometime between May 7 and 9, and it was seen with the herd briefly on May 13. Thus, it appears that the doe may spend some two to three weeks before and after parturition as a peripheral or unstable member of the breeding herd.

Young fawns spend much of the day lying quietly hidden in a patch of grass, being visited only at intervals by the doe. One fawn, about two days old, crouched with neck and head extended along the ground as I approached to within 12 feet before it ran 350 feet away and crouched once more. The doe seems to have little influence on when or where the fawn lies down. One five-day-old fawn, for example, nibbled on grass briefly while standing beside the doe, then left without obvious signal from her and walked 200 feet to a strip of high grass. There it reclined, one minute later moved 50 feet, and then rested again. The doe looked up once and continued to forage. When a doe wants to find her young, or when she approaches it, she emits an "orr," call to which the fawn replies with a bleating "maa," according to Walther (1960), but I never heard these sounds. On one occasion, a doe approached her hidden fawn, but when she was still 125 feet from the spot at which it was lying, it rose and trotted toward her. She lowered her head, the two touched noses briefly, and the young then suckled for 50 seconds while she licked its rump. The touching of noses and subsequent licking of the rump was seen several times at initial contact, probably serving as a means of recognition. One day-old fawn suckled several times, totalling about 250 seconds, in a period of 15 minutes. Young approach from the side, give the udder a vigorous butt, and suckle with their tails beating wildly and a forefoot pawing the air.

Comparisons with the Nilgai

Nilgai (*Boselaphus tragocamelus*) are rare at Kanha but occur in the same dry deciduous and thorn forest areas as the blackbuck from Gujurat, Rajasthan, and Punjab south to Madras. Since very little information about the behavior of the nilgai has been published, except for brief observations on captive animals (Hediger, 1955; Walther, 1958), my notes on this species, collected primarily in the Keoladeo Ghana Sanctuary, are of interest for comparison with the blackbuck.

The nilgai are horse-sized antelopes, with bulls weighing up to 600 pounds and standing 54 inches high at the shoulder (Prater, 1934). Adult bulls have an iron-gray to blue-gray head, back, and sides, a black neck, chest, legs, and belly, and a white rump; the insides of the thighs and the underside of the tail are also white (Plate 14). There is a conspicuous white throat patch, a white crescent on the cheeks, and white spots around the muzzle, over the eyes, inside the ears, and above the hooves. The mane is short and bristly, and a tuft of hair projects from the throat. Bulls have short smooth horns some 6 to 8 inches long. Cows, young bulls, and calves have a tawny pelage in contrast to the black and gray of the adult bulls but otherwise are similarly marked. Two adult females weighed 240 and 290 pounds, respectively (Crandall, 1964).

The nilgai population at Keoladeo Ghana comprised an estimated 110 animals, with ratios of 59 bulls : 100 cows : 68 calves (Schaller and Spillett, 1966). In the Vanbihar Sanctuary, 66 nilgai were classified in the course of two days and ratios of 37 bulls : 100 cows : 107 calves obtained. Bulls have a tendency to segregate from the cows, possibly making my bull count too low, but calves were definitely more abundant at Vanbihar than at nearby Keoladeo Ghana. About 25 percent of the nilgai in the latter area were yearlings.

Nilgai have no regular rutting season, according to Prater (1934) and Asdell (1946); Heape (1901), on the other hand, stated that mating occurs from March to May. During the time of my visit, the majority of calves at Keoladeo Ghana and Vanbihar were an esti- mated four to eight months old, with a few perhaps as old as ten months, indicating that they were born between June and October of the previous year. The gestation period of the nilgai has been variously reported to be 8 months (Crandall, 1964), not more than 8¼ months (Brown, 1936), and 8 to 9 months (Sclater, 1863). With a gestation period of 8 months, most young were conceived between October and February, with some perhaps as early as September. Although some young may be born during every month, a definite rutting season with a possible peak in November and December exists in eastern Rajasthan. Captive nilgai rut in the spring (Bed- ford and Marshall, 1942). Births at the London zoo occurred throughout the year, but 42 percent of the 113 young were born in April and May (Jarvis and Morris, 1962). Nilgai have either single young or twins, the latter being quite common.

The animals usually foraged until about 0830 hours and then rested in the shade or sun until 1500 to 1600 unless disturbed by the numer- ous villagers in the sanctuary. In addition to grass, they consumed a considerable amount of browse from *Acacia* and other trees, some- times standing up on their hindlegs to reach a branch, behavior not observed in the blackbuck.

Nilgai bulls establish territories and form breeding herds during the rut much like the blackbuck, each herd consisting of 1 bull and 2 to 10 cows (Dharmakumarsinhji, 1959). All except one breed- ing herd that was isolated in the northern end of the sanctuary had broken up when I reached Keoladeo Ghana. This herd consisted of 1 large bull, 9 cows, and 3 calves, and it retained its composition for the ten days of my stay there. The animals ranged over about two hundred acres of thorn forest. Five dung piles, up to three feet in diameter and four inches high, were found within the territory.

The composition of the nilgai herds, excluding the breeding herd, changed constantly, but three kinds of herds were discernible: (1) small herds consisting of 1 or 2 cows with young calves, (2) small herds composed of 3 to 6 adult and yearling cows with an occasional calf, and (3) bull herds varying in number from 2 to 18 animals.

Bulls readily joined the cows, and on one occasion about 50 nilgai formed a loose herd.

In addition to the large bull with the breeding herd, the sanctuary contained two others, in the eastern and western part, respectively. Each of these animals appeared to be dominant in the area it occupied, and each was characterized by a greatly swollen neck and an intensely black pelage. The necks of all three bulls were heavily scarred, indicating that their short horns were used for actual combat rather than predominantly for display, as were the long, ornate horns of the blackbuck.

Two of the large bulls roamed considerably within their respective parts of the sanctuary, often alone, but sometimes with cows for brief periods. Although they also joined bull herds on occasion, contact rarely lasted long because of their aggressiveness. In one typical instance a large bull wandered alone through the forest at 1450 hours. At 1510 hours he joined 6 cows and 2 calves. When 3 young bulls appeared three hundred feet away, he advanced toward them holding his neck horizontally in a threatening attitude. The 3 bulls fled at a trot. After returning to the cows, he sniffed the vulva of one briefly, exhibited *flehmen* with muzzle raised and back hunched, and walked to a dung pile one hundred fifty feet distant. He pawed several times with a foreleg and defecated with rump lowered and hindlegs spread, sprinkling some urine at the same time. He maintained this position for thirty seconds after finishing, then departed alone.

Bulls display their dominance in a number of ways. Most frequently seen is the head-up display, with the bull raising his muzzle and exposing the white throat patch to the opponent. A threatening bull characteristically stretches his neck and head horizontally or obliquely downward, making the tuft of hair on the throat conspicuous, lays the ears back in such a way that the black and white pattern on their insides is exposed, and either presses the tail close to the body or holds it horizontally, a position illustrated by Walther (1958). This horizontal-neck display is similar to the head-low threat of the moose (Geist, 1963). Other threatening gestures include jerking the head down, pointing the tip of the horns at the opponent, and chasing briefly. An intimidation display, closely resembling the head-down display of the chital, was seen on three occasions. The bull holds his neck erect, tucks his chin in, humps his back, and raises his tail horizontally as he stands broadside to the other bull or slowly circles him with a stiff-legged gait, head slightly averted and the eyes turned so as to make their whites visible. The horizontal-neck display and the head-down display were not observed in the blackbuck.

Only one sparring match was seen. On that occasion 2 young bulls touched horns lightly, then pushed with their shoulders, and at the same time jabbed with their horns at each other's neck. When one bull dropped to his knees, apparently an invitation to spar, his opponent walked away. The kneeling posture is also sometimes used when grazing and suckling. Walther (1958) described sparring by nilgai when they were kneeling on their carpal joints, and he also observed a fight in which bulls crossed necks as one tried to push the other down.

CHAPTER 7

THE GAUR

The subfamily Bovinae includes the bisons of the old and new world, the buffaloes, and the domestic and wild cattle of the genus *Bos*. In addition to domestic cattle (*Bos taurus* and *B. indicus*) and the yak (*Bos grunniens*), the genus contains several species of wild cattle, all confined to the Oriental region of the world. The rare kouprey (*Bos sauveli*) is found in Cambodia, the banteng (*Bos banteng*) in Java, Borneo, Malaya, and parts of Indochina, and the gaur (*Bos gaurus*) from Malaya (where it is known as seladang) to India. A fourth species, the gayal (*Bos frontalis*) of Assam and Burma, is believed to be a domesticated form of the gaur. These wild cattle share certain physical features, such as white feet, a ridge along the back, and a dewlap in two parts, but the gaur is the most impressive of them all. Three subspecies of gaur are generally recognized: *B. g. gaurus*, occurring in India and Nepal; *B. g. readei*, in Burma and Indochina; and *B. g. hubbacki*, in Malaya.

Information concerning the behavior of *Bos* is adequate only for domestic cattle (Hafez and Schein, 1962; Schloeth, 1961), very little work having been done on the wild members of the genus (Brander, 1923; Hubback, 1937; Wharton, 1957).

Gaur were studied only in Kanha Park, where the shyness of the animals and the dense undergrowth which they frequented made sustained observations difficult. I stalked the animals often along the base of the hills, hoping for a good view of them, but they either moved from sight or, spotting me first, gave a trumpet-like snort and bolted. Consequently, I rarely was able to watch them undisturbed. From late March to early June, however, herds of gaur commonly came to the Kanha meadow to drink and graze, and it was during this period that most information on the species was obtained.

Description

A bull gaur has a massive yet rangy body supported on rather dainty-looking legs. He stands 64 to 72 inches high at the shoulder, and his total length is 11 to 12 feet, including about 3 feet of tail. Recorded weights of bulls, shot in the wild, are as follows: 1,297, 1,720, 1,900, 2,049, and 2,071 pounds (Meinertzhagen, 1939; Morris, 1947). Adult bulls have a shiny black, short-haired pelage, except for white stockings, a gray boss between the horns, and rusty-colored hairs on the insides of the thighs and forelegs. Young bulls are dark brown like the cows. There is a conspicuous dorsal ridge, formed by the extension of the spinous processes of the third to eleventh vertebrae, which terminates abruptly near the middle of the back. A small dewlap hangs below the chin, and a large one drapes down between the forelegs (Plate 15). The heavy horns sweep sideways and upward. The horns of young bulls are smooth, yellow-orange in color, and tipped with black, whereas those of old bulls are corrugated, a dull olive in color, and sometimes frayed at the tips (Plate 16). The horn length of one of the largest bulls seen at Kanha (which was killed by a tiger) was 24 inches; the world record is 31½ inches (Ward, 1922).

Cows are considerably smaller than the bulls, and their dorsal ridges and dewlaps are not prominently developed. One cow weighed 1,546 pounds (Meinertzhagen, 1939); another cow which was found dead at Kanha weighed 969 pounds (excluding blood). The pelage of cows is dark brown in color and the horns are slenderer, more upright, and with a more inward curve than those of bulls (Plates 15 and 17).

Young calves have a light brown coat and lack the conspicuous white stockings, which do not appear until they change into a dark brown pelage at the age of about three months. One light brown young, just killed by a tiger, weighed 95 pounds.

Distribution

According to Ellerman and Morrison-Scott (1951) the gaur occurs in "Malay States, Indo-China, Burma, Assam, Nepal, Peninsular India in forest areas, south to Travancore," a rather vague outline of the animal's distribution. In order to determine the present range of the gaur in India, I corresponded with and interviewed numerous foresters, hunters, and other persons about the status of the animal

FIG. 10.–The distribution of gaur in India. The black spots indicate isolated populations or known concentrations of animals. The shaded areas represent extensive forests probably inhabited sparsely by gaur.

in the areas known to them, and the resulting information is summarized in Figure 10.

The gaur is found predominantly in the hills, and its present range encompasses three widely separated geographical areas that correspond to the major mountain systems in India: the Western Ghats, the central Indian highlands, and the foothills of the Himalayas, including the hills south of the Brahmaputra River. The animals in each area are typically divided into several more or less isolated populations, a result largely of the extensive clearing of forests, especially in the central part of India. But even in large continuous forest tracts, gaur have the tendency to congregate in some parts of the forest almost to the exclusion of other and seemingly just as favorable parts. It was not possible to obtain sufficient information to delineate the range of the gaur precisely in Figure 10, and even the relatively small local areas indicated on the map may include several distinct populations. For example, although the gaur in the Mandla district are represented on the map as one population, the animals in that area are separated into at least five more or less distinct aggregations.

Gaur are found in the Western Ghats from Mysore southward to Kerala and Madras. In Mysore, they are said to occur in the districts of Mysore, Coorg, Hassan, Himoga, Chickamagalur, South Kanara, and Karwar (Spillett, pers. comm.), but I was unable to obtain precise information about the status and distribution of the species from the state forest department. A sizable population, estimated at 300 to 400 animals by Krishnan (letter, August 23, 1965), inhabits Mudumalai Sanctuary. Two isolated populations survive along the Madras-Kerala border in the Anaimalai Hills and around Periyar Lake.

A distance of at least 400 miles separates the gaur in the Western Ghats from those in central India. Widely scattered populations occur over a block of country some 200,000 square miles in extent, principally along the Eastern Ghats of Orissa and in the Mahadeo Hills and the Maikal Range of Madhya Pradesh. A few herds survive in northern Andhra Pradesh, in the Bastar District of Madhya Pradesh and the adjoining Chanda District of Maharashtra, and in the Palamau and Singhbhum districts of Bihar. I was unable to assess the status of most of these populations. A few localities such as Kanha Park support a fair number of animals, but in many areas, among them the West Bastar District, heavy illegal hunting has reduced the herds to a few stray individuals; "in one instance in

Sukma zamindary a herd of 19 bison were beaten into nets and the whole lot slaughtered" (Rooke, 1908). Elimination of habitat and epidemics of rinderpest and foot-and-mouth disease have also greatly decimated the central Indian populations (Baker, 1890; Stewart, 1928; Ali, 1953).

Along the foot of the Himalayas the gaur is found from central Nepal to eastern Assam. Gee (pers. comm.) saw one gaur in the Chitawan Valley of Nepal in 1959, a locality which probably is near the western boundary of the species' range. A few gaur survive in northern Bengal: a herd of about fifteen animals exists in the Jaldapara Sanctuary and a few stragglers roam the surrounding hills, such as the Sukna Range of the Kurseong Division (Rao, 1961). The forests of Assam both north and south of the Brahmaputra River are so vast that I was able to do little more than outline the approximate distribution of the animal there. Higgins (1935) listed the species as rare in Manipur.

The habitat of the gaur is characterized by (1) large, relatively undisturbed forest tracts, (2) hilly terrain below an altitude of 5,000 to 6,000 feet, (3) availability of water, and (4) an abundance of forage in the form of coarse grasses (including bamboo), shrubs, and trees. A comparison of the vegetation map (Fig. 2) with the distribution of the gaur shows that the animal is largely confined to the evergreen, semi-evergreen, and moist deciduous forest areas but that it has also penetrated the dry deciduous forests at the periphery of its range. The apparent preference of gaur for hilly terrain may in part be due to the conversion of much of an earlier habitat in the plains into fields, whereas the hills have until recent years been left relatively undisturbed. At least it may be assumed that the gaur at one time must have lived on the plains, since in order to reach central India they had to traverse the Gangetic plains and in order to reach southern India they had to cross the upland plateau.

Population Dynamics

In the absence of animals of known age, several size classes were established. Bulls that are considerably larger than cows and have a black pelage are referred to as black bulls. Such bulls are probably five or more years old. Brown bulls are about the size of adult cows, with some being slightly larger or smaller. Yearling bulls and cows, aged roughly ten to twenty months, are smaller and less bulky than adult cows. Calves were divided into three age classes based on size in relation to adult cows. Small calves, until the age of about three months, have a light brown coat and weigh about 80 to 130 pounds (Plate 15). Medium-sized calves have acquired their brown coat, are about one-third the size of a cow, and weigh up to an estimated 350 pounds. Large calves are about half the size of a cow and weigh some 500 to 600 pounds. When young reached two-thirds the size of a cow, they were classified as yearlings. This crude and relative age scale served its purpose during the brief period of the year when gaur were observable, but an accurate aging technique based perhaps on horn length and shape, as was used for the American bison by McHugh (1958), would be desirable for a more detailed study.

POPULATION SIZE AND COMPOSITION

Both the habitat and the habits of the gaur make censusing difficult, and sample counts in a limited area may produce highly variable results (Table 2). In addition to their extensive travels within the park, some animals probably move back and forth across the park boundaries. The census figures and information from residents leave little doubt that in general the population has been increasing steadily in recent years, the only wild ungulate species in the park to do so. During the 1956 census only 19 gaur were tallied, but over 100 are now commonly seen. The majority of animals frequented the forests surrounding the Kanha meadow in April, as indicated by foot transects through the hills and in other valleys. My population estimate for the Kanha valley at that time was about 125 to 150 gaur, with perhaps another 40 to 60 animals, in particular bulls, scattered in other areas of the park, for a total of about 200. The largest number seen on a single morning was 68.

A total of 2,303 animals were classified singly and in herds at Kanha during 1964, most of them between April and June, giving ratios of 80 bulls: 100 cows: 42 calves. The bull count may be somewhat low since a few animals remained solitary and rarely if ever frequented the Kanha meadow, where most data were obtained. The importance of including solitary bulls when determining the population composition is shown in Table 38, which presents the ratios of bulls to cows in herds at various times of the year. Roughly half of the bulls were not with cows in any given month. From January to June the calf to cow ratio remained relatively stable at between 39 and 45:100 but dropped to 29:100 during the second half of the year (Table 38). Of 109 medium-sized and large calves that were sexed, 55 were male and 54 were female, an equal sex ratio. A total of 16 gaur calves were born in the National Zoological Park between 1937 and 1958, and of these, 9 were males and 7 were females (Reed, 1959). In terms of percent of the total population, black bulls comprised 20 percent, brown bulls 12 percent, yearling bulls 4 percent, adult cows 39 percent, yearling cows 6 percent, and calves 19 percent.

THE RUTTING SEASON

Most mating in central India occurs in December and January, with calves being born in August and September (Brander, 1923). Stebbing (1911) and Sanderson (1912) gave similar months but also noted that calves may be born in April, May, and June. The peak rutting period in southern India is from November to March (Morris, 1937*a*). In Burma calves are born throughout the year (Peacock,

TABLE 38

GAUR HERD SIZE AND COMPOSITION

Month	Total Number of Herds Classified	Largest Herd Classified	Average Herd Size	Total Number of Animals Classified	Bulls : 100 : Calves Cows		
January–February. . . .	6	10	5.5	33	44 :	100 :	39
March.	18	24	8.3	148	34 :	100 :	45
April	54	26	9.1	503	52 :	100 :	45
May.	72	23	10.2	735	43 :	100 :	44
June.	30	20	9.7	291	18 :	100 :	39
July–December	16	29	10.5	169	36 :	100 :	29
Total	196			1,879			

1933), and in Malaya young ones are seen at all times except from October to December (Hubback, 1937).

Rutting bulls have a characteristic call, which I heard for the first time at Kanha on December 6 and for the last time with the onset of the monsoon in mid-June. The frequency of calling and other aspects of sexual behavior reached a peak in March and April. The gestation period of the gaur, like that of domestic cattle, is about nine months (Hubback, 1937). A rut from early December to mid-June thus means a calving period from early September to mid-March, with a peak in December and January. A few newborn calves were also noted in April, May, June, and July, indicating that some mating occurs in every month. Captive gayal have repeated estrous cycles of about three weeks' duration throughout the year (Heape, 1901), and this is probably true of the gaur also.

RATE OF REPRODUCTION

Gaur cows, like American bison cows (McHugh, 1958), appear to mate for the first time when about two years old and have their first calf at three years of age. Adults probably have one calf per year, and there is no evidence to support Brander (1923), who stated that, since calves remain with their mothers for two years, "these do not breed again until the third year." Single births are the rule, there being no records of twins.

MORTALITY

Rinderpest is a widespread cause of death in gaur; the disease has been reported in this species from southern India (Anderson, 1954) and central India (Baker, 1890; Stewart, 1928). A virulent epidemic of rinderpest killed many gaur in the Kanha Park area in the years 1925–26 (Mehta, n.d.). Gaur have also been reported to die from foot-and-mouth disease (Ali, 1953) and anthrax (Peacock, 1933). There was no evidence of disease at Kanha in 1964. One cow that was autopsied contained light infestations of nematodes (*Oesophagostomum radiatum* Rud., 1803) in the large intestine and trematodes (*Gastrothylax crumenifer* Creplin, 1847) in the rumen. Ticks (*Boophilus microplus*) were found on two adults checked for ectoparasites.

Physical injuries were conspicuous in the gaur, in contrast to the other species studied. Four different bulls limped severely, the lower leg of one animal having healed unevenly after a break; one calf also limped. Three bulls had what appeared to be horn punctures, two in the thigh, one in the neck. One bull had lost an eye, and another had a healed cut on the dorsal ridge. One cow had a piece of skin about eight inches in diameter torn from her side, and a second cow had a deep cut in her flank. Some of the injuries, particularly those on the legs, may have resulted from falls on the rocky hillsides, and several wounds were undoubtedly incurred in fights, but a few of the cuts were perhaps the result of attacks by tigers.

The primary cause of death in 1964 was predation by tiger, prin-cipally on the calves. In April, after most calves had been born, the ratio of calves to adult cows was 53:100. A small percentage of the cows classified as adult had not yet given birth to their first calf, a few had calves later in the year, and others were perhaps sterile, had abortions, or in other ways failed to produce young. If all these factors are taken into consideration, an estimated 80 percent rather than 53 percent of the adult cows should be accompanied by calves or about 27 percent more than were seen at that time of year. The ratio of yearlings to adult cows was 24:100, 56 percent less than the expected calf to cow ratio. This suggests that about half of the calves die before they reach the age of one year. The population of gaur in the Kanha valley was estimated at 125 to 150 animals, of which roughly 50 to 60 were adult cows. Of these, perhaps 90 percent, or 45 to 54 cows, bore young during the year. With a mortality of 50 percent, about 23 to 27 calves were taken.

In contrast to the high death rate of calves, mortality in adults was so low that the population apparently showed an annual increase with a yearling percentage of only 10 percent. Tigers attack adult gaur infrequently, a fact verified by the kills found. A total of fourteen old and recent kills were located (Table 51), of which six were calves and eight were yearlings and adults. The large bones of adult gaur are easier to discover than those of calves, since they remain visible on the forest floor longer. The small number of adult remains that were found support the conclusion that mortality in this age class is low. Added to this is the potential longevity of the gaur, which probably exceeds that of any other hoofed animal in the park. In a zoo one bull lived for about twenty years and a cow for about twenty-four years (Crandall, 1964), but such records are not wholly indicative because the animals usually do not thrive in captivity. McHugh (1958) found that three out of five tagged free-ranging American bison cows were pregnant or lactating at the age of over thirty years, and some gaur may also reach such an advanced age in the wild.

The villagers do not appear to poach the gaur very often at Kanha, although a few young may be taken in snares. According to the local forest officer, poachers find it difficult to handle and dispose of an adult quickly and efficiently, and the Hindu population in the towns abjure gaur for the most part because of the animal's resemblance to the sacred cow.

General Behavior

The gaur is a forest animal, coming out onto the meadows only to eat and drink during the hot season after its forage in the forests has been burned and the stream beds are dry. Most of the gaur's activity is at night, and a typical sight at Kanha is a line of gaur filing from the meadow into the forest at dawn. By 0700 hours most animals are in the shelter of trees, and after 0800 hours they are rarely seen in the open; once, on January 11, a herd rested on the meadow until 0840 hours, an exceptional instance.

DAILY ACTIVITY CYCLE

During the day the animals lie scattered near the forest's edge, in a bamboo grove or on the slope or top of a grassy knoll. They usually recline on the belly with legs folded under the body, but occasionally an animal will lie flat on its side with legs stretched out. A few may groom themselves, licking their hides or rubbing their necks, rumps, or sides against a tree trunk. One cow scratched her hump with the tip of her horn. Some may chew cud slowly at the rate of about forty-five chews per minute, and others just stand quietly, only their tails swishing from side to side. A herd sometimes forages in cursory fashion at mid-day, but generally there is little activity before 1700 hours and often not until 1730 to 1830 hours. Feeding continues steadily into the night. During the early morning, the animals generally rest, occasionally on the open meadow.

FOOD HABITS AND FEEDING AND DRINKING BEHAVIOR

Gaur are both grazers and browsers, preferring green grass when available but otherwise consuming coarse, dry grasses and a large variety of forbs and leaves (Tables 10 and 11). This varied diet has undoubtedly played an important role in enabling the species to colonize a wide range of vegetation types. In addition to the forty kinds of plants listed in the tables, Brander (1923) noted that gaur eat the bark of *Adina cordifolia* and the fruit of *Aegle marmelos*. During the cool season, when the animals were mostly on the slopes and ridge tops, they ate various forbs (*Vernonia divergens*, *Leucas mollissima*) and particularly the leaves and sharp-pointed seeds of bamboo, as well as grass and the leaves from trees like *Terminalia* and *Bauhinea*. By late March they concentrated their foraging along stream beds and in moist depressions where tall coarse grasses (*Vetiveria zizanioides*, *Coix lachrymajobi*) abounded. Sal, bamboo, *Moghania*, *Phoenix*, and *Cordia myxa* were also browsed extensively during the hot season.

Rumen samples from four gaur killed by tigers were obtained during the hot season. Coarse, semidry to dry grasses formed the bulk of the animal's diet at that time, averaging 85 percent (range 66–100 percent) by volume; browse averaged 10 percent (trace to 33 percent). One rumen contained a few *Cassia fistula* seeds, and another numerous *Bauhinea* seedpods and *Cordia myxa* fruit (18 percent).

The members of a foraging herd are typically scattered over 200 to 600 feet of terrain as each animal searches for food, moving at the rate of about 500 to 1,500 feet per hour. At a site of abundant forage, such as a clump of bamboo or a grassy swale, a herd may remain as long as an hour in an area 150 feet in diameter.

Gaur have a long, prehensile tongue well adapted for browsing. When feeding on bamboo, for example, the animal extends its curved tongue, hooks a twig with it, and draws the food into its mouth (Plate 17); when picking up leaves from the forest floor, however, the tongue is not extended past the lips. Leaves out of reach in the crown of a sapling are pulled down by several means. The animal may bend the stem with a sideways sweep of the neck, by walking into it and pushing it down with the weight of its body, or by biting into the stem and snaping it with a twist of the head. One large calf attempted to break a sapling eight times by the latter method before the stem ceased to snap erect and it was able to reach the leaves.

One member of the herd, usually an adult cow but occasionally also a brown bull, sometimes stood motionless with head raised in an alert posture for as long as five minutes while the other animals fed. This behavior was not in response to an obvious visual or auditory stimulus, and it failed to elicit a reaction in the others. The gaur gave the impression of being a sentinel. Nothing comparable was observed in the other species studied.

Several man-made salt licks were located on the Kanha meadow. These were visited very rarely by blackbuck, infrequently by barasingha, but quite commonly by chital, sambar, and gaur. When gaur were encountered on the meadow during the cool season and monsoon, they were usually crowded together at a salt lick, licking the soil for as long as forty-five minutes without interruption.

The gaur drank at least once a day during the hot season, usually in the evening. Rarely more than five minutes elapsed between the arrival at a pool of the first member in a herd and the departure of the last member; the animals were obviously nervous when approaching a water source in a ravine. One cow drank steadily for 85 seconds, another cow for 25 seconds, and a black bull for 45 seconds.

RANGE AND MOVEMENTS

The movements of the gaur at Kanha encompassed the whole valley and the surrounding hills, an area of at least thirty square miles. A majority of the animals probably remained within this area, but a few had perhaps a still larger range. The gaur were scattered in small herds along the base of the slopes and on the ridges for much of the year. I sometimes came across them there in a thicket or moving toward a seepage spring, where the trampled earth and radiating trails clearly indicated their frequent visits. Most animals spent the cool season in the mixed forest of the hills, but with the advent of the hot weather, they moved into the sal forest. At first they remained along stream beds and near the base of the slopes. As progressively more of the forest was burned they congregated around the Kanha meadow, in part because of the availability of food and water and perhaps also because of mutual attraction during the rut. Most herds remained in an area of ten to fifteen square miles until the beginning of the monsoon and then dispersed into the hills again.

Gaur herds ranged more widely in their day-to-day movements than any other ungulate species studied. Occasionally several herds appeared to travel in loose association; they would be present in one locality for a number of days only to abandon it and turn up suddenly in another locality some two miles away. There was no evidence to support Forsyth (1889) who wrote that "each herd appears to possess a tract of country tabooed to other herds." The extent of daily movement of a herd seemed to average about two to three miles but sometimes was considerably less. On several occasions I watched animals emerge from the forest in the evening, graze and rest nearby all night, and then retreat into the shade during the day, having remained in an area of about two hundred acres. Solitary bulls may take up residence along a particular stretch of stream bed for several days, and in one instance, a black bull rested in the same patch of grass for three days in succession. Rutting bulls often travel extensively within their range, walking along steadily at some two to three miles per hour.

RESPONSE TO PREDATORS

Gaur are exceptionally alert to potential danger, and they respond to alarm signals from their own and other species with a characteristic series of sounds and gestures. As in American bison (McHugh, 1958), the alert posture consists of lifting the head above the level of the hump and facing the source of the disturbance. The muzzle is sometimes raised as if the animal is sniffing the air. The sense of smell of the gaur is acute — the animals were able to wind me at distances exceeding four hundred feet. The tail of an excited animal may be whipped back and forth at a faster than usual rate.

Gaur frequently enhance the effectiveness of the alert posture as a signal by producing a number of sounds. When danger is not imminent, the sounds consist of a series of soft snorts, audible for less than one hundred feet, which may be given while the animal continues to graze. When one cow spotted my car, for example, she blew air through her nose softly three times, and two gaur within fifty feet looked first at her and then toward the car. When a herd is startled or put to flight, one or two of its members usually blow a trumpet-like blast of air through the nose, accompanied occasionally by a growling sound — a harsh, rolling bru-u-u-u. As the animal flees it often gives a series of rather stiff-legged bounds, some two to eight in number, with the forelegs brought down hard in unison to produce a series of distinct thumps. After thumping, it usually trots off without making further sounds other than the usual commotion of a large animal moving through the forest. The thumping undoubtedly alerts others to danger and indicates the flight direction. Only one or two gaur of either sex in a fleeing herd were observed to thump; solitary bulls also do so. Once, when I encountered two bulls on foot, one of them snorted while the other thumped.

These various responses were elicited predominantly by man and tiger, but one gaur also snorted after having spotted a jungle cat. The flight distance of a herd from a man on foot was about 200 to 300 feet, the animals commonly watching the approach of the potential danger from the protection of a thicket before suddenly wheeling around and crashing away. Solitary black bulls were not as shy and alert as herds, and I was sometimes able to walk to within 100 feet of an animal before it detected me. Occasionally a solitary bull responded to my approach by swinging around with head lowered aggressively and then retreating with a snort, sometimes jabbing the air in my direction with his horn before trotting away. The animals showed little fear of a car, and it was often possible to drive to within 150 feet of herds, and even to within 50 feet of some bulls, without disturbing them. A good account of the shyness and elusiveness of the gaur when hunted is found in Forsyth (1889).

The gaur's response to a tiger depended on the circumstances of the encounter. Once a bull and a cow watched a tiger walk past at 250 feet. Both stood alertly and the cow snorted, but neither fled. Another time, a tigress walked along, trailed at 150 feet by eight gaur. They calmly followed her for 200 feet until she disappeared in the high grass. But, on another occasion, when a cow spotted a tiger stalking the herd, she snorted and fled, followed by the others.

The gaur is the only wild ungulate in the area formidable enough to stand its ground successfully against a tiger. At 0800 hours, on December 20, we heard a loud snort and saw a black bull facing a copse of trees. He snorted three times, spray flying from his nostrils, and then just stood with lowered head; occasionally he blew air softly through his nose and nibbled on some grass. At 0825 he approached the trees to within 90 feet, and a tigress growled. Slowly the gaur turned and walked away. He had a severe limp. The tigress made no effort to follow. A herd of gaur in Malaya encircled a calf killed by a tiger and prevented the cat from approaching (Foenander, 1952), and in the same country Ogilvie (1953) observed a herd of eight gaur facing a tiger. According to Toogood (1937), two bulls once approached and sniffed at the body of a freshly shot tiger. On the other hand, a cow at Kanha whose calf had just been killed made no effort to attack the tigress and merely walked around in an agitated fashion.

Social Behavior

Details of social interactions of known individuals within a herd were difficult to obtain chiefly because of the nocturnal habits of the species and the unstable membership of herds. When the animals moved onto the meadow at dusk, they were largely preoccupied with grazing, and I quite commonly watched a herd for thirty or more minutes without noting a single overt interaction. The following information on social behavior was obtained largely at a time when the rut of the gaur was at or near its peak, a fact that must be taken into account when evaluating the results.

HERD SIZE AND COMPOSITION

Herds ranged in size from 2 to about 40 animals each and averaged 8 to 11 (Plate 18, Table 38). The largest herd seen at Kanha numbered between 36 and 38 individuals. On one occasion a total of 45 gaur in three herds were near each other, and they appeared to have been together earlier that morning. Inverarity (1889) noted that the average herd contains 12 to 20 animals, Brander (1923) 8 to 12, Russell (1900) 10 to 20, and Sanderson (1912) about 12 but occasionally as many as 30 to 40 and, rarely, up to 100. In Burma, herds average 10 to 20 animals in size, with as many as 50 together on occasion (Peacock, 1933), and in Malaya 10 to 12 is the usual number (Hubback, 1937). All these figures agree very well with my observations at Kanha. Fuller (1960) found that the herds of American bison in the forest environment of Wood Buffalo National Park in Canada also average some 6 to 30 animals each; herds of plains-living American bison, however, numbered several hundred individuals during the rut (McHugh, 1958).

The composition of herds varied. Occasionally a cow and calf were found alone in the forest. Cows with small calves and with larger ones each tended to form their own herds. Average herd composition in May was 1.0 black bulls, 1.0 brown bulls, .4 yearling

TABLE 39

PERCENT OF GAUR HERDS CONTAINING ONE OR MORE
BLACK OR BROWN BULLS AT VARIOUS TIMES OF THE YEAR

Month	Total Number of Herds Tallied	Percent of Herds Containing One or More Black Bulls	Percent of Herds Containing One or More Brown Bulls
January–February . .	6	50	50
March	18	56	28
April	54	65	52
May	72	56	63
June	30	43	27
July–December . . .	16	31	68

bulls, 4.7 cows, .8 yearling cows, and 2.3 calves. However, the number of bulls in a herd changed with the time of the year, black bulls associating with the cows primarily during the rut. In April, the peak of the rut, 65 percent of the herds were accompanied by a black bull, a figure that dropped to 31 percent during the second half of the year. The percentages of brown bulls in the herds fluctuated rather widely for unexplained reasons (Table 39). Yearling bulls remained with the herds except on rare occasions; my observations thus do not support Powell (1964), who stated that young bulls usually live away from herds. Frequently 2 to 3 and as many as 5 to 8 brown and black bulls were found in the same herd. One herd contained 6 black bulls and 4 younger ones, a total of 10; another contained 8 black bulls and 6 others, a total of 14. There was no evidence to support Brander's statement (1923) that the master bull drives all others from the herd.

Bulls not in herds led a solitary existence or associated with other males in bull herds, behavior also noted in the American bison by Fuller (1960). Of 418 bulls tallied alone or in bull herds, 71 percent were black, 28 percent were brown, and 1 percent were yearlings; since black bulls are nearly twice as abundant in the population as brown ones (a ratio of about 63 brown:100 black bulls), these figures indicate that the former left the cows somewhat more readily than the latter. Fifty-three percent of these bulls were solitary, 26 percent were in bull herds of 2, 10 percent in herds of 3, 7 percent in herds of 4, and 2 percent each in bull herds of 5 and 6. Of the solitary bulls, 88 percent were black, showing that brown bulls usually accompanied another bull when they left herds rather than becoming solitary.

Some herds undoubtedly retained the same composition for several days and perhaps even weeks when they were isolated from others. During the rut, however, when herds commonly came into contact, changes were frequent. On several occasions herds emerged from the forest at dusk and then split into two or three units, each of which drifted off in a different direction; at other times new herds arrived at a feeding site and joined the animals already there. One herd, for example, consisting of 6 bulls and 6 cows split into three units, with 1 bull going off alone, another bull and 3 cows heading in one direction, and the rest of the herd drifting in another direction; on another occasion, 1 bull with 7 cows and 5 calves joined a herd consisting of 4 bulls, 2 cows, and 1 calf. One distinctive small herd, composed of 2 bulls, 2 cows, and one calf, was still together after one and a half days, although during that time an additional bull and 3 cows had associated with them. The same 4 cows and newborn calf remained together for a minimum of five days, but during this period at least 3 different bulls and 1 cow had joined with and parted from them. The only changes in one herd of 19 animals between dusk and dawn appeared to be the departure of one bull and one cow.

It is unlikely that black bulls remain with a particular herd for more than a few days during the peak of the rut. One distinctive black bull was seen alone on March 25. On April 12 he was part of a herd containing 6 black bulls, 2 brown bulls, and 6 cows, and on April 15, he was in a bull herd with 2 others. On June 11 he was solitary again. This constant change from a lone life, to one in a herd, and back to a solitary existence appears to be typical of many bulls. However, a few black bulls appeared to remain solitary most or all of the time, seemingly ignoring herds with cows in the vicinity. One excerpt from my field notes illustrates the constant changes in a herd at the height of the rut:

0110 hours. Two black bulls, 1 brown bull, 6 cows, and 1 calf are on the meadow. The 2 black bulls stand parallel to each other in a lateral display for about 5 minutes before one turns away and leaves the herd, calling several times as he does so. Ten minutes later the second black bull departs from the herd. At 0140 a new black bull approaches, his nose almost touching the ground as he snuffles and snorts. He calls once, then joins the herd. Four hundred feet away two more black bulls approach slowly, making a total of 5 that have been around this herd in the past half hour. One of the last bulls snorts and jabs a horn at a sapling, and then both of them join the herd. The larger of the two sniffs the rump of a cow, and the other suddenly leaves the herd alone. He stops 300 feet away, sweeps his horn into a bush, and then continues. After 20 minutes the other bull departs, calls once, jabs a horn into a sapling, and moves from sight. At 0150 the herd consists of the black bull which joined at 0140, the brown bull, and the cows and calf.

Bull herds were generally unstable, although in several instances two animals associated closely. Once 2 brown bulls were seen together for three consecutive days. On another occasion 2 black bulls traveled together for a half hour across a meadow. One of them had a severe limp, which slowed his walking speed down considerably; yet the other one remained by his side.

LEADERSHIP

A leader was usually not evident when the members of the herd were foraging, but when they moved in single file, an adult cow led the procession in 73 percent of 41 instances recorded (Plate 18). Brown and black bulls led the remaining herds. Black bulls often brought up the rear, although their position in the line was highly variable. Sometimes a bull initiated a movement in a certain direction, but a cow soon took over the lead. On several occasions a bull stood at the periphery of the herd facing a certain direction for as long as five minutes before the others ceased to forage and joined him. The leading animal was frequently 60 to 100 feet ahead of the herd and highly alert, looking around with muzzle raised, whereas the others trudged along seemingly paying little attention to their surroundings.

AGONISTIC BEHAVIOR AND DOMINANCE

Various displays and forms of aggressive behavior are used by the gaur to establish rights of priority to a place at a salt lick, to a cow in heat, and to other limited objectives, as well as to a position in the social structure of the herd as a whole. Threatening gestures, most of which are of low intensity, consist of walking directly at the opponent perhaps with head slightly lowered and of jerking the head down and up, often accompanied by a lateral sweep of the horns. A gentle nudge with the horn tip is usually sufficient to make a neighboring animal move. A head-up display, resembling that of the other ungulates in the park, consists of an upward jerk of the head while facing the other animal. This gesture may be followed by a threat with lowered horns. When gaur are involved in a tense situation, such as the approach of a high-ranking animal or a person, or the courtship of a cow, they frequently flip their heads up briefly, seemingly a nervous gesture related to the head-up display.

A bull holds his head low when approaching a rival, muzzle almost touching the ground and horn tips pointing forward, at the same time swinging his head and even his forequarters from side to side. Air is blown out through the nose, emitting a spectrum of sounds from gentle snuffles to violent snorts. He may interrupt his approach, extend his muzzle, and give a hoarse bellow. Sometimes he jabs a horn into a sapling with an upward swing of the head or pushes a bush down with his forehead before thrashing it with his horns, both forms of redirected aggression. The display has in most instances enough of an intimidatory effect that the other bull either turns aside, stands with head and neck pointing toward the ground, or begins to graze, apparently all gestures of submission. Occasionally a bull threatens in return, and in one instance, four bulls bellowed, jabbed the soil, and swept their horns at each other for twenty minutes.

American bison horn certain trees until the bark hangs in shreds (McHugh, 1958), behavior not observed in gaur. Domestic cattle (Schloeth, 1958a, 1961) and American bison also rub their heads and necks vigorously on the ground and paw the soil during aggressive encounters. The former type of behavior was not seen in gaur, and pawing was limited to infrequent and cursory sweeps of a forefoot.

Sparring was observed eighty-one times. It occurred most frequently between brown bulls (48 percent), between brown bulls and adult cows (10 percent), and between adult cows (14 percent). Black bulls were not seen to spar with each other, but their wounds and tattered ears attested to the fact that they did so on occasion. Most matches consisted of gently touching horns and light pushing and twisting with the head. Only four matches were classed as vigorous, and all were between bulls. After challenging each other with lowered horns, the animals drove each other back and forth while twisting their heads sideways, the full force of their effort absorbed on the bony boss. In order to readjust his position while sparring, a bull sometimes stepped sideways, which caused his opponent to move sideways, too, apparently in an attempt to remain face to face. The first bull then moved some more, and the two were soon circling rapidly while keeping their horns locked. The majority of bouts seemed to come to an indecisive conclusion, but whenever one animal was clearly victorious, it was the larger of the two combatants. Black bulls sparred less frequently than brown bulls, and in this context it is probably significant that various forms of redirected aggression, such as thrashing bushes, were more prevalent in the former than in the latter. On one occasion a bull pressed his forehead against the neck of the other bull and kept it there, thus preventing further sparring. This gesture resembled the "clinch" described by Hafez and Schein (1962) in domestic cattle. On another occasion a cow lowered her head and her small calf placed its forehead against hers and pushed with braced legs.

One black bull stood with head raised while a yearling bull jabbed his exposed throat lightly; an adult cow behaved similarly to a yearling cow. The significance of this behavior could not be determined.

The most striking behavior pattern of the gaur is a lateral display in which the animal presents its impressive profile, particularly the dewlaps and dorsal ridge, to an opponent (Plate 19). The displaying animal stands parallel to the other with head lowered and back hunched. The opponent then often assumes a similar posture. The two bulls face either in the same or in opposite directions ten to thirty feet apart, with their heads slightly averted from each other. One may start to circle, moving very slowly and stiff-legged, while the other stands in one spot but shifts his position to keep his broadside toward the opponent. The animals sometimes continue to display for five to ten minutes, and in one instance for fifty-five minutes, until one is intimidated and accepts the subordinate position. Bellowing and horning the soil or bushes may precede or succeed the display. Usually only one or two bulls are involved, but occasionally three or four mill around displaying to each other. Two typical instances from my field notes describe the behavior:

1) *A herd of 4 bulls, 8 cows, and 4 calves moves in single file across the meadow. Last in line and walking parallel about 30 feet apart are two black bulls. The smaller of the two drops behind, then hurries to catch up, but as he draws near, the other bull turns and presents his broadside to him.*

PLATE 16.—An adult gaur bull, showing his gray boss and the corrugated horns; a mynah bird sits on his head (May 13, 1964).

PLATE 17.—A female gaur feeds on bamboo leaves (June 20, 1964).

PLATE 18.—A female gaur leads a herd followed by an adult bull; another adult bull brings up the rear (March 29, 1964).

PLATE 19.—One adult bull expresses his dominance with a lateral display while the other adult bull slowly circles him (March 20, 1964).

The small bull advances with head lowered, blowing air softly through his nose, then passes by the rump of the other bull in the direction of the re- treating herd. Both bulls walk parallel to each other once more. The large bull steps ahead and again assumes the lateral display, upon which his opponent swerves aside and moves toward the forest alone.

2) A black bull walks steadily along at 0615 hours; at 0625 he comes across a scattered herd consisting of 1 black bull, 2 brown bulls, and 4 cows, which is foraging in the forest. He enters the herd walking very slowly with his head lowered threateningly. The larger of the 2 brown bulls walks up and stands parallel to him 20 feet away. Less than one minute later the black herd bull, which is larger than the newcomer, arrives and places himself at right angles to the other two bulls. All three stand with heads lowered for one minute. The brown bull then leaves and joins the cows. The new bull grazes in cursory fashion while the other black bull slowly walks until he is 30 feet away and parallel to him. Both face in the same direction, saliva dribbling from their mouths. Occasionally the new bull takes a bite of grass, and whenever he moves, the herd bull adjusts his position so that their bodies remain parallel. Once they circle each other only 10 feet apart. At 0645 hours, the new bull suddenly faces at right angles away from the herd bull, and the latter emits a lowing u-u-u-u-u. When the new bull walks a few steps away, the herd bull follows and once more presents his broadside. Finally at 0654 the new bull leaves the herd alone, moving from sight in the forest at 0700 hours.

The lateral display appeared to be one of the principal means by which bulls, particularly black bulls, established their rank without actual physical contact. Antonius (1932) mentioned that the lateral display in gaur preceded attack, which perhaps was true in the zoo where his observations were made, but in the wild the display func- tioned as a substitute for fighting. Once the rank order between two bulls was established, the subordinate animal had the choice of re- maining in the herd, at the periphery, or of leaving it entirely: the dominant bull made no attempt to drive the other animal from the vicinity of the herd. Interactions between bulls in a herd were usually peaceful, for each animal assumed its position in the hierarchy on or soon after entering it. Brown bulls rarely took part in a lateral display, perhaps because they could assess their rank in relation to black bulls and to other brown bulls easily by visual means. Spar- ring is probably also important in establishing and reinforcing the rank of brown bulls — 48 percent of all sparring matches were be- tween brown bulls and 70 percent contained at least one brown bull. On two occasions black bulls displayed to my Land Rover when I parked within fifty feet of the animal. In both instances I maintained the vehicle's lateral position until the bull turned aside, accepting a subordinate rank. The lateral display has also been reported from domestic cattle, American bison (Schloeth, 1958a), and gayal (Antonius, 1932).

The general opinion regarding the status of bulls in the herd was expressed by Sanderson (1912): "On the leading bull's strength declining with age he is ousted by more youthful rivals and thence forward invariably, I believe, leads a solitary life, unless he is able to force himself for a season into a herd whose chief is in worse case than himself." Brander (1923), Forsyth (1889), Fletcher (1911),

TABLE 40

DOMINANCE INTERACTIONS IN A GAUR HERD,
MARCH 18, 1964, BETWEEN 1735 AND 1900 HOURS

DOMINANT ANIMAL	SUBORDINATE ANIMAL					TOTAL
	Brown Bull	Cow	Cow	Yearling Bull	Bull Calf	
Brown bull. . . .		4	4	3	1	12
Cow.			2	1	1	4
Cow.				2	1	3
Yearling bull. . .						0
Bull calf.						0
Total						19

and others have made essentially similar statements. The evidence of my observations clearly refutes this interpretation. Rather than on strength, bulls base their rank order primarily on size. The relative position of the bulls in the hierarchy changes constantly and requires frequent readjustment as some join and others leave of their own volition.

Size is a major criterion for determining rank in all members of the herd: black and brown bulls are dominant over adult cows, which usually rank higher than yearling bulls; yearling bulls in turn take priority over yearling cows; and calves are at the bottom of the hierarchy. Reversals in this sequence may occur. On three occasions a cow hooked a black bull in the side when he inadvertently crowded her small calf, and once a cow jabbed a brown bull that attempted to mount her. Schloeth's statement (1961) that among cattle external properties such as "size of body, strength of the horns are only of limited importance for social rank order" is undoubtedly a valid conclusion for the small captive herd studied by him, because in such a situation the animals know each other individually and respond on the basis of repeated previous contacts. In the wild, however, where meetings with strangers are frequent, the animals probably determine their status in most instances by assessing each other's physical attributes visually without overt interaction, as has already been described for the chital.

Schloeth (1961) and Schein and Fohrman (1955) observed a linear dominance hierarchy in herds of domestic cattle, as did McHugh (1958) in a captive herd of American bison. The existence of a linear hierarchy in free-living gaur was difficult to determine because of the frequent changes in herd composition and the paucity of interactions. On one occasion, the members of a herd consisting of 2 bulls, 2 cows, and a calf interacted aggressively a total of nineteen times while crowded together at a salt lick, revealing a linear hierarchy (Table 40), but a similar relationship of cows and subadults in large herds could not be established.

Sexual Behavior

Extensive roaming and calling by bulls mark the onset of the rut. Black bulls walking alone through the forest stop at intervals and emit a call which Peacock (1933) described as a "thin, whining" note and Brander (1923) as an "absurd piping or whistling sound" but which I have called a song in my notes because of its musical quality. The bull raises his muzzle and with slightly opened mouth produces a clear, resonant u-u-u-u-u about one to three seconds long, either constant in pitch or slightly rising and falling. This note may be followed by a second one somewhat lower in tone, by a third one still lower, and so forth, giving the impression of someone practicing musical scales. As many as ten seconds sometimes elapse between the first and last note. Although the call does not seem to be particularly loud, it carries for about one mile through the forest. Calling predominates at dawn and dusk but continues throughout the night during the peak of the rut. One of my most pleasant memories from Kanha is the song of the gaur floating across the dark and silent meadow.

Large brown and black bulls called in a variety of situations, which were similar to those described for American bison bulls by McHugh (1958): (1) when walking alone through the forest, (2) when approaching a herd, (3) while moving around in a herd, especially if a cow in heat was present, (4) in response to the call of another bull, and (5) in response to an imitation of the call by man. Cows appeared to be attracted by the sound; once, for example, when four females and a yearling bull heard a call about seven hundred feet away, the lead cow changed her direction and moved toward the sound. A black bull appeared at the forest's edge, joined the herd, but after giving a lateral display for five seconds to the yearling bull, called again and continued on alone. Solitary bulls also responded to a call, and in that fashion probably found herds which they otherwise might not have encountered in their dense forest environment. On one occasion, I heard a solitary black bull call at 1445 hours and receive an answer from a great distance. He walked steadily toward the sound, calling at intervals and each time receiving a reply. I followed on foot. At 1515 hours he was within a quarter mile but still out of sight of the other bull, which stood on a bamboo-covered knoll with a number of cows and calves. The bull continued to advance, but now his horns were lowered, his head swung from side to side, his tail flicked back and forth, and he snorted. Once he jabbed his horns into a clump of dead bamboo stems, rattling them loudly. He bellowed harshly, then grazed briefly, while the other bull snorted once. At 1530 hours the two bulls approached each other with lowered heads; unfortunately at that point a cow winded me, and all animals bolted.

Wallowing, a conspicuous activity of American bison during the rut (McHugh, 1958), was rare in gaur and was probably associated with grooming rather than with sexual activity. On two occasions, I found a muddy depression in which a gaur had reclined, and once I came across a churned site where an animal appeared to have taken a dust bath. Hubback (1937) saw no evidence of wallowing in the Malayan gaur. Domestic cattle do not wallow, but as Schloeth (1961) has pointed out, they paw and rub their necks and heads on the ground while kneeling on their carpal joints, which in some other species are actions preliminary to wallowing. The fact that gaur were never seen to behave in this fashion suggests that wallowing features even less in their behavioral repertoire than it does in that of domestic cattle.

On entering a herd the bull is apparently able to determine by olfactory and perhaps visual means if a cow is in estrus. Occasionally he merely walks through the herd and continues on alone without pausing, but at other times he sniffs the vulva of one, two, or three cows in succession, the tip of his tongue sliding in and out of his nostrils and saliva dribbling from his lips. *Flehmen*, with raised muzzle and curled lip, is common in such situations, especially after the bull has sniffed urine or feces. If a cow is in estrus, he remains with her, standing either by her rump or her side; when she grazes, he waits; and when she takes a step, he does, too, behavior termed "tending" by McHugh (1958). The two animals usually face in the same direction, but occasionally they stand head to tail, which is apparently the usual position for domestic cattle (Schloeth, 1961). One courting pair sparred lightly three times, and the bull then jabbed the cow once gently in the udder with the tip of his horn. If the cow stands still, the bull may place his chin on her rump, an action which is often followed by an attempt to mount.

TABLE 41

FREQUENCY OF SEXUAL BEHAVIOR PATTERNS IN THREE AGE CLASSES OF GAUR BULLS

Age Class	*Flehmen*	Tending	Attempted Mounting or Mounting	Percent of Bulls in Each Age Class in Population
Total number of observations. . .	29	9	16	
Black bull.	62%	89%	50%	55%
Brown bull	38	11	44	35
Yearling bull . . .	0%	0%	6%	10%

Courting pairs tend to remain in or near the herd. During the long mid-day rest period, the two may lie side by side; mutual licking of head and neck are common at this time. On one occasion a black bull tended a cow away from a herd. They moved three hundred feet in eighteen minutes, while another black bull tagged one hundred fifty feet behind, stopping and moving whenever they did.

The frequency with which various patterns of sexual behavior were seen in three age classes of bulls is presented in Table 41. The brown bulls appear to be sexually almost as active as the black ones as indicated by mounting but less so by tending. Since most successful copulations are probably the end product of a prolonged tending period, it seems unlikely that the hurried mountings by brown bulls result in an appreciable number of conceptions.

The black bulls obviously lost a considerable amount of weight during late April and May, presumably as a result of rutting during the hot time of the year when nutritious forage was scarce, but by July they had regained their prime condition.

LICKING

Licking as a form of social contact in deer is largely confined to females licking their young and males licking the vulva of females.

In gaur, however, this activity is also conspicuous during courtship, with cows and bulls licking each other's necks, shoulders, and rump, occasionally for as long as ten minutes without interruption. Bulls also lick each other at times, and in five out of seven instances the subordinate animal licked one of higher rank. A summary of all licking interactions seen during the study is presented in Table 42.

FEMALE-YOUNG RELATIONS

Cows about to give birth leave the herd and remain separated from it for about four days, according to Sanderson (1912). Cows with small calves were seen alone in the forest on three occasions. On one of these the calf rested beneath a tree, its muzzle tucked into

TABLE 42

LICKING INTERACTIONS IN GAUR

ANIMAL LICKING	ANIMAL LICKED						TOTAL
	Black Bull	Brown Bull	Yearling Bull	Adult Cow	Yearling Cow	Calf	
Black bull. . . .	0	1	0	5	0	0	6
Brown bull . . .	2	4	0	2	1	0	9
Yearling bull. . .	0	0	0	0	0	0	0
Adult cow. . . .	8	1	0	7	3	16	35
Yearling cow. . .	0	0	0	1	0	0	1
Calf	0	1	0	3	1	3	8
Total. . . .							59

its flank, while the cow foraged two hundred feet away. On May 25 a newborn with part of the umbilical cord still attached was in a herd with four cows, indicating that females may not remain separated from the herd for long after parturition. The calf tends to stay close to its mother, usually at heel, although it may stray to other parts of the herd. Small calves frequently rest nearby while the cow forages. Once a cow nudged her sleeping calf with her nose until it rose and followed her. But on another occasion, a herd moved away from a grazing area leaving a small calf behind; seventy minutes later it was still there alone. Domestic cows commonly moo when seeking their calves (Schloeth, 1961). I heard female gaur moo in similar situations, but calves did not vocalize when separated from their mothers, nor did they reply to the call of the cow.

Suckling was observed thirteen times, always in calves estimated to be less than six months old. The calf approached from either side, butted the udder with its nose, and suckled, its tail beating wildly. A typical suckling sequence went as follows: a calf approached from the left side, butted the udder once, and suckled; after 2½ minutes it butted once more, and again at 5½, 6, and 7 minutes. After suckling for 7 minutes 36 seconds, it walked to the right side and drank for another 1 minute 15 seconds while the cow walked slowly chewing her cud. Seven suckling periods that were observed varied from 4 minutes 7 seconds to 8 minutes 51 seconds (average 6 minutes 2 seconds) in duration. Schloeth (1958b) found that the average duration of suckling in domestic cattle is about 10 minutes.

CHAPTER 8

ECOLOGICAL AND

BEHAVIORAL COMPARISONS

Although the species have in some instances been compared briefly in the text at the appropriate places, a number of topics need elaboration or emphasis. Some of the comparisons are intended to help clarify the similarities and differences of the species in adapting to the same general environment, and others serve to draw together the scattered data and provide a brief summary of certain important aspects of behavior.

Biomass

The number of individuals in each ungulate species per unit area multiplied by their weight provides an estimate of the biomass supported by a certain habitat, a useful index for ultimately determining the optimum carrying capacity of the range. Bourlière (1963) summarized the published information on ungulate biomasses in various parts of the world, noting figures as low as .3 kilograms per square kilometer in the Sahara to 31,028 kilograms per square kilometer in a severely overgrazed area of Uganda. No data are available for India or any other part of the Oriental region, and an attempt was therefore made to derive the biomass of the hoofed animals in the 123 square miles of Kanha Park (Table 43). As discussed earlier, the estimate of numbers of the different species was derived from direct counts, transects and other censuses, and in some instances from guesswork based on the frequency with which the animals were seen in mid-1964. According to figures supplied by the forest department, about 2,500 head of cattle and buffalo graze more or less permanently within the park, but from March to June an unknown number of others are brought into the area illegally. These additional animals are not considered in the computations of biomass. The weights of the wild ungulates were taken primarily from published sources. In gaur, chital, and sambar, species with an unequal sex ratio and a large difference in size between adult male and female, the biomass was based on the actual composition of the population, using weights as indicated in Table 43. The

TABLE 43

POPULATION DENSITY AND BIOMASS OF UNGULATES
IN KANHA NATIONAL PARK, JUNE, 1964

Species	Estimate of Numbers	Density per Square Mile	Average Weights Used in Computations (In Pounds)	Biomass per Square Mile (In Pounds)
Wild				
Gaur.	165–210	1.3–1.7	Ad. ♂ 1,900; yg.500; others 1,300	1,690–2,151
Chital	900–1,000	7.3–8.1	Ad. ♂ 140; ad. ♀ 125; yrl.100; yg.50	732–809
Sambar. . . .	200–300	1.6–2.3	♂ 450; ♀ 350; yg.100	513–761
Barasingha . .	75	.6	350	213
Wild pig . . .	150±	1.2	60	73
Nilgai	20±	.2	400	65
Barking deer .	125±	1.0	40	40
Four-horned antelope . .	100±	.8	40	32
Blackbuck . .	18	.1	50	7
Total. . . .	1,853–2,098	14.1–16.0		3,365–4,151
Domestic				
Elephant . . .	2	.01	8,000	130
Cattle and buffalo . . .	2,500±	20.3	500	10,162
Total. . . .	2,502±	20.3		10,292
Grand total	4,355–4,600	34.4–36.3		13,657–14,443

Ad. = adult; yrl. = yearling; yg. = young.

biomass for the other species was obtained by multiplying the number of individuals by the approximate minimum adult weight. Cattle were estimated to weigh 400 pounds, buffalo 600 pounds, for an average of 500 pounds. As Bourlière (1963) has pointed out, "Overestimation caused by attributing to the young the weight of an adult is more or less compensated for by the underestimation of the weight of the oldest individuals."

The number of large wild ungulates in Kanha Park appears to lie somewhere between 1,850 and 2,100 animals, or 14 to 16 per square mile, half of these being chital. The biomass is on the order of 3,365 to 4,151 pounds per square mile (937–1,178 kg/sq km), about half of it represented by gaur. The amount of cattle and buffalo exceeds that of the wild ungulates both in number and in biomass, the live-stock's biomass being two and a half times as large. If the biomasses for the wild and domestic animals are combined, a figure of 13,657–14,443 pounds per square mile (3,880–4,103 kg/sq km) is obtained. This figure is comparable to the wild ungulate biomass of 3,400 kilograms per square kilometer in the National Bison Range of Wyoming and the 4,418 kilograms per square kilometer in the open woodland of southern Rhodesia (Bourlière, 1963).

The biomass in Kanha Park reflects, of course, only the condi-tions prevailing in 1964 and does not indicate the size of the standing crop that the area can support. About half of Kanha Park is more or less heavily grazed by livestock, some areas along the boundaries and around the villages being overgrazed. On the other hand, the forage in much of the hills and the central part of the park is only lightly to moderately cropped by the herbivores, and there is no evidence of range deterioration. My twenty-square-mile study area contained nearly all the barasingha, two-thirds of the chital and gaur, perhaps one-quarter of the sambar, and a small sample of the other species, a biomass of about 13,000 pounds per square mile, for much of the year without signs of overgrazing. This figure for wild un-gulates is similar to the one derived for the whole park when the livestock is included. Large parts of the park appear to be able to support a biomass of wild ungulates as large as the one in my study area, but either the carrying capacity of these localities has been ex-ceeded by livestock or the wildlife has been decimated by poachers. The available data suggest that Kanha Park is capable of maintain-ing a permanent biomass of around 13,000 pounds per square mile (3,693 kg/sq km) of a variety of wild ungulates under optimum con-ditions after the exclusion of cattle and buffalo from the forests.

An intensive census over the whole 11 square miles of the Keo-ladeo Ghana Sanctuary revealed a population of 375–400 chital, 110–20 nilgai, 70 blackbuck, fewer than 40 wild pigs, and fewer than 15 each sambar and hog deer (Schaller and Spillett, 1966), giving a biomass of 8,318–9,145 pounds per square mile (2,362–2,609 kg sq km), over twice as high as the wild ungulate biomass in Kanha Park. In addition, 1,640 cattle and 4,016 buffalo obtain most if not all of their forage in the sanctuary, a biomass of 257,090 pounds per square mile. The total biomass supported by this small area is about 266,000 pounds per square mile (75,568 kg/sq km).

Although most buffalo feed in a swamp which is not used by the wildlife, the standing crop of livestock exceeds the range's carrying capacity to such an extent that it is deteriorating rapidly to desert conditions.

Ecological Separation of Species

Although the large ungulate species in Kanha Park occupy essentially the same environment, each one is adapted to certain habitat conditions which separate it to some extent ecologically from the others. The summary in Table 44 shows similarities between the sambar and gaur: they are both predominantly nocturnal, prefer large unbroken tracts of forest, frequent the hills as well as the valleys, and subsist on a large variety of leaves and other browse in addition to their preferred grasses. They are less specialized in their habitat requirements, particularly with regard to food habits, than the other species, which no doubt is responsible for their wide distribution in India and southeast Asia. Ecological differences between

TABLE 44

PREFERENCES FOR CERTAIN ECOLOGICAL CONDITIONS
IN SEVERAL SPECIES OF UNGULATES AT KANHA PARK

Species	Diurnal Activity	Tolerance of Direct Sun	Amount of Browse Eaten	Coarse Grasses Eaten	Water Requirements	Preference for Open Habitat	Preference for Flat Terrain
Chital.	++	++	+++	+	++++	++	++
Barasingha . . .	+++	+++	++	+++	++++	+++	++
Sambar.	+	+	++++	+++	+++	+	+
Gaur	+	+	++++	++++	++++	+	+
Blackbuck. . . .	++++	++++	+	+	+	++++	++++

+ = the least relative amount; ++++ = the most.

the two species consist primarily of a greater tolerance by sambar for dry, open habitats and high altitudes and a seeming preference by gaur for coarser grasses and bamboo.

The chital are more diurnal, depend to a greater extent on grass as forage, and generally frequent more open habitats than the sambar and gaur. They are characteristically animals of the forest edge and of open glades and woodlands, with shade, water, and a good understory of tender grasses being requisites. These habitat preferences, together with their general avoidance of steep terrain and large forests with an unbroken canopy, have hindered the expansion of the animal into much of the range occupied by the sambar and gaur.

That the barasingha are essentially adapted to an open habitat, such as the reed beds in which they once occurred over most of their range, is suggested by their tolerance of sun, their subsistence on grass, and their predilection for concentrating on meadows during much of the year. The animals also enter the forest readily, however, and ascend the hills, being very adaptable in their use of different vegetation types at Kanha although confining their foraging almost entirely to grasses.

The blackbuck remain on the meadow at all times. They are more diurnal and more tolerant of direct sun, and they eat less browse and require less water than the other species studied, all adaptations to life on the plains.

The gradation of habitat preferences from meadow to forest edge to deep forest has tended to separate the species ecologically to some extent. In addition, their food preferences are somewhat different and complementary. Young green grass is avidly eaten by all species when available, particularly during the monsoon. However, since adaptation is a measure of response not to an optimum condition but to one of stress, it is during the hot season that the differences in food habits become important. Blackbuck continue to nibble on whatever grass shoots remain on the meadow; chital search for tender grass blades especially along the forest border, also taking some browse in the form of leaves and fruits; barasingha eat dry grasses and moderately coarse ones along the ravines; sambar forage on coarse grasses and a considerable amount of browse in the forest; and gaur graze down the tall coarse grasses taken by none of the others and break down saplings to get at the leaves. This division in habitat preferences and food habits ensures that the ecosystem is fully exploited by the herbivores, a fact also stressed by Huxley (1961) in his discussion of the "ecological division of labour" among the ungulates of East Africa.

The Reproductive Season

The ungulates of temperate latitudes, both in the northern and southern hemispheres, have a well-defined period of rut in autumn, and the young are born the following spring at a time of equable weather and ample green forage, thus missing the low temperatures, shortages of high-quality food, and other adverse conditions. Young green and growing plants are far more nutritious than full-grown, dead, or dormant ones, being particularly high in protein

(Leopold *et al.*, 1951; Taber and Dasmann, 1958). A high plane of nutrition is thought to be important to the female when she is lactating and to the young when it is being weaned. The whole yearly cycle of reproduction in temperate latitudes is correlated with the environmental conditions in such a way that the selective advantage to the species is obvious. That the availability of green forage coincides with the birth of young has also been noted in the white-tailed deer of Mexico (McCabe and Leopold, 1951) and in the wildebeest of Tanzania (Talbot and Talbot, 1963).

In central India the most unfavorable season of the year for the availability of nutritious green forage is from late March to mid-June, when in the searing heat the grasses dry up, the trees drop their leaves, and food in general is scarce or of low nutritional value.

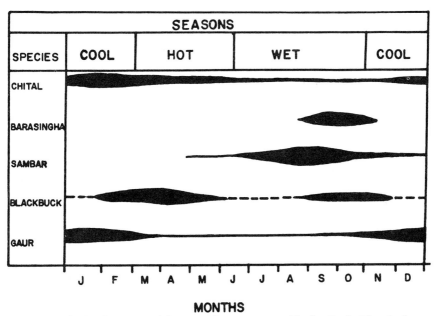

Fig. 11.—The birth season of five ungulate species in Kanha Park. The thickness of the black line represents the relative number of young born each month.

The most favorable time is from mid-June to mid-September. Solely from the nutritional standpoint of the lactating female, June would be the most suitable birth month. Yet fewer young appear to be born in this month than in any other (Fig. 11). The young of chital and gaur are born primarily during the cool season at a time of diminishing food resources, and they continue to suckle during the hot season, many being weaned or almost weaned at the onset of the rains in June. The sambar gives birth primarily during the monsoon and the barasingha toward the end of it. Lactating females have ample good forage available, but the young have the unfavorable seasons ahead of them. The blackbuck has two birth seasons, the major one during the hot period and the other one during the latter part of the rains. A direct correlation, which encompasses all five species, between fawning time and the availability of young green forage is obviously lacking.

Other periods in the reproductive cycle may of course be as important nutritionally as the time of fawning. The fetus grows very rapidly during the last three months of its development, and an adequate diet may be necessary to the female then (Wallace, 1945). The barasingha and to a lesser degree the sambar and blackbuck benefit in this respect from the monsoon, and the females of the other species are in advanced stages of pregnancy during the cool season when green forage is still moderately abundant.

The incidence of multiple ovulation in domestic sheep is increased by bringing the ewes to a high plane of nutrition about three weeks before mating (Wynne-Edwards, 1962). In black-tailed deer, the "rate of ovulation seems to be strongly affected by the level of nutrition just prior to and during the rut" (Longhurst et al., 1952). In order for this so-called flushing effect to have its maximum influence on the ungulates at Kanha, the most favorable time to mate would be in July. Of the species studied only the blackbuck reaches a rutting peak during the monsoon.

Chital, gaur, and blackbuck may mate and bear young during every month, a good indication that environmental conditions are not so rigorous that selection has favored only restricted rutting and birth seasons. Some green forage is usually available throughout the year, since even in February and March a few showers brought by the southwest monsoon stimulate the growth of grass.

The annual reproductive cycle is the result of both internal and external factors which bring the population into breeding condition. There is the internal physiological rhythm of the species, which, however, must be set off and synchronized by external stimuli (Amoroso and Marshall, 1956). The sexual rhythm of deer, according to Wislocki (1943) and Wislocki et al., (1947) is determined by seasonal factors which affect the antler and sex gland development by way of the pituitary. In the white-tailed deer, for example, seasonal changes in the size of the testes are evident. They are small in the spring when the antlers are in velvet. Spermatogenesis begins in July and reaches a peak in October during the rut, then diminishes by December. The loss of velvet is precipitated by a rise of testosterone in the blood, and the antlers are shed as a result of a subsequent drop in this hormone level (Severinghaus and Cheatum, 1956). It is probable that the stages of antler development in the deer at Kanha coincide with a similar annual rise and fall in the amount of testosterone. Since the chital sheds its antlers throughout the year, however, it does not appear that the physiological rhythm of this species is wholly synchronized by external stimuli but that each animal follows its own internal rhythm to some extent. The blackbuck and gaur appear to be sexually active at all seasons, although more so in some than in others.

Light intensity and temperature are two environmental variables that may have an influence on the reproductive cycle. According to Amoroso and Marshall (1956), "The ruminating ungulates, with a few possible exceptions, stand out in marked contrast to the majority of mammals in breeding in late summer and autumn when daylight is diminishing." Most mating in the chital and gaur occurs at a time of increasing day length, and most mating in the sambar and barasingha begins during a decreasing period but continues into an increasing one. The peak of the rut for the last two species occurs during the coolest time of the year and for the chital and gaur during the hottest time. The blackbuck reaches mating peaks during periods of both increasing and decreasing day length (Fig. 12).

The striking differences in the annual reproductive cycle between the species at Kanha make it obvious that no single environmental factor or combination of factors influences all animals equally. The obvious correlation between plant phenology and climatic conditions with the season of birth in temperate latitudes is not applicable to central India. Ansell (1960) and Dasmann and Mossman (1962) found a similarly inconclusive relationship between breeding and environmental factors in the ungulates of central Africa. It is clear that generalizations cannot be made until the factors influencing each species have been analyzed separately. For example, the onset of the rut of the barasingha may well be influenced by a drop in temperature but that in the chital by a rise in the temperature. The social habits of the species may also have an effect on the annual reproductive cycle. Both the gaur and chital, which have a similar social organization, rut primarily during the hot season when the

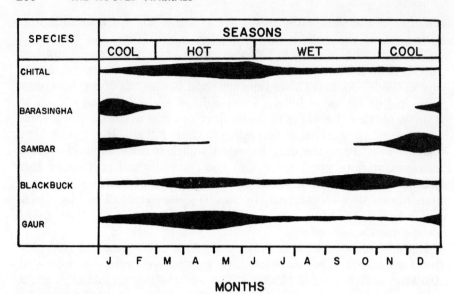

Fig. 12.—The mating season of five ungulate species in Kanha Park. The thickness of the black line represents the relative amount of rutting activity each month.

animals are concentrated near the remaining water and food sources. It may be that sexual activity in these species at Kanha is stimulated and synchronized by social contact and that the rutting peak is reached by the animals as a result of having been brought together by adverse environmental conditions, a system of obvious biological advantage to species whose members are widely scattered through the forest at other times of the year.

It is probable that external conditions play on the whole a less prominent role in synchronizing the sexual cycle of ungulates in the subtropical and tropical regions than in the temperate regions. This becomes evident when a species is transported to a different latitude. Red deer, for example, when moved from England across the equator to New Zealand where the seasons are reversed, adapted rapidly to the new conditions. The males shed their antlers twice in one year after introduction and then became fully synchronized after eighteen months; the females reversed their estrus cycle within two years. Similarly, red deer shipped from New Zealand back to England readjusted to their original seasons within two years. Such reversals in the cycle have also been observed in white-tailed deer, wapiti, moose, and chamois (Marshall, 1937). On the other hand, deer and antelope moved from India to the temperate zones do not adapt to the new conditions. Chital, which have now ranged freely at Woburn Abbey in England for half a century, still fawn throughout the year and especially in February and March, just as they do in India. The published birth records of barasingha, sambar, nilgai, hog deer, and blackbuck from the London zoo and New York Zoological Park (Crandall, 1964; Jarvis and Morris, 1962; Zuckerman, 1953) all indicate that these species have failed to adapt their sexual cycle to local climatic conditions. The principal change in the cycle of zoo animals appears to be a partial to complete disappearance of the rutting and fawning peaks found in the wild.

Although the reproductive cycle of wild ungulates in India appears to be dependent on an inherent endocrine cycle little influenced by obvious environmental conditions, it is surprising to note the striking differences in the rutting and fawning times within the same species from area to area. As discussed earlier, such differences were noted in the chital, to some extent in the sambar and hog deer, and particularly in the barasingha. The sexual cycle is presumably adapted to local circumstances, which implies that the endocrine system retains the potential to respond to the environment to a limited degree.

Social Behavior

Although a society has many functions, one of the most important of these in ungulates is to organize the members of a species in such a way that most mating is accomplished by the prime adult males. The males establish a system of land tenure or a hierarchial pattern that partly or wholly excludes a certain percentage of their sex from active participation in the rut. The means by which this is accomplished varies from species to species.

Social Systems

Every kind of ungulate at Kanha has two basic social systems, although the distinction between them is sometimes not sharply defined: one at the peak of mating and the other during the rest of the year. When little or no mating occurs, the ungulates are broadly divisible into solitary species, such as hog deer, barking deer, and four-horned antelope, and herd-living species. Herd size varies considerably between species and appears to be dependent at least in part on the habitat. In general, ungulates living in open environments tend to form larger herds than those in dense forests. Black-buck and barasingha were once found in herds of thousands. Chital, which are deer of the forest edge, average 5 to 10 animals per herd, although sometimes as many as 200 or more individuals came to-gether. The forest-dwelling gaur forms temporary aggregations rare-ly exceeding 40 animals, and the average is around 8 to 10. The sambar has a still smaller social unit, as many as 10 deer infre-quently remaining together. The composition of these herds is fluid, with individuals joining and parting at intervals. The only stable social relationship is between a female and her young and some-times also a yearling. Adult males tend to become solitary or form herds of their own. The significance of this widespread type of herd structure is obscure. "There is no existing and generally-accepted theory regarding the purpose of the herding habit in mammals," and it may simply be the alternative to a solitary life (Wynne-Ed-wards, 1962).

During the peak of the rut, on the other hand, the social structure of the ungulates shows some striking differences between species: (1) In the chital and gaur the adult males roam widely, entering and leaving many herds, apparently in search of estrous females. The male associates with any female in heat and defends her individually from other males until copulation has been completed. There is no attempt to prevent males from entering the herd, and no territory is established. (2) Most adult sambar males appear to confine them-selves singly to a limited range, in which they join or are joined by females for varying lengths of time. (3) The barasingha form breed-ing herds, numbering 30 to 50 individuals each, composed of a num-ber of adult males, females, and young. Males establish a dominance hierarchy, with the highest ranking male taking priority to any estrous female. The composition of the herd changes somewhat from day to day, but the same animals tend to associate for a week or more. (4) As many as 20 to 30 hog deer males and females aggre-gate loosely in certain localities at Kaziranga. Each male seemingly attempts to acquire one estrous female and, when he has done so, leaves the area with her, the two animals presumably remaining to-gether only until they have mated. (5) Blackbuck and nilgai males establish territories which they defend against other males. Attempts are made to retain whatever females enter the territory, and ulti-mately, a typical breeding herd consists of an adult male and sev-eral females and young, often with a few subordinate males at the periphery of the territory. These breeding herds may remain constant in composition and confined to one locality for prolonged periods.

According to the concepts developed by Wynne-Edwards (1962), social organization, particularly during the rut, is a means of providing competition among the members, the degree of competition maintaining the proper balance between population size and food supply. In addition, competition helps to determine the dominant individuals, which then take priority to estrous females. The genetic selective advantage of having the largest and most vigorous males doing most of the mating is readily apparent, although the environmental and social conditions which foster one system rather than another are not at all clear. Blackbuck and nilgai, for example, which frequent open habitats with good visibility, establish a more cohesive social system than the chital, gaur, and, to a lesser degree, sambar, which are forest-dwellers. It is also possible that differences in social systems serve to lessen the chances that individuals of two related species, such as the sambar and barasingha, will interbreed.

DOMINANCE

Males in a small herd tend to establish a rank order. The existence of a hierarchy was apparent in blackbuck and gaur throughout the year, but in the male deer, with their deciduous antlers, there was considerable seasonal variation in the degree of dominance displayed. A difference between relative and absolute dominance was pointed out by Leyhausen (1965b). In the former type, the animal is dominant only in its own territory and not outside of it. No evidence for relative dominance was found in the ungulates studied. In an absolute hierarchy the rank of individuals remains constant under all circumstances. "The main prerequisite of its proper functioning is, of course, that all members of a community know each other individually" (Leyhausen, 1965b). This type of hierarchy was evident in the blackbuck, among which it persisted unchanged throughout the period of study. The barasingha males on the Kanha meadow, which probably also recognized each other individually, displayed an absolute hierarchy until they shed their antlers. The animals lost their rank with the loss of their antlers, and no hierarchy seemed to be actively maintained until the new set was free of velvet.

In addition to the absolute hierarchy based on individual recognition, another absolute type needs to be considered — that based solely on a rapid mutual appraisal of physical characters. The populations of gaur and chital are large, and herds change constantly in composition, making it highly improbable that all males know each other. Yet a hierarchy becomes established, often without overt interaction, whenever several males come together. The antler length in the chital appears to be one of the main factors determining the status of the individual, the longest antlers conferring dominance. In the gaur, general size and the prominence of the dorsal ridge and dewlaps seem to be symbols of rank. A system of dominance based primarily on a visual assessment of certain characters rather than on repeated contacts would seem to be a distinct advantage to species with a fluid social organization since it would lessen the amount of strife and make the establishment of rank almost instantaneous when two individuals met. Although this form of absolute hierarchy rarely persists for more than a few hours as males join and part from the herd, its manner of assertion and effectiveness do not differ from the one based on individual recognition.

All males in this study, and also female gaur, have horns or antlers which are formidable weapons, symbols of the animal's power to attack and hurt an opponent. Although the potential to do damage is always implied, actual fights are rare. Only 2 out of 309 (.06 percent) barasingha and one out of 284 (.03 percent) chital sparring bouts that were observed were actual fights in the sense of one animal seemingly attempting to subdue another. Most sparring among chital, barasingha, gaur, and blackbuck was proportionally far more frequent in young males than in fully adult ones, with the animals apparently attempting either to reassert their position or to test their strength. Dominance is largely determined by a number of conventions, to use Wynne-Edward's (1962) term. All species threaten with their antlers or horns by pointing them at the opponent; and several displays, such as the head-up, head-down, and lateral displays, are used to intimidate, as are various forms of redirected aggression (Table 45). Added to these conventions are several olfactory and auditory signals, all of which help to establish the male's position in the hierarchy.

The social competition between males and the resulting hierarchy confer one obvious advantage on the high-ranking individuals: they are given priority to estrous females, as pointed out earlier. The selective force, which enhances the effectiveness of the structures such as antlers that have enabled the animal to achieve a high rank in the first place, is therefore strong. In polygynous ungulate social systems, where only a small percentage of high-ranking males do most

TABLE 45

COMPARISONS OF SOME MALE AGGRESSIVE AND SEXUAL BEHAVIOR PATTERNS
IN SEVERAL INDIAN UNGULATES

Behavior Pattern	Chital	Barasingha	Sambar	Hog Deer	Blackbuck	Nilgai	Gaur
Preorbital gland marking. . . .	+	+	+	+	+	?	
Thrashing bushes with horns. . .	+	+	+	+	+	?	+
Rubbing bark off tree trunks with horns.	+	+	+	?			
Preaching. . . .	+		+				
Pawing with foreleg	+	+	+	+	+	?	+
Defecating on dung piles. . .					+	+	
Wallowing. . . .		+	+				
Stamping ground.			+				
Head-up display .	+	+	+	+	+	+	+
Head-down display	+		?	+		+	
Lateral display. .	+	+	+	+	+	?	+
Horizontal-neck display						+	
Low-stretch display	+	+	+	?		?	
Sparring.	+	+	+	+	+	+	+
Loud rutting call.	+	+	+				+
Flehmen.	+	+	+	+	+	+	+

of the mating, a large number of seemingly excess males are present. The function of these males possibly "lies in maintaining the high level of competition" (Wynne-Edwards, 1962).

DISPLAY PATTERNS

The males exhibit a number of different behavior patterns which tend to make them look conspicuous and impressive, at least to the human observer, by emphasizing their size, movements, special markings (such as a white throat patch), and special structures (such as antlers). An impressive appearance is presumably of importance to the animal in the presence of an opponent and when courting a female, and it is in these two situations that most displays are seen. The head-up display, in which the muzzle is raised, making the animal appear large and exposing the white throat patch in chital, barasingha, and nilgai, is used by all species studied (Table 45). The lateral display, with two animals standing parallel to each other, is often used in conjunction with the head-up. However, the emphasis placed on each of these displays differs somewhat with the species. The head-up in the gaur is infrequent and appears to be far less important as a communicatory signal in the daily life of the animal than the lateral display. In the deer and blackbuck the reverse is true in that the head-up is more commonly employed and the lateral display is less ritualized than in the gaur. In this context, it is significant to note that the gaur has structures — the dorsal ridge and dewlaps — which emphasize its appearance only in profile, whereas the other species lack such attributes. These two displays are exhibited during aggressive encounters as well as during courtship, functioning apparently by intimidating males, on the one hand, and by impressing estrous females, on the other. In contrast, the head-down display, and also the horizontal-neck display of the nilgai, seems to occur only during aggressive encounters, functioning primarily in intimidation.

The majority of animal displays are thought to be derived from intention movements, displacement activities, and redirected aggression (Moynihan, 1955). The head-up display is perhaps based on an intention movement to rear up and strike the opponent with the forelegs, a method of fighting in deer but not in the gaur. The lateral display may possibly be the outcome of a balance between the opposing tendencies to attack and to flee, with the animal neither advancing nor retreating. The head-down display may have a similar derivation, except that the lowered neck and averted head are gestures of submission and indicate that a direct challenge is not intended. The low-stretch display, seen only in sexual situations, appears to contain both an aggressive component, the raised head, and a submissive one, the lowered neck; or it may be derived from an intention movement to lick the vulva. Several forms of redirected aggression, which involve attacking an inanimate object rather than an opponent, are also exhibited by males. Prominent among these are pawing the ground and thrashing bushes and trees with horns and antlers (Table 45). Three other types of behavior, all perhaps containing elements of redirected aggression, occur but are not widespread among the ungulates, and the significance of their presence in some species and not in others is unknown. Preaching, with the animal standing on its hindlegs and wiping its face in a leafy branch, is confined to the chital and sambar; wallowing during the rut occurs in the sambar and barasingha; and establishing stamping grounds has been observed only for the sambar (Table 45). These forms of behavior may serve to intimidate an opponent either directly or indirectly by marking the environment with visual signals and with scent from the preorbital and other glands.

Males sometimes interrupt their courtship to thrash vegetation and to paw, actions indicating that the female releases both aggressive and sexual behavior. Each display probably contains aggressive, submissive, and sexually mediated components, with the final emphasis depending on the circumstances. It is, therefore, not surprising that similar displays may be elicited in dissimilar situations and that the function of the gesture varies with the situation. In the chital, for example, the vertically raised tail and the exposed white rump patch are evident in four different circumstances: (1) in conjunction with the head-up display to another male, the gesture is an aggressive action, tending to cause submission or evasion; (2) to a female in estrus, it is a part of courtship, presumably attracting her; (3) in flight, it becomes a danger signal to which the other animals respond similarly; and (4) in play by the young, it elicits no obvious response other than occasional alertness.

RANGE AND TERRITORY

All ungulates occupy a range in which they spend their lives and which they share with other members of their species. This range may be relatively small, like the two to three square miles frequented by a blackbuck, or it may be large like the thirty square miles used by a gaur. In addition, the males of some species lay claim to a small piece of ground within their range at certain times of the year — a territory — from which other males are excluded but within which females are permitted to remain. Of the species studied, only the blackbuck and nilgai showed this territorial behavior.

Rutting males of all species mark their range with a number of auditory, visual, and olfactory cues, apparently serving to draw attention either to the animal itself or to its recent presence in the area. The rutting call of the chital, barasingha, gaur, and others is a long-distance auditory signal, lacking in the territorial nilgai and blackbuck. The thrashing of vegetation with horns, as practiced widely among the ungulates, leaves a visual signal of tattered branches, often enhanced by an olfactory signal of the scent from the preorbital glands. Other visual and olfactory signals include wallows, pawing marks, scoured tree trunks, and preaching trees. Pocock (1910) noted that the metatarsal gland of deer secretes an oily substance, which may serve to mark the resting spots used by the animals. It is perhaps significant that the sambar, the most complete forest-dweller and least social of the deer studied, exhibits the most complex signaling system. Such signals have sometimes been taken as evidence of territorial behavior, but it is obvious that non-territorial species use the same means to mark their environment as territorial species, with the exception of defecation at localized sites (Table 45). The markings in a territory differ from those in a range only in their concentration in a small area and in their being largely the work of one male.

It may be inferred that the signals, whether in a territory or scattered over the range, combine two opposite qualities: attracting and

TABLE 46

COMPARISONS OF SOME BEHAVIOR PATTERNS OF SEVERAL INDIAN UNGULATES IN RESPONSE TO A POTENTIALLY DANGEROUS SITUATION

Behavior Pattern	Chital	Barasingha	Sambar	Hog Deer	Blackbuck	Nilgai	Gaur
Alert posture with neck and ears erect	+	+	+	+	+	+	+
Raising tail vertically . . .	+	+	+	+	+	+	
Exposing rump patch.	+	+	+	+	+	+	
Stamping forefoot. . . .	+	+	+	+	+	+	
Alarm call. . . .	+	+	+	+	+	+	+
Thumping forefeet in unison . . .		+	+				+
Thumping hind-feet in unison .	+	+	+	+			
Spronking. . . .					+	+	
Standing motionless. . .			+				
Sneaking away in semi-crouch . .			+				

drawing individuals together and subsequently spacing them out as a result of intraspecific rivalry. The territory is in itself a spacing mechanism which prevents overcrowding in a particular locality. The density of males in non-territorial species is controlled by more subtle means, perhaps by causing scattering and emigration when the number of sign posts in an environment exceeds an optimum level. Some evidence for this was found in the barasingha. There is another possible result of a too high concentration of signals: the degree of mutual sexual stimulation may decrease rather than increase, with some males becoming sexually inactive. The relatively small number of vigorously rutting chital males at the peak rutting season lends some support to this conjecture.

LEADERSHIP

Herds tend to move in single file, a trait common in many social mammals including man. Such a mode of progression has several advantages over other patterns of movement: it prevents the animals from becoming separated, it provides each member with the best possible route, often a well-worn trail, and it lessens the probability of encountering a hidden predator. The animal leading the herd usually behaves more alertly than its followers.

Adult females characteristically lead herds, although males also do so on occasion. Any animal may be a herd leader as long as it elicits following in others. The reason for the predominance of female leaders may be related to the instability of the males as herd members and to the tendency of the young to follow only their mothers until well over a year old, behavior which possibly becomes generalized later in life to include all adult females.

Communication of Danger

Each species has evolved a number of visual, auditory, and olfactory signals which communicate the existence of potential danger to other members of the herd (Table 46). Some of these signals, like the raised tail, alert only animals in the immediate vicinity, but others, like the alarm call, may transmit information over long distances. The gaur appears to have the least complex signal system of the species studied, its repertoire consisting predominantly of raising the head, snorting, and thumping the forefeet. The deer and antelope also raise their tails, exposing the rump patch, which in all species except the sambar is highly conspicuous. It is likely that the interdigital glands of fleeing deer deposit scent, olfaction thus adding another dimension to the communicatory system. Since the visual, auditory, and possibly olfactory signals of danger used by one species are readily understood and responded to by other species, there is an interconnecting system of responses to predators such as tiger and man involving the whole ungulate population in a particular area.

PART III

THE PREDATORS

Although a number of different kinds of large carnivores occur in Kanha National Park, the tiger is by far the most important as a predator on the populations of hoofed animals. An attempt was therefore made to obtain as much information as possible on the behavior of this cat and its role in the ecology of the area. The bulk of the data in this part of the report is devoted to the tiger at Kanha, supplemented with observations from the literature when pertinent. The leopard, potentially an important predator on the deer and antelope, was uncommon in the study area, and I obtained very little information on its behavior. The jackal, jungle cat, and sloth bear are capable of preying on young ungulates, and with this in mind I investigated their food habits. The other large predators — wild dog, hyena, fox, and python — were so rare that their effect on the wildlife was negligible.

CHAPTER 9

THE TIGER

Few living mammals have become creatures of myth in the minds of man to as great an extent as has the tiger. Its large size, nocturnal habits, solitary nature, and elusiveness, coupled with its reputation as the "embodiment of devilish cruelty, of hate and savagery incarnate," as Inglis (1892) put it, have endowed the animal with an aura of mystery and fear, a feeling which has been intensified by the cat's occasional predilection for preying on humans. Even the earliest historical record of the tiger in the Indian region, a seal about five thousand years old found at Mohenjo-Daro in the Indus valley, depicts a man sitting in a tree angrily addressing a tiger waiting for him below (Burton, 1933). Yet although the tiger has been feared for some of its attributes, it has been admired for such others as the stealth, speed, power, and ruthlessness of attack and the lithe beauty of its appearance. For the Koreans, for example, the tiger is the king of beasts, the symbol of physical beauty, strength, and fighting force (M. Taylor, 1956), as it is also for the numerous sporting teams, military units, and other organizations which have named themselves after it. Therefore, it is not surprising that the tiger has been relentlessly pursued by hunters, who derive status from killing so formidable a beast, whether it is done sportingly with bow and arrow from horseback, as it was formerly in Korea, or otherwise with a rifle from the safety of a tree platform or even the inside of a car, as is usually the case in India today.

Although the literature on the tiger is voluminous, most of it is devoted to a discussion of how to shoot the animal, to arguments concerning its size and power to scent, and to interminable anecdotes about dangerous encounters with it. The natural history of the tiger has been studied predominantly along the sights of a rifle, and even authors like Champion (1927, 1933) and Berg (1936), who specialized in obtaining admirable photographs rather than skins, contributed little new information about the cat. Several maharajas, such as those of Gwalior and Dholpur, frequently fed tigers at certain sites for the amusement of visitors (Gee, 1964; P. Singh, 1959) and thus had remarkable opportunities for making observations, but no detailed records were kept. Some hunters, however, have written informative regional accounts, notably Baikov (1925) for Manchuria, Bazé (1957) for Indochina, Locke (1954) for Malaya, and Burton (1933) for India. Perry (1964) has presented a good, though uncritical, compilation of the literature concerning the tiger, but the over-all effect of the book is to emphasize the lack of knowledge about the habits of this species.

The purpose of this chapter is to present information about the behavior of tigers in Kanha Park. Factual material from the literature has been included to supplement the data, but no attempt has been made to summarize all the available information about the animal throughout its vast range, this having already been done to a large extent by Perry (1964).

My conclusions regarding some aspects of the tiger's behavior may not be applicable to other parts of its range, for it is an eminently adaptable animal readily changing its habits to conform with the prevailing conditions. The tigers in central Kanha Park have not been actively pursued there since about 1952, and it may be conjectured that their behavior accurately reflects their natural inclinations in particular situations, whereas the tigers in most of India give the responses of constantly harried animals. The Kanha tigers, for example, return to their kill even after having been disturbed repeatedly by man, but in other localities they are said to abandon the carcass with very little provocation.

Ellerman and Morrison-Scott (1951) recognize six subspecies of tiger of which *Panthera tigris tigris* occurs throughout India and Indochina, *P. t. virgita* around the Caspian and Aral seas, *P. t. longipilis* in Manchuria, *P. t. coreensis* in northern Korea and adjacent parts of China, *P. t. amoyensis* in south China, and *P. t. lecoqi* in Chinese Turkestan. In addition, some authors (see, for example, Jarvis, 1965) retain subspecific names for the Sumatran, Javan, and Balinese tigers (*P. t. sumatrae, sondaica, balica*). The physical differences between subspecies, which have been described by Pocock (1929), are slight. "While the tigers of the frigid north are large, long-coated, and pale in color, there is a gradual reduction in size and length of coat as well as a deepening of color toward the south, so that the island races are noticeably small, dark, and short-haired" (Crandall, 1964). In their general habits the tigers appear to be essentially similar throughout their range, judging by the published information, but unless stated otherwise, all data in this report pertain to Indian animals.

Description

The tiger is the largest existing member of the Felidae and, like most others in the family, adapted for stalking its prey rather than running it down. It has a lithe, elongated body, a short neck, and a compact head with a relatively short muzzle that contains a formidable set of canine teeth. The legs are stout and of moderate length, the forelimbs being more muscular than the hindlimbs, and the broad paws are armed with retractile claws (Plate 20). "A well-fed tiger is by no means a slim figure, but on the contrary it is exceedingly bulky, broad in the shoulders, back, and loins, with an extraordinary girth of limbs, especially in the fore-arm and wrist" (Baker, 1890).

Males are considerably longer and heavier than females. The average total length, including the tail, of an unspecified number of males measured by Brander (1923) was 8 feet 9 inches to 10 feet 3 inches and that of 39 females 7 feet 10 inches to 9 feet 1 inch. In general, the body of a male is about 6 feet long and the tail 3 feet long, with females 6 to 12 inches shorter in body (Finn, 1929). Numerous weights of tigers, shot in the wild, have been published. Brander (1923) found that the average weight of the males recorded by him was 420 pounds (range 353–515). Cooch Behar (1908) weighed 26 males and obtained an average of 482 pounds, the heaviest animal scaling 546 pounds, but his records are biased because only very large animals were recorded. Twenty weights of males taken from Hewett (1938), Inverarity (1888), Baker (1890), Burton (1933, 1948), Hornaday (1885), Meinertzhagen (1939), and Sanderson (1912) gave an average of 242 pounds, with a range of 349 to 590 pounds. Exceptionally heavy animals include one of 645 pounds (Ward, 1922) and one of 705 pounds (Smythies, 1942). The average weight of 39 females was 290 pounds, the heaviest being 343 pounds (Brander, 1923). The heaviest female among a total of 365 tigers shot by Cooch Behar (1908) weighed 360 pounds.

The color of the tiger's pelage varies from orange-red to tawny yellow, broken with a series of transverse black stripes of varying length and width. The cheeks, throat, abdomen, and the insides of the ears and legs are white. The back of the ears is black, with a conspicuous white spot in the center. The stripe pattern varies considerably among tigers. The black markings in the patch of white hair above each eye were found to be so distinctive that individuals could readily be distinguished by them (compare, for example, Plates 22 and 26), and I used this means of recognition to determine the number of different tigers that frequented the study area. The sole male tiger in the center of the park had a thick ruff of hair around his neck from about October to March but not at other times of the year.

Distribution and Status

The geographical distribution of the tiger once spanned some six thousand miles of Asia from Mount Ararat in eastern Turkey and the Caspian Sea to the Sea of Okhotsk in Russian Manchuria. In the western part of their range the animals (*P. t. virgita*) occurred in northern Afghanistan and Iran and into the U.S.S.R., their northern boundary being Lake Balkhash and the Aral and Caspian seas. Ognev (1962) documented the former distribution and recent extirpation of the Russian populations in detail. Except for an estimated 80 to 100 tigers in the Mazanderan and Bujnurd districts of northern Iran near the southeastern shore of the Caspian Sea (Perry, 1964) and for stragglers in southern Turkmenia (Novikov, 1962), this subspecies appears to be extinct.

Tigers were formerly found throughout China from the Altai Mountains and the borders of Mongolia eastward to the South and East China seas, including Hong Kong, and northward into Chinese Manchuria, but hunting and deforestation have almost eliminated the species in that country. The tiger in Chinese Turkestan (*P. t. lecoqi*) has become extinct within the past few years; the Korean subspecies exists primarily along the North Korea–China border and in the northern Yenpien area and the northeastern part of the Kirin Province of China; the last strongholds of *P. t. amoyensis* are along the Yangtze River, where scattered populations occur in the provinces of Hupei, An-hui, and Kiangsu, and also in Fukien Province opposite Taiwan (Kirk, 1966). Populations of *P. t. tigris* are found in the southern part of Yünnan Province where China, Burma, and Laos meet and along the North Vietnam–China border. The Manchurian tiger exists in small numbers in the Kirin Hills of eastern Manchuria. Although tigers were once common in neighboring Russian Manchuria from the vicinity of Lake Baikal and the Yablo-

PLATE 20.—A tigress strides across the Kanha meadow (June 21, 1964).

PLATE 21.—A tigress sprays scent against a clump of grass (March 1, 1964).

PLATE 22.—A tigress grimaces after having sniffed her own scent (March 1, 1964).

PLATE 23.—A bare spot scraped by a tiger's hindpaws with a pile of feces on it (October 11, 1964).

PLATE 24.—A large tiger cub, one year old, snarling (November 16, 1964).

PLATE 25.—Two tiger cubs, one year old, attack a tethered buffalo while the tigress (standing on the left) watches; another one of her cubs looks on alertly just before entering the melee; a fourth cub, nine months old (only head visible), belongs to a different litter (November 17, 1964).

novy Mountains to the Sea of Japan and the Island of Sakhalin in the Sea of Okhotsk, only an estimated 80 to 90 animals still survive in several isolated areas (Abramov, 1962; Anon., 1965a), primarily along some of the eastern tributaries of the Ussuri River and in the Sikhote-Alin chain of hills (Novikov, 1962).

The tiger is widely distributed throughout northern Vietnam, Laos, Thailand, Cambodia, and Burma. Locke (1954) estimated that 3,000 tigers exist in Malaya, and he noted that tracks were seen in Singapore as recently as 1950. The species failed to colonize Borneo, but it penetrated the Indonesian chain of islands as far east as Bali. Tigers remain quite common in parts of Sumatra (Anon., 1964a), but only about 9 animals survive in Java, all in the Udjong Kulon Sanctuary on the western tip of the island; and possibly 3 or 4 tigers still occur in Bali (Anon., 1964b).

The tiger is found in many parts of India, from Assam westward through Bhutan and Nepal to Himachal Pradesh and from Uttar Pradesh and Rajasthan southward over the whole peninsula, but not including the island of Ceylon. At one time the species also occurred in the Indus valley of West Pakistan, but the last animal in that region was shot in 1886 (Burton, 1952).

The wide geographical distribution of the tiger implies a great adaptability to different environmental conditions, and indeed the only requisites for its survival appear to be some form of vegetative cover, a water supply, and sufficient prey. In the western part of the range, it inhabited the marshes and reed beds of the lowlands upward through the cork and tamarisk forests to an altitude of 8,000 feet (Ognev, 1962). In China it occupied grass thickets and oak and poplar forests. Farther north in its range "pine and fir trees predominate throughout the whole taiga, but on the Manchurian side the increased number of deciduous trees is noticeable, particularly of oak trees. The slopes of hills are well-wooded with scrub-oak, birch, walnut trees, and a thick, tangled undergrowth" (Baikov, 1936). According to Ognev (1962) the cedar woods and rocky slopes at altitudes of 2,000 to 4,500 feet are particularly favored by tigers. The climate during the winter is severe in Manchuria, with snow lying several feet deep on the ground and temperatures falling as low as −30°F. In Indochina, Burma, and Indonesia the habitat consists predominantly of hot and humid rain forests but also, in Cambodia and Thailand, of grass thickets and, in northern Sumatra, of mangrove swamps.

The tiger is found in all major forest types of India — thorn, dry and moist deciduous, semi-evergreen, and evergreen. It also occurs in the mangrove swamps of the Sunderbans in West Bengal and East Pakistan, where it swims from island to island (Pocock, 1939). The animal appears to be equally at home among the tall grasses of the Kaziranga Sanctuary, a type of habitat which has now largely disappeared in India. In the Western Ghats tigers ascend to an altitude of 7,000 to 8,000 feet, where they inhabit a grassland–scrub forest mosaic (Dang, 1962). The pine and oak forests in the foothills of the Himalayas, however, are rarely visited, most tigers remaining below an altitude of 4,000 feet. On the other hand, Turner (1959), Baldwin (1877), and Hewett (1938) reported stray tigers at altitudes of 6,000 to 10,000 feet. Kinloch (1892) noted that animals may be found as high as 12,000 feet, and Gupta (1959) noted that they cross a mountain pass at 11,000 feet between Sikkim and Nepal, with a few ascending as high as 13,000 feet.

An idea of the former abundance of tigers in India and Nepal can be gained from the number of animals shot by certain individuals. Gordon-Cumming (1872) shot 73 tigers in one district along the Narmada River in 1863 and 1864, and he once shot 10 tigers in 5 days along the Tapti River; Forsyth (1911) shot 21 tigers in 31 days in Uttar Pradesh; George V and his party shot 39 tigers in 11 days in Nepal in 1911–12 (Smythies, 1942); Rice (1857) shot or wounded 158 tigers, including 31 cubs, in Rajasthan between 1850 and 1854; the Maharaja of Nepal and his guests shot 433 tigers, as well as 53 Indian rhinoceros, between 1933 and 1940 (Smythies, 1942); Colonel Nightingale shot over 300 tigers in the former Hyderabad State (Perry, 1964); the Maharaja of Udaipur shot at least 1,000 tigers during his lifetime (K. Singh, 1959); the Maharajkumar of Vijayanagaram, who is still actively hunting, has shot 323 tigers to date (letter, April 5, 1965); and the Maharaja of Surguja wrote to me in a letter dated April 6, 1965: "My total bag of Tigers is 1150 (one thousand one hundred and fifty only.)"

Although the range of the tiger has shrunk considerably with the expansion of the human population and the concomitant deforestation, the animal still occurs sparsely in most large forest tracts of India, except in the states of Gujarat, Punjab, and Kashmir. In recent years a decline in the number of tigers has been apparent in Assam (Stracey, 1961), where as late as 1940 rewards were paid for their destruction (Prater, 1940), and in peninsular India, according to most foresters and hunters with whom I talked. The forest-clad foothills of the Himalayas, for example, made famous by the tiger-hunting exploits of Corbett (1957), now contain only widely scattered animals. I found far less evidence of tigers in the form of tracks, droppings, and other spoor in Corbett Park and in the Kheri forest divisions, considered to be among the best localities for tigers in the state, than at Kanha. A total of 1,074 tigers were shot on license in government forests of the state between 1929 and 1939 (Prater, 1940), and if the number of animals shot on private lands and illegally without license were added to this figure, the actual kill would probably be twice as high. In one of the most remote areas of peninsular India, the West Bastar District of Madhya Pradesh, thirty-four hours of walking along transect lines through a three hundred square mile tract of forest revealed only two fresh sets of tracks. The tiger is also becoming scarce in the dry woodlands of eastern Rajasthan, largely because the villagers find and kill many small cubs in the heavily exploited forests (Sankhala, pers. comm.). In the Arawalli Hills, between Ajmer and Idar, the tiger population is said to have been reduced from more than 150 to perhaps 10 in recent years (Singh, 1963). As recently as May, 1964, however, a maharaja was able to shoot 6 tigers in two weeks in that state. In Kerala and Madras the tiger has become quite rare, so much so that the latter state has given protection to it. In Mysore, where tigers were once abundant and treated as vermin, with a bounty of 50 rupees paid for each animal killed (Russell, 1900), the decline in the past few years has been drastic, partly as a result of poisoning by villagers, who place insecticide into cow carcasses (Anon., 1965b).

Corbett estimated that only 2,000 tigers survived in India in the mid-1940's (Stracey, 1961). Gee (1964) recently placed their number at 4,000, a figure which, even if it were underestimated by 100 percent, indicates the need for strong conservation measures if the species is to survive in the country. Legal and illegal killing has been the major cause in the decline of tigers throughout the forested areas. Males, females, and young are destroyed indiscriminately, although many states now have regulations which prohibit the shooting of tigresses when accompanied by cubs. However, the shooting season is opened for the convenience of the hunters during the hot weather when the females are more likely to be pregnant or have small young hidden somewhere than at other times of the year.

Population Dynamics

Although there were more tigers at Kanha than in any other area of similar size that was visited, the population was too small to provide much data on its dynamics during the year of study. However, information from the literature and from zoos, as well as from my own notes, provides a general picture of some of the factors influencing tiger populations.

POPULATION SIZE AND COMPOSITION

The forest department estimates the number of tigers in Kanha Park each year by measuring the size of pug marks around water holes on a certain day in early June. The census technique is based on the assumptions that tigers drink once a day and that the pug marks of every individual are distinctive. The figures obtained by this method between 1958 and 1965 varied from 7 to 25. The pug marks of tigers are often so similar in size that the cursory measurement of one set of prints cannot be used to distinguish between animals, especially since no consideration is given to the facts that the configuration of the print varies somewhat with the substratum and that the forepaws of a tiger are larger than the hind ones. Small tiger prints can also be confused with those of leopard unless care is taken. The unreliability of this type of census was illustrated in 1964 when the tally in my study area revealed a total of 16 adult tigers and leopards when in fact it is doubtful if even half that number were there at the time.

Kanha Park lies within a forest block exceeding five hundred square miles in size. Since some tigers undoubtedly range partly in the park and partly outside of it, and since others may visit the area only as transients, it was very difficult to make a precise estimate of the number of tigers using the park. A total of 11 different tigers, excluding cubs dependent on their mothers, were seen in the study area in 1964, but of these only 4 were residents that frequented the central part of the park repeatedly. The prevalence of droppings, tracks, and other spoor indicated that more tigers used the study area than the surrounding forests, which suggested in turn that the 123 square miles of the park supported about 10 to 15 adult tigers all or part of the time. This estimate does not include an unknown number of casual visitors, dependent cubs, and animals whose range only touches the periphery of the park. Sanderson (1912) reported a total of 8 tigers — 6 males, 1 female, and 1 large cub — in an area of 200 square miles in Mysore, and Forsyth (1911) shot 21 tigers within a month in an area of similar size along the Nepal border. Locke (1954) estimated a population of 32 tigers in an area of 324 square miles in Malaya.

Of the 10 adults identified individually in the study area, 8 were females and 2 were males, a sex ratio of 4:1. Adult tigers were encountered on 121 occasions, and of these, 102 were females and 19 were males, a ratio of about 5:1. Both methods of computation reveal a great disproportion in the sexes. Although social interactions may well skew the sex ratio in a small area (see Ranges, p. 236), a preponderance of females appears to be typical of the population as a whole. Similarly, Forsyth (1889), Sanderson (1912), and Lydekker (1924) noted that tigresses are more common than male tigers, and Locke (1954), in Malaya, reported a ratio of 55 females to 45 males. Rice (1857) estimated a ratio of 2:1 in favor of females, even though he apparently encountered more male tigers than tigresses while hunting. During the fiscal year 1961–62, a total of 56 tigers were legally shot in Uttar Pradesh, of which only 16 were females (Hingorani, 1962); in 1962–63 a total of 79 were shot, of which 30 were females (D. Misra, pers. comm.). Prater (1940), who collected data on the number and sex of tigers shot by license holders in government forests throughout India in the late 1930's, found that of 575 tigers whose sex was reported to him 384 were males and only 191 were females, a ratio of 2:1. However, kill records probably do not reflect the composition of the population accurately because males wander more widely and are said to approach baits more boldly than tigresses. Of 1,791 North American pumas killed by bounty hunters, 911 were males and 880 were females, an almost equal sex ratio (Young and Goldman, 1946).

The disproportionate sex ratio of adult tigers is not apparent in the young. Rice (1857), Burton (1933), Richardson (1890), and Toogood (1936) determined the sex of a total of 25 fetuses in tigresses shot by them and found 12 males and 13 females. Of the 5 large cubs in the study area, 2 were males and 3 were females. The sex ratio of 196 cubs at birth in various zoological gardens was 100 males to 100 females (Table 47). Robinette et al. (1961) reported a sex ratio of 96 males to 100 females in 229 puma young.

Of the 8 tigresses identified during 1964, only 2 (25 percent) were known to have cubs. In addition, the tracks of another tigress with 2 small cubs were seen in December of that year. Rice (1857) and Gordon-Cumming (1872) shot a reported total of 71 tigresses, of which about one-third appeared to have been accompanied by cubs. Some litters were probably overlooked by them, but their method of hunting by using a large number of shouting villagers to drive the animals from their restricted cover assured a reasonably accurate tally. These figures indicate that a large percentage of adult tigresses

TABLE 47

LITTER SIZES AND SEX RATIOS OF TIGER CUBS BORN IN CAPTIVITY*

	LITTER SIZE			SEX RATIO		
Total Number of Litters	Number of Young in Litters	Average Number of Young in Litter	Source	Male	Female	Source
5	2–3	2.4	Delhi zoo (pers. comm.)	6	6	Delhi zoo (pers. comm.)
9	2–4	3.3	Basel zoo (pers. comm.)	21	9	Basel zoo (pers. comm.)
11**	1–4	2.9	Crandall (1964)	21	15	New York Zoological Park (pers. comm.)
15**	1–4	2.2	Lincoln Park zoo (pers. comm.)	14	13	Lincoln Park Zoo (pers. comm.)
8**	1–4	2.9	National Zoological Park (pers. comm.)	5	5	National Zoological Park (pers. comm.)
17		2.3	Zuckerman (1953)	12	14	Jarvis and Morris (1963)
8**	1–3	2.7	Sadleir (1966)	12	23	Jarvis (1965)
6	1–5	3.3	Animal Training Center (pers. comm.)	7	13	Animal Training Center (pers. comm.)
79				98	98	

* Data from several subspecies.
** All litters from same female.

do not have cubs. Similarly, only 41 percent of 299 mature female puma had young at the time of capture (Robinette *et al.*, 1961).

REPRODUCTION

Little has been published regarding the age at which tigers reach sexual maturity. One tigress in the New York zoo reached the menarche at 3 years 8 months (Crandall, 1964). One female at the Whipsnade zoo is said to have produced a litter at 2 years of age (Pocock, 1939). A tigress at the Animals Training Center produced her first litter at the age of 4 years 5 months (Baudy, pers. comm.); and another at the Basel zoo had her first litter at the age of 4 years 6 months (Lang, pers. comm.). Blanford (1888–91) gives the age of sexual maturity as 3 years, and Abramov (1962) and Novikov (1962) as 4 years. Copulation in captivity, however, sometimes begins when the animals are only 2½ years old (Baudy, pers. comm.). In captivity, female lions become cyclic at 36 months of age, according to Crandall (1964), but as early as 24 to 28 months, according to Cooper (1942). Maturity in wild lions is reached at the age of 4 years (Guggisberg, 1961); the lioness raised by Adamson (1961) in a semi-wild state conceived at the age of about 3 years 8 months.

The Felidae appear to be seasonally polyestrous in the temperate regions and completely polyestrous in the tropics (Asdell, 1964; Crandall, 1964). For precise data on the length of the estrous cycle in tigers I am indebted to E. Lang. Estrus in one tigress at the Basel zoo was observed 21 times with an average interval of 51.9 days (range 20–84 days); in another tigress it was recorded 18 times with an average interval of 54.2 days (range 27–83 days). The interval between the mid-points of 3 consecutive estrus periods in one tigress varied from 45 to 55 days, and the average length of receptivity during 14 estrus periods was 7.1 days (Sadleir, 1966). Crandall (1964) and Baudy (letter, January 21, 1966) reported that receptivity lasts about 5 days on the average.

According to Inverarity (1888), Brander (1923), and others, the tiger in India has no definite mating and birth seasons. Sanderson (1912), for example, found newborn young in March, May, October, and November, and Burton (1933) in March, April, and December. Brander (1923) noted, however, that most young are born in November and April, and Rice (1857) stated that the small young are most prevalent in late June. Mating in Indochina, as well as in southern India (Morris, 1937a), is said to be most common in November and April (Bazé, 1957), whereas in Malaya most mating occurs between November and March (Locke, 1954). The Manchurian tigers mate only from December to February (Baikov, 1936; Ognev, 1962). At Kanha certain aspects of the tiger's behavior indicated that the peak of sexual activity was from November to about February (see Vocalizations, p. 256), with some mating probably occurring throughout the year. One litter of cubs was estimated to have been born in November, the other in February. The gestation period of tigers has been variously given as 98 to 109 days (Eckstein and Zuckerman, 1956), 100 to 108 days (Crandall, 1864), and 95 to 107 days (Abramov, 1962). The two litters were, therefore, conceived in about early August and early November, respectively.

The size of litters varies from 1 to 7 (Brander, 1923). Richardson (1890) and Inverarity (1888) both found 6 embryos in a tigress, and Hewett (1938) heard of one containing 7. However, Burton (1933), Fletcher (1911), Abramov (1962), and others noted that a tigress is rarely accompanied by more than 2 to 3 cubs. Forsyth (1889) never saw more than 3 cubs with a tigress. Locke (1954) mentioned 4 tigresses each with 1 cub and 1 tigress with 2 cubs. Morris (1927) reported that one tigress was accompanied by 5 cubs, an exceptional instance. Two tigresses at Kanha had 4 cubs each and one had 2 cubs. The number of young seen with a female is of course not an accurate measure of litter size at birth. In the puma, for example, Robinette *et al.* (1961) found that the average number of young in 66 prenatal litters was 3.4 but that in 258 postnatal litters it had dropped to 2.9. The average size of 79 tiger litters born in zoos was about 2.8 (Table 47). The average of 64 lion litters in captivity was 2.5 (Cooper, 1942).

Tigers have a high reproductive potential. In zoos, where the cubs are usually removed from the mother at birth, one litter per year is common. One tigress at the New York Zoological Park, for example, had 11 litters between 1948 and 1959 (W. Conway, pers. comm.). A tigress at the London zoo had 8 pregnancies between 1961 and 1964. She gave birth to 2 cubs on January 16, 1962, to 3 cubs on August 11, 1962, and to 2 dead cubs on December 16, 1962 — 3 litters in one year. In seven instances, from 16 to 56 days (mean 28) elapsed between the removal of her young and the return of estrus (Sadleir, 1966). A free-living tigress that loses her cubs in some mishap is thus potentially able to have a new litter within about 5 months.

Estrus is in most instances held in abeyance while the tigress has her cubs. "Silver Hackle" (1929), Inglis (1892), Burton (1933), and

Brander (1923) all state that cubs are largely dependent on the female for about two years in the wild, and this was confirmed in one instance during the present study, as will be discussed fully below. It seems probable that, if the young survive, each tigress has a litter at most every two to two and a half years. If from each litter an average of two cubs reach independence, a reasonable assumption if conditions are favorable, the average number of young raised per adult tigress per year is about one. Tigresses may on rare occasions be accompanied by cubs of different ages (Brander, 1923). Stewart (1928) shot a pregnant tigress which was followed by a cub about ten months old, and Hewett (1938) heard of a tigress with unborn cubs "which had at her heels cubs of about a year old." Captive lions have been known to go into estrus while nursing young (Cooper, 1942).

The maximum longevity of tigers under zoo conditions is about 20 years, an age which is probably not exceeded in the wild. Flower (1931) and Crandall (1964) reported no tiger as having lived longer than 19 years, but recently two of them reached the age of 20 years (Anon., 1965c). If a tigress in the wild produces her first litter at the age of 4 years and raises on the average one cub per year until she dies at the age of 18, her total lifetime production is on the order of fourteen animals. This potential can, of course, be realized only under optimum circumstances, and under the conditions existing in India today, a tigress that raises even half that number before her death is doing better than average.

MORTALITY

Most tigresses at Kanha seemed to lack cubs, and only one independent young was observed in the area. This low percentage of litters in the population in spite of the high reproductive potential of females is perhaps attributable both to a failure to conceive and to high prenatal and postnatal mortality. Of 239 lion "breedings" recorded by Cooper (1942) in captivity, only 38 percent resulted in births; but the fact that males and females were permitted to remain together for only a short period may have influenced the results. In the house cat, and most likely also in the tiger, ovulation is not spontaneous but is induced by copulation (Asdell, 1946). If for some reason no fertilization occurs, the animal may become pseudopregnant; that is, it may behave as if actually pregnant, its abdomen and nipples even enlarging after ninety days, until past the expected parturition time. Such pseudopregnancies have been reported in the lion (Cooper, 1942) and tiger (Reed, pers. comm.); they may in some instances be due to a sterile male or to a lack of synchronization between the behaviorally receptive stage of the female and the physiological readiness of the ovum.

One tigress in the London zoo aborted two out of eight litters during the latter part of pregnancy, and two further litters were born dead (Sadleir, 1966). Guggisberg (1961) wrote of one lioness in the wild: "After having parted from her grown-up family in June 1957, she had cubs twice within 12 months, but on both occasions left them to perish." Captive lionesses occasionally eat their young while consuming the afterbirth (Cooper, 1942). Tigresses probably behave similarly at times.

Although tigresses give birth to 4 cubs quite commonly, they rarely are accompanied by more than 2 large ones. One tigress at Kanha raised 4 cubs successfully to an age of sixteen months, but another female lost 3 of her 4 young between the ages of one and a half and two and a half months, a 38 percent mortality in this small sample of 8 cubs during the first year of life. The cause of death of these and other cubs is in most instances unknown. One of the young when seen on April 11 was obviously weak and sickly and was barely able to keep up with its siblings. Inglis (1892) reported that a herd of domestic buffalo trampled one small cub to death. Possibly jackals and hyenas prey on newborn young when the tigress is away hunting. In times of food shortage, the weakest members of a litter probably die of starvation. And numerous young cubs undoubtedly succumb when their mother is shot.

Many authors (Rice, 1857; Forsyth, 1889; Finn, 1929; Powell, 1957; Anderson, 1961; Ognev, 1962) are of the opinion that the male tiger kills cubs whenever he encounters them, especially when they are small. Inglis (1892) heard of an instance in which a mauled cub was found at the site of a fight between a male and female, and Smeeton (1961) reported a similar fight in which two cubs were killed. Brander (1923) related that on two occasions a young male was killed by a large male at a carcass.

A difficult time in the life of cubs is the transition period from partial to complete independence, when they are abandoned for varying periods by their mother before they have learned to hunt and kill efficiently. Male cubs appear to become independent at an earlier age than female cubs and because of their inexperience are probably killed at times when attacking such prey as wild boar and gaur or when harassing livestock in the vicinity of villages. According to Sanderson (1912), a tigress with two large cubs attacked a gaur, but one young was gored in the process. The unequal sex ratio in adults favoring females can no doubt be attributed in part to differential mortality among large cubs. In the Kruger National Park, only about 50 percent of the lion cubs survive to the age of two years, according to Stevenson-Hamilton (1954), and the death rate of tiger young is probably of similar magnitude.

More adult tigers undoubtedly die as a result of having been shot, speared, snared, or poisoned by man than through any other cause. Occasionally a wild pig and a tiger fight and seriously wound each other (Inglis, 1892; Turner, 1959). Anderson (1961) found a boar and a tigress sixty yards apart, both dead after a fight; and Baldwin (1877), Shakespear (1860), and K. Singh (1959) related similar instances. Accidents in dealing with porcupines can lead to severe injury and death. Anderson (1954) came upon a dead tiger whose forelegs were badly infected and filled with long, sharp quills, and Corbett (1957) related numerous instances of tigers having been almost incapacitated by quills in their paws and faces. Locke (1954) noted that crocodiles may attack tigers.

The Indian wild dog, a canid weighing about forty-five pounds, has been known to fight with tigers and even to kill them (Burton, 1940). Connell (1944) reported an instance in which a pack of wild dogs attacked and ate a tiger, although not until the cat had managed to kill twelve of the dogs. According to Strachan (1933) a pack drove a tiger from its sambar kill. Khajuria (1963) heard a tiger and several wild dogs fighting in Kanha Park in February, 1963; later examination of the site showed that the dispute may have arisen over a dead chital doe. Anderson (1954) witnessed an encounter between a tigress and a pack of dogs:

The dogs had spread themselves around the tigress, who was growling ferociously. Every now and again one would dash in from behind to bite her. She would then turn to attempt to rend asunder this puny aggressor, when a couple of others would rush in from another direction. In this way she was kept going continually, and I could see she was fast becoming spent. . . . I heard the whistling cry of the main pack, galloping to the assistance of their advance party. The tigress must have also heard the sound, for in a sudden renewed fury, she charged two of the dogs, one of which she caught a tremendous blow on its back with her paw, cracking its spine with the sharp report of a broken twig. . . . The tigress then followed up her momentary advantage by bounding away, to be immediately followed by the five remaining dogs. They were just out of sight when the main pack streamed by, in which I counted twenty-three dogs. . . .

The dogs cornered the tigress five miles away, where she was found partially eaten the following day. Five dead dogs, some of them partly devoured, were also at the site.

Disease does not appear to be a prominent cause of death in tigers. Burton (1950) reported two cases of rabies, both animals having Negri bodies in the brain. The tick *Hyalomma kumari* Sharif, 1928, has been reported from a tiger in Assam (Kaiser and Hoogstraal, 1964), and Gee (1937) noted a tigress who was heavily infested with ticks. Two species of cestode were found in feces at Kanha — *Taenia pisiformis* Bloch, 1780, and *Diphyllobothrium erinacei* Rud., 1819; the tiger had probably become infected with the latter species by eating frogs (Belding, 1952). In addition, one specimen of *Moniezia benedeni* Moniez, 1879, a parsite of cows, was collected from a dropping beside a cow kill; the worm had apparently passed through the digestive tract of the tiger. Eleven fresh droppings were collected and checked for ova by G. Schad, the various kinds occurring with the following frequencies: *Diphyllobothrium*, 82 percent; *Paragonimus* (probably *westermani*), 55 percent; *Taenia*, 36 percent; and *Toxocara* (an ascarid) 36 percent. The oriental lung fluke, *Paragonimus westermani*, was discovered in 1877 in a tiger at the Amsterdam zoo. Man is an important definitive host of this fluke, as are cat, dog, goat, pig, opossum, and muskrat. The first intermediate host of this fluke is a snail and the second intermediate host a freshwater crab or crayfish (Belding, 1952). The tigers at Kanha probably ate infected crabs which occur in the streams there. Although no crab remains were found in the feces, Burton (1936) and Perry (1964) listed crabs as being part of the cat's diet.

Ranges

To trace the movements of a tiger in its dense forest environment is a difficult task, and most data were obtained by plotting sight records of known individuals on a map and by following tracks until they were lost. Tigers were identified individually 91 times between January 1, 1964, and January 17, 1965; on 33 other occasions during this period tigers were seen but could not be recognized either because of darkness or because it was not possible to scrutinize their faces closely enough to distinguish the individual markings. The tracks of one male tiger were so distinctive that his movements could be traced by them alone. Of eleven large tigers recognized individually, only two were seen with any regularity, two were en-

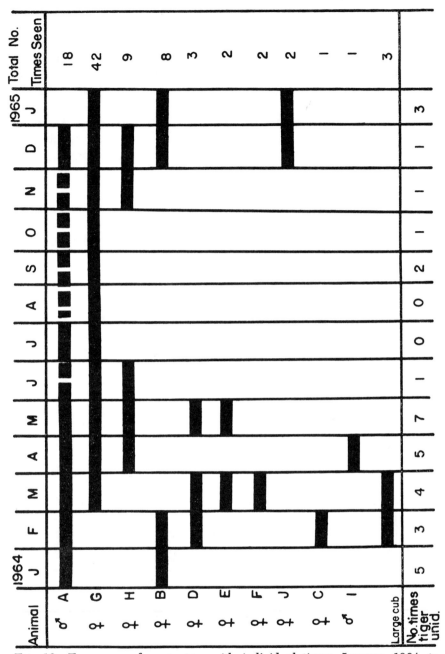

Fig. 13.—Frequency of encounters with individual tigers, January, 1964, to January, 1965. The dashed line in certain months for male A indicates that only his tracks were seen.

countered occasionally, and the others were noted one to three
times each (Fig. 13). Thus, four of the tigers were residents, using
the study area wholly or in part, and seven were transients, remaining from a few days to perhaps a month or two and then disappearing.

The two regular residents, a male and a female, ranged over almost completely overlapping areas in the Kanha valley and across a
ridge into the valley to the southwest. The total range encompassed
by the travels of the tigress during the year of observation was about

TABLE 48

SIZE OF HOME RANGES OF TIGERS

Approximate Size in Square Miles	Source	Comments
1,500	Corbett, 1957	Man-eater, India
600	Anderson, 1954	Man-eater, India
250	Anderson, 1954	Man-eater, India
100	Anderson, 1954	Man-eater, India
315	Hewett, 1938	Man-eater for eight months, India
"Not more than 150"	Locke, 1954	Man-eater for eleven months, Malaya
9+	Gilbert, 1889	Man-eater; spent most of time in area, India
200	Sanderson, 1912	Tigers in general, south India
187–250	Novikov, 1962	General winter range, Manchuria
115	Abramov, 1962	Tigress with two large cubs, Manchuria
80	Baker, 1890	Cattle-eater, India
25±	This study	Tigress with four cubs, India
25–30	This study	Male tiger, India

25 square miles; that of the male appeared to be somewhat larger,
perhaps as much as 30 square miles. A number of range sizes
have been reported in the literature (Table 48). Most of the estimates appear to be based only on rough impressions, but they indicate the general size of ranges. Over half of the records pertain to
man-eating tigers because such animals tend to draw attention to
themselves. A number of factors, including the sex of the animal, its
reproductive state, and the availability of food, undoubtedly influence range size. For comparison, a pride of lions consisting of one
female with three cubs used 8 square miles in the Nairobi National
Park, Kenya; another pride containing two lionesses and eight cubs
in the same sanctuary frequented 13 square miles; and two males
there ranged over 54 square miles of terrain (Guggisberg, 1961).

The number of different tigers that frequented the study area either as residents or transients indicated that ranges were not exclusively occupied by one individual. Three adults were together on one occasion, and two adults of the same or opposite sex were encountered a number of times (see Table 49). In addition, two tigers sometimes called near each other, and tracks showed that the animals used the same area at night. The ranges appeared at first glance to be communal, with no effort made on the part of one ani-

TABLE 49

THE COMPOSITION OF LARGE TIGER GROUPS

Male	Female	Young	Total	Source	Comment
1	1	2	4	Aramilev, 1959	Manchuria; on deer carcass
1	1	2	4	Bazé, 1957	Indochina
2	2		4	Bazé, 1957	Indochina
2	2	3	7	Bazé, 1957	Indochina; in adjoining caves
1	1	4	6	Smythies, 1942	Nepal; driven out during hunt
1	1	2	4	Smythies, 1942	Nepal; driven out during hunt
1	2	3	6	Brander, 1923	India; on deer carcass
5	1		6	Powell, 1957	India; driven out during hunt
1	1	2	4	Anderson, 1961	India
2	2	3	7	N. Negi (pers. comm.)	India; seen several times on buffalo kill, Corbett Park, 1963
2	3	4	9	Journal of the Bombay Natural History Society, 1948	India; together in same ravine (count perhaps one too many)
1	2	4	7	This study	Seen once around kill
1	1	4	6	This study	Seen three times on kill
	2	4	6	This study	Seen three times on kill; once while walking together

mal to prevent another from hunting there. Of the ten adult tigers identified, however, only two were males, one of them a transient seen only once in company with the resident male. No other adult males were seen in the study area. On the other hand, three tigresses used the same range, and five others passed through as transients. An unequal sex ratio favoring females probably cannot explain the fact that only one male frequented the whole central part of Kanha Park; instead, it is likely that his range was a selectively defended territory, shared freely with females but not with other males. Locke (1954) noted that a male tiger resists "any attempt on the part of another tiger to poach upon his reserve," and according to Berg

(1936), a male drives another male from his territory but tolerates transients.

The territories of some mammals are so large that they cannot be surveyed readily by the owner, as Leyhausen (1965a) has pointed out, and this seems to be particularly true in the case of the tiger. Strangers cannot, therefore, be prevented from entering the area, because a defense of all boundaries is impossible except by such indirect means as marking with scent. As a result, the presumed territorial system of male tigers appears to be less rigid than that, for example, of many antelopes and birds. Two adult males have often been reported to frequent the same general range and even to associate amicably at a kill. Brander (1923) once saw three males together, and Bazé (1957) shot two males on a small river island. Two males accompanied by one or more females have been reported on several occasions (see Table 49). It is possible that territorial behavior may be modified under certain environmental conditions, such as a shortage of water or cover. Thakur told me of encountering three males and one female in an area of six square miles of grass and brush surrounded by an extensive burn. In the heavily populated parts of Indochina, the tigers retreat to the isolated rocky hills, where a number of animals may occupy adjoining caves (Bazé, 1957). When several males are found in a limited area, some are undoubtedly transients which remain only for brief periods; others perhaps share the same range after establishing a rank order. Such sharing of ranges appears to be prevalent in the lion (Guggisberg, 1961). In the house cat, Leyhausen (1965a) found that males are very tolerant toward trespassers into their range. When meeting for the first time, they may fight fiercely until a rank order is established, but thereafter they avoid fights either by displays or by keeping out of each other's way.

A female in estrus travels widely and is sometimes followed by several males. Powell (1957) once found five males and one female in the same area, and Ognev (1962) reported as many as six males together. Such aggregations probably include a resident male, transient males, and a number of males from adjoining ranges through which the tigress has passed. Similar behavior has been reported in the puma, among which as many as four to five males may follow a female in heat (Young and Goldman, 1946), and in the jaguar, among which "during the love season the males congregate, eight or sometimes more together" (Azara, 1838, quoted in Wynne-Edwards, 1962).

There was no evidence of territorial behavior in tigresses at Kanha, and they readily shared their range with each other and with the male. Some self-limiting trend, however, appeared to be operating in the tiger population on a local level, perhaps based on intraspecific intolerance when meeting or sharing a kill and, more subtly, on various visual and olfactory signals left in the environment. During the hot season, when the wild ungulates concentrated around the water holes, leaving the hills almost deserted, the number of resident tigers in the study area did not increase (Fig. 13). As many different tigers were seen in December, when the wildlife was scattered, as during May, when it was concentrated. Most transient tigresses moved through the study area during the cool and hot seasons (activity which appeared to be in part correlated with estrus), but in spite of an abundant food supply, they failed to remain there. Tigers moved little during the monsoon.

The land tenure system of the tiger appears to be in some respects similar to that of the lion, as described by Guggisberg (1961): "For the lioness, the territory means simply a hunting ground, while for the lion it is a region containing a certain number of lionesses which from time to time are ready to mate with him. The territory of a lion can therefore encompass the hunting grounds of various family and single lionesses. . . ."

The male tiger at Kanha retained the same range for at least twelve months, and the evidence from the literature indicates that some animales may stay in a particular locality for several years. "When a tiger becomes old and fat he usually settles down in some locality where beef and water are plentiful, and here he lives on amicable terms with the villagers, killing a cow or bullock about once in four or five days" (Sanderson, 1912). Berg (1936) photographed a male and a female in the same area one year apart, and Smythies (1942) reported a tiger and a tigress that had supposedly lived together for seven years. Baker (1890) noted that a male stayed for fourteen years in a particular locality, killing five hundred cattle in that time; Brander (1923) stated that one tiger remained fifteen years near some villages; and Sanderson (1912) claimed that one tiger was a cattle-killer for twenty years. Although these lengths of time may well be highly exaggerated, the reports attest to a probable long occupancy in one locality.

One tigress with four cubs at Kanha inhabited the study area from March, 1964, to at least March, 1965, a period of thirteen months.

Since I did not see her until March, even though she was a highly distinctive animal, it is likely that she either moved into the area at that time or switched the center of her activity to a part of her range not used extensively before.

In addition to the resident tigers, there is a segment of the population that seems to lack established ranges. Berg (1936), Blanford (1888–91), and others have commented on the fact that if a tiger is shot in a certain locality another tiger may soon occupy it. Wanderers are sometimes encountered far from their usual haunts. One animal traveled fifty to sixty miles over cultivation (Burton, 1933) and a tigress appeared two hundred miles from the nearest known habitat (Perry, 1964). Some of the unestablished animals are probably young adults which, having reached maturity, are moving away from the area of their birth into unoccupied terrain. Others may be adults unable to establish a range in the limited habitat available to them. And still others are tigresses in heat which probably have left an established range somewhere to roam widely. Several of the transients at Kanha fell into the last category, the shyness of some of them indicating that they probably came from outside of the park. Thus tigers exhibit a wide variety of land tenure patterns — from exclusive use of an area that seems to be defended against others, to peaceful sharing of ranges, to lack of established ranges — depending on the sex, physiological condition, and perhaps individual inclination of the animals involved.

A tiger appears to have a center of activity within its range where it spends much of its time. One tigress with cubs concentrated her activity in about seven to eight square miles around the Kanha meadow. The male tiger favored a mosaic of forest, ravines, and small meadows about two miles northeast of the Kanha meadow. The two other resident tigresses apparently centered their activity outside of the main study area. Corbett (1957) described the life of one tiger which had his home base in a hollow tree, and Bazé (1957) found that the tiger "is very strongly attached to his permanent quarters and uses them as his base for his foraging expeditions." Jerdon (1874) noted that the tiger returns to the same lair at dawn. These and other observations indicate that in some areas a tiger appears to have a more or less permanent abode to which it returns each day. In forests with scanty undergrowth, localized water supplies, and heavy disturbance by man and livestock, it seems probable that the tiger retreats daily into one of several pieces of preferred cover. At Kanha, however, where shade, water, and other requirements are widespread, the tigers have no predilection for certain lairs, a finding which is similar to that of Locke (1954) in Malaya.

Social Organization and Interactions between Adults

The tiger is usually pictured as an unsociable beast living a solitary life in its jungle realm. The well-known Chinese proverb "one hill cannot shelter two tigers" appears to have been taken literally. Inglis (1892), for example, wrote: "In their habits they are very unsociable, and are only seen together during the amatory season. When that is over the male betakes himself again to his solitary predatory life. . . . Pairs have often been shot in the same jungle, but seldom in close proximity, and it accords with all experience that they betray an aversion to each other's society. . . ." In Malaya, Locke (1954) noted "that a male does not appear to resent the presence of a tigress in his area, especially if she has young with her, but they do not consort or share kills. . . ." Scattered throughout the literature, however, are observations which contradict the idea that the tiger is always unsociable. Forsyth (1889) stated that "I have twice known five, and once, seven, tigers to be driven out of one cover." A male and two females have often been seen together (Brander, 1923), and Sanderson (1912) once observed two females and a male on a kill brought down by the latter animal. Hewett (1938) noted that "a family will be met of father, mother and two or three cubs, sometimes nearly as large as the mother before they leave her." According to Berg (1936), "One often meets tiger and tigress in company; they kill and eat an animal together and camp a few days near each other. But they soon part again."

The social interactions of adult tigers can best be understood when considered separately in the contexts of hunting, mating, and feeding at a kill. In 82 encounters with tigers either hunting or just walking along, two adults were together in only two instances; the others were solitary animals or tigresses accompanied by one or more young. On one of these occasions two tigresses, one of them with cubs, crossed the Kanha meadow, and on the other the resident male and a transient male strode along at the rate of about 3.5 miles per hour parallel to each other, the intruder emitting a series of rasping grunts. Hunting in tigers is essentially a solitary activity — in contrast to the communal hunting and stalking sometimes practiced by lions (Guggisberg, 1961). Brander (1923) maintained that he once saw two adults hunting in company; Bazé (1957) watched a male tiger and a tigress stalk deer in Indochina; and Baikov (1936) implied that in Manchuria two tigers frequently hunt together. Two or more tigers are also said to stalk pigs communally (Ognev, 1962). But the evidence for this type of hunting is meager.

Since several tigers may hunt through the same general range, meetings between individuals are probably quite common. Baikov (1936), for example, watched a male and a female arrive from different directions at a river bed, join, and then move away together. Most such meetings are undoubtedly brief and casual, with the animals soon drifting apart to continue their solitary hunts.

Tigers associate, of course, when mating. Blanford (1888–91) and Fletcher (1911), among others, maintained that the tiger is monogamous, but this conclusion is contradicted not only by the frequency with which one male and two females are seen together (Table 49) but also by the land tenure system in which several females may occupy the same range as a male. The male undoubtedly mates with whatever estrous females, resident or transient, are found within his range. Sometimes several males are attracted by the calls and scent trails of an estrous tigress (see Communication, p. 251); fighting between the males on such occasions is the frequent outcome. "I have spent many nights in the taiga alone with my fellow hunters, sitting by the fire and listening to tigers challenging their rivals — resounding through the frost-bound forests; but though the battle ground is invariably drenched with blood, such encounters never end in death" (Baikov, 1925). Forsyth (1889) reported similar behavior, and Hanley (1961) gave an eye witness account of a fight between three males over a female which has the ring of authenticity.

Tigers appear to socialize more at kills than on any other occasion. It is significant that most of the large groups reported in the literature and observed during the study were at kills. I spent a total of 11 nights in observing tigers at a kill in 1964, and more than one adult was present on 7 of these; on the other hand, in March, 1965, when eleven head of livestock were fed to tigers in one locality over a period of two weeks, only one tigress with four large cubs was seen. Strachan (1933) has published a detailed description of the behavior of two adults at a kill:

Now he turned and walked slowly in the direction of the tigress. . . . She was still lying in the same position, and at first took no notice of his approach, but as he drew nearer she turned to face him, then crouched as if to spring. The male strode slowly as if in studied indifference to her presence, while the body of his spouse seemed to sink gradually into the ground as she flattened herself as a cat does on the near approach of its prey.

With blazing eyes, ears laid back, and twitching tail, her attitude for the moment was anything but that of the loving wife. Waiting till the tiger was within a few paces, she sprang towards him as if bent on his annihilation, lifted a fore-paw, and gently patted him on the side of his face. Then she raised her head and obviously kissed him.

To these symptoms of affection the male at first seemed rather indifferent, but when she rubbed herself against his legs and playfully bit them, he condescendingly lay down, and a mock battle ensued between the two beautiful animals. This was conducted in absolute silence, save for the occasional soft "click" of teeth meeting when the widely opened jaws came in contact with each other.

Sometimes locked in a close embrace, playfully kicking each other with their hind-feet, sometimes daintily sparring with their fore-paws, they rolled about thus for nearly a quarter of an hour. . . .

Then the male was shot.

I observed the interactions between adults at a kill on six occasions, and three of these are described below as examples:

1) At 0350 hours on December 7 our servant wakened me, saying that a tiger was in our shed behind the house. We found that a tigress had clawed a hole 22 x 13 inches in size through the woven bamboo wall, killed a buffalo, and, unable to haul it away, had taken a sheep and disappeared. We dragged the buffalo 900 feet away and tied it to a tree at 0630 hours. Langurs and chital barked intermittently all day indicating that the tigress was in the vicinity.

At 1810 hours the tigress — the mother of 4 large cubs — suddenly appears and begins to eat at the rump. Five seconds later the male cub approaches, but he walks away without feeding when his mother growls. After devouring meat steadily for 65 minutes, she leaves the kill and, as she meanders nearby from 1920 to 2035 hours, roars a total of 266 times, sometimes loudly, at other times softly. At 2040 hours 4 tigers advance down the road toward the kill — the 3 female cubs trotting ahead, and the tigress walking behind. While the 3 cubs eat, the tigress disappears from sight. They feed intensively for 15 minutes, the only interactions being a sharp cough by one cub, which causes the threatened animal to jerk back, and a snarl by another cub when crowded too closely by a sibling. The male cub returns at 2055 hours, as does the female. All cubs eat steadily until 2150 hours, when 2 of them lie down and rest. The tigress then begins to eat but stops 5 minutes later. Between 2200 and 2250 hours at least one cub is at the kill. The others rest, wander around, and lick themselves; one cub reaches up on a tree trunk and rakes the claws of its left forepaw about 6 inches down the bark, then does the same with the right paw. The tigress feeds between 2305 and 2325 hours; when she stops the kill is unattended for the first time since 2040 hours. Five minutes later, however, she and one cub return to the carcass. The cub rubs its head against hers and then paws the ground 4 times with its left foreleg. Intermittent feeding continues until 2400 hours. One cub coughs, then growls at another cub, but otherwise the animals are silent for 2 hours. I think the tigress left the vicinity of the kill.

At 0210 hours another tigress—the mother of one large cub—appears alone by the kill. She growls loudly as she approaches and slaps at the male cub with a forepaw as he appears from the grass. One female cub feeds with her for about 5 minutes, but after that she remains alone at the carcass until 0300 hours. After she moves from sight, a cub snacks occasionally. She returns at 0430 hours and eats alone until 0520 hours, growling loudly several times. Suddenly she emits deep, rolling growls as the mother of the 4 cubs comes into sight and then rushes for 30 feet toward her. The tigresses face each other at 10 feet, growling harshly and swiping a forepaw in the air. The intruding female retreats even though she is the larger of the two and, at 0535, roars twice as she departs, leaving the female with the 4 cubs in possession of the kill.

The cubs then feed intermittently. One rips off a foreleg and carries it into the high grass of a shallow ravine nearby. The female scratches dirt over the kill, making a total of 19 sweeps with a paw. All cubs approach her, and two of them rub themselves against her at the same time. When she squats to urinate, a cub sits down beside her and places the top of its head against her chin. At 0625 hours all but one cub loll around. The female returns to the carcass, pulls off a scapula and, after gnawing on that for awhile, tears off a piece of meat. At 0720 hours she jerks the head loose and carries it into the high grass, followed closely by her cubs. She drops it, returns to the kill site, and chews briefly on 2 leg bones. Two cubs lie in the sun; they touch noses, then disappear in the grass. All are out of sight at 0745 hours.

The remaining edible portions of the buffalo were eaten during the night. The tigers lingered in the high grass nearby during the day but moved away the following evening.

2) I tied a buffalo to a stump at 1630 hours and waited in a blind 80 feet away. At 1940 hours a tigress attacked the animal, which died 8 minutes later, as described in detail below (see Killing techniques, p. 289).

The tigress pulls on the rump of the carcass for 5 minutes in an attempt to drag it away. Finally she lies down and cuts the skin and meat on the hindquarters with her carnassial teeth, pulling pieces of it loose on occasion. At 2020 hours she leaves, apparently to fetch her 4 cubs.

Barasingha and chital bark vigorously in the distance at 2155 hours, and 15 minutes later I first hear, then see, the large cubs, which are 9 months old, rushing down the slope to pounce on the kill. The largest of the cubs, a male, begins to eat immediately at the rump, and another cub starts at the neck: but when a third cub tries to crowd in, the male cub jerks up his head and emits a coughing roar, which causes the other cubs to jump back. Five minutes after the cubs arrive at the kill, the tigress appears and right behind her is the male tiger. Three cubs bound 50 feet toward her and rub their heads and necks against her face and throat.

Before the female had returned, at 2105 hours, a tiger roared in the direction opposite to the one she had taken, and it is likely that the male met the female on the road near the kill where they socialized while the cubs went ahead to eat.

Three cubs are at the kill, the male cub at the rump and two others at the neck; the smallest cub is with the adults 70 feet away. One cub coughs and rears up on its hindlegs, slapping with a forepaw at another, which responds in similar fashion. The smallest cub approaches the kill, rests 15 minutes beside it without eating, and then rejoins the adults. The male rises at 2250 hours and walks to the kill. Two cubs nuzzle his face and neck. He circles the kill, grunting repeatedly, a sound similar to the one emitted by females when inducing small cubs to follow. One cub trails behind the male. He lies down 30 feet from the kill, and a cub rubs its body against his.

All 4 cubs feed at 2310 hours while the female lies on her back; all 4 feet held limply in the air. She then eats for 5 minutes — the first time since her return to the kill at 2210 hours. One cub lunges forward with an explosive "wow" and slaps another on the head with a forepaw. The tigress commences to eat again at 2405 hours; once she growls loudly at a cub beside her. The male tiger walks to the kill, picks it up by the neck, drops it, and returns to his resting spot. The cubs continue to feed intermittently, from 1 to 4 of them being at the kill at the same time. The tigress leaves the carcass at 2425 and approaches the male with a series of rasping grunts. She licks her chest and forelegs, then lies down beside him and licks her paws. A cub also reclines nearby and cleans its paws. Ten minutes later the tigress descends into a ravine, followed by 3 cubs. The fourth and smallest cub rubs its face against the neck of the male, and both go to the kill and eat, the first time since the male's arrival 2½ hours earlier that he has taken a bite.

By 2440 hours the female and cubs rest out of sight in some tall grass while the male tears at the meat alone until 0110 hours. As soon as he ceases to feed, the tigress and cubs return and eat intermittently until 0210 hours.

All animals rest between 0210 and 0455 hours. Once the male tries to drag the remains away, and when he stops, the tigress gives the carcass several violent jerks. Having no more success than the male, she turns around and scratches earth and grass over it with 17 sweeps of a forepaw. She pulls on the remains again, then scratches 8 more times with one paw and 5 times with another. When the female leaves, the male tears off a foreleg and hauls it out of sight into the high grass, followed by 2 cubs. The *tigress subsequently pulls out a lung and, after trying to cover the kill with 4 swipes of a paw, returns into the high grass at 0535 hours.*

The tigress returns to the kill at 0535 hours with 3 cubs. She paws dirt on it 10 times, then pulls at the meat, thereby undoing whatever progress she has made in covering the remains; she paws 8 times more, goes to the other side and paws a final 5 times. A cub stands parallel to her and also takes a sweep with its paw. Rain pours down at 0550 hours. At 0755 hours the tigress rips a piece of rib cage off and carries it into the high grass where her cubs stand waiting.

No tigers feed between 0800 and 1825 hours.

At 1825 hours the tigress returns to the remains, consisting now solely of the head, some vertebrae, and a piece of skin, the other bones having been scattered the previous night. She tears off a piece of skin and leaves. A cub walks by and picks up a piece of bone and at 1910 hours another piece; at 1925 hours a cub chews on the head. The male jerks on the remains at 2010 hours and, when the rope with which the head is tied suddenly snaps, tumbles backward and flees, leaving the head behind. Five minutes later the tigress picks it up. The tigers are occasionally visible during the night as they wander around. At 0520 hours the tigress and one cub check the kill site for any remaining scraps. As one cub enters the undergrowth, another pounces playfully toward it, the first cub jumping aside with a growl. Ten minutes later several soft grunts are audible in the distance. Apparently the male tiger is leaving the site alone. The tigress and her cubs remain nearby until about 1845 hours, when the tigress leaves alone.

3) *At about 1730 hours on April 26, a tigress killed a domestic bull in a ravine. When a villager approached the site, having heard the bellows of the dying animal, the tigress charged at him in bluff. Tourists watched the kill from a car until about midnight. After their departure, the tigress apparently brought her 4 cubs to eat. I began observations the following morning, sitting hidden in the branches of a solitary tree along the bank of the ravine 120 feet from the kill.*

The female walks back and forth among the reeds at 0510 hours. She paws the vegetation 5 times with a foreleg, then urinates. After walking 60 feet to the carcass of the bull, which lies partly submerged in the creek, the five-month-old cubs join her. They lie around, then at 0540 hours file up a slope and disappear in a patch of high grass. A few minutes later, 5 tourists casually approach the kill on foot, but when the tigress steps out of the reeds and heads slowly in the direction taken by the cubs, they flee. The tigress stops, looks after the retreating forms, circles around in the grass near her cubs as if undecided about her course of action, and finally moves off at 0615 hours without taking her young. Although numerous vultures are at the kill site all day, the tigress does not return.

Between 2000 and 2020 hours chital barked at 3 different localities on

*the meadow, and examination of tracks on the roads the following morning
suggested that 2 tigresses and a male tiger arrived at the kill from different
directions. From the small amount of the carcass eaten, it is likely that only
the tigress and her cubs were present the previous night. The other tigers
may have been attracted to the site by the behavior of the vultures.*

*At 2025 hours a tigress walks into the stream, another tigress at her heels.
One emits a series of soft grunts. The first tigress picks the bull up by the
neck and drags the carcass out of sight into some high reeds. The second
tigress watches. Both feed until 2110 hours without a sound except for the
cutting of meat and the crunch of bones. One tigress then walks steadily
away, roaring a total of 49 times until the call is barely discernible in the
distance. I fail to note the time of arrival of the male, but at 2200 hours he
and the tigress circle the kill. She angles up the slope, stands still, and calls
softly bru-u-u-u, before turning abruptly and descending to the carcass.
Two minutes later her 4 cubs follow in single file, the tigress' call apparently having been the signal to which they responded.*

*At 2230 hours stinging ants invade the tree in which I am sitting, forcing
my retreat.*

*All tigers are resting when I return at 0455 hours. At 0530 hours a tigress
with 4 cubs leaves. Last in line is another tigress, probably the same one
that was seen the previous evening. There is no sign of the male tiger.
While the tigress with the 4 cubs moves from sight, the other female lags
behind, stops, walks a few steps, stops again, and then turns and trots back
toward the kill now covered with vultures and crows. Suddenly she charges
ahead and with a roaring "woo" rushes among the flushing birds. Finally
she leaves the area at a fast walk in the direction taken by the others.*

These observations, as well as two instances described below
(see Behavior of Female and Young, p. 264), indicate that the responses between individuals vary. Only three different adults—a
male and two females—were known to have been involved in the
encounters. The meetings between the tigress with four cubs and
the male tiger were friendly, with no growling, coughing, or other
overt aggressiveness. On the other hand, the meetings between
the two tigresses were often marked by various forms of agonistic
behavior, and the whole demeanor of the animals attested to the
fact that they were tense in each other's presence.

A rank order based on size would place the male at the top, the
tigress with one cub in the middle, and the tigress with four cubs at
the bottom. On one occasion, the smaller female rolled on her back
in a submissive gresture when attacked by the larger one, an action
which would seem to verify her subordinate position. However, at a
kill, the larger and hence stronger of two adult tigers did not necessarily appropriate the best feeding spot or, if the meat supply was

limited, the carcass as a whole. Once the male tiger waited two and
a half hours at a kill until the tigress and cubs had eaten before he
proceeded to feed; on another occasion the male did not feed at
all when he met the same tigress and her cubs at a kill although
he had obviously not eaten much the previous night. Bazé (1957)
saw a female eat on a freshly killed deer while the male sat nearby
"awaiting his turn." In every instance observed, the female with
four cubs ate more and stayed with the remains longer than the female with one cub, even though the latter was larger. During two
nights, for example, the two tigresses ate for the following number
of minutes on a buffalo carcass: during the first night, the female
with four cubs ate 180 minutes and the female with one cub 55;
during the second night, the former ate 191 minutes and the latter
90. It is significant that whenever two or more adults were observed
at a carcass, the small tigress with four cubs had actually done the
killing. This suggests that a tiger had priority rights to its own meat
supply even in the presence of a larger and stronger animal.

Large social groupings may also occur for no apparent reason. A
group of 9 tigers was reported by the editors of the Journal of the
Bombay Natural History Society (1948) in Madras (see Table 49),
and when 3 of these were shot, the others partially ate 2 of them.
One hunter shot 5 tigers within one hour in Assam "and estimated
that perhaps ten more were collected in the same place" (Perry,
1964), the largest aggregation on record. In the house cat "males
and females come to a meeting place adjacent to or situated within
the fringe of their territories and just sit around," according to Leyhausen (1965a). Possibly tigers behave similarly on occasion.

The main point that should emerge from this description of the
tiger's social organization is that, although the cat is essentially solitary, it is not unsociable. Adults readily join for brief periods, particularly at a plentiful food supply, but their association rarely persists long. Solitary mammals, as Leyhausen (1965a) has stressed,
have a communal organization, just as those that normally live in
groups. The resident tigers at Kanha shared a range with its associated network of trails, and they probably knew each other individually by sound and smell in addition to sight. They lived a
solitary existence, but they seemed to be quite aware of each other's
doings, as suggested by the frequency with which they suddenly
appeared to share a kill.

The basically solitary habits of the tiger are shared by most members of the Felidae, one conspicuous exception being the lion.

Groups of lions may number up to 30 animals (Wright, 1960). For example, three large groups tallied by Adamson (1964) in the Serengeti Plains of Tanzania were composed of 2 males, 5 females, and 16 young, a total of 23; 1 male, 5 females, and 15 young, a total of 21; and 3 males, 6 females, and 10 young, a total of 19.

It may be conjectured that the solitary habits of the tiger are an adaptation to the average size and availability of its prey. Much of the tiger's food consists of relatively small mammals such as pigs and deer, which, if shared with several other adults, would not provide enough meat for them all. The prey is usually scattered and time-consuming to find and stalk in the forests. Under such conditions, a solitary search for prey is probably more efficient than a communal hunt. Once the tiger has killed, it can readily hide any remains in the undergrowth and rest in the vicinity, for several days if necessary, until all the meat has been devoured. The lion, on the other hand, inhabits relatively open habitats for the most part, where prey tends to be concentrated in herds and easily visible. Zebra, wildebeest, and other large mammals constitute a substantial percentage of the lion's prey in East Africa (Wright, 1960; Talbot and Talbot, 1963). Scavengers are numerous, and the open terrain may make it difficult to hide and protect excess meat from them. "In general, it can be said that on the open veld prides tend to be considerably larger than in dense bush. The largest prides are naturally found in regions where game is plentiful" (Guggisberg, 1961).

Communication

Tigers use a number of different sounds, postures, and gestures to communicate with each other when they are together. In addition, because of their nocturnal and solitary habits, they require other means of communication which will enable them to find and keep in contact with each other as they roam across their large communal range. Most of this section is devoted to long-distance signaling. Facial expressions and other gestures have been treated extensively by Leyhausen (1960) in his monograph on the behavior of captive cats, and his work provides many details lacking in my observations on free-living animals.

SCENT AND VISUAL SIGNALS

Male and female tigers mark their range primarily by spraying scent, as pointed out by Locke (1954), and by making their feces conspicuous. As a tiger walks along, it pauses at intervals, swivels its hindquarters around to face some object like a tree or bush, and, with slightly elevated rump and almost vertically raised tail, squirts a single jet of fluid (Plate 21). This liquid shoots upward at an angle of about thirty degrees, hitting the vegetation three to four feet above ground. Tigresses eject a rather wide spray, male tigers a narrow stream. On two occasions a tiger stopped and sniffed the scent, grimacing afterward with nose wrinkled and tongue hanging out (Plate 22), a gesture described as *flehmen* by Leyhausen (1950). It was twice possible to examine the fluid closely after a tigress had sprayed some leaves. Much of it consisted of a clear, pale yellow liquid, apparently urine. Several clumps of a granular, whitish precipitate were in it. Observations of a scent-marking male showed that the fluid was ejected caudally from the penis. Tiger urine by itself, however, did not have a particularly strong odor, whereas this fluid smelled very musky, readily discernible to the human nose at a distance of ten to fifteen feet. The white precipitate was apparently a secretion from the anal glands, which are also found in the house cat. The scent adhered to the vegetation for a long time. One tuft of grass still smelled pungent to me after one week; on tree trunks the scent persisted for three to four weeks, except when it rained heavily; and in one instance I detected the odor on the bark of a sal tree for three months.

Tigers squirted scent at all times of the year. Sometimes a cat walked along for half a mile without scent-marking, but at other times it would do so repeatedly, particularly at points where it changed its direction of travel. One tigress, for example, walked down a forest road for 600 feet and sprayed a tree once, leaving a wet spot six inches in diameter; when she turned off the road into the forest, she squirted another tree and 200 feet farther on a third one. Another tigress sprayed scent on one post and three tufts of grass as she ambled .4 mile along a road. In yet another instance a tigress squirted once, then kicked each hindpaw backward as if scraping soil; after 50 feet she sprayed again, then squatted to urinate. Scent-marking followed by urinating was also seen on two other occasions.

One tigress, apparently in estrus when encountered on February 6, sprayed scent along her route of travel repeatedly. Several barasingha barked at 1620 hours and watched her cross the meadow. She walked slowly, stopped to look at the deer, then emitted a muffled roar. She meandered among some trees, roaring — almost groaning — several times. After passing my car at a distance of 70 feet, she sniffed the trunk of a tree, looked up the bole of another tree, and then continued on. Her eyes were glazed; she seemed to be "in a kind of dazed ecstatic trance," as Allen (1960) termed it. Twice within 100 feet she squirted scent against trees. She entered a patch of grass, and I moved to where I expected her to reappear. She stepped into the open 50 feet from the car, rubbed her body with a sinuous movement along a bush, and deposited scent on the leaves. She sniffed it, grimaced, and at 1700 hours walked from sight, moaning once.

Male and female house cats also mark their range with scent (Leyhausen, 1965a), as do lions, according to the description for a tame lioness by Adamson (1960): "Elsa was now eighteen months old and I noticed, for the first time, that she had, temporarily as it proved, developed a strong smell. She had two glands, known as the anal glands, under the root of her tail; these exuded a strong-smelling secretion which she ejected with her urine against certain trees, and although it was her own smell she always pulled up her nose in disgust at it."

The scent serves a number of possible functions: (1) it could enable tigers to follow each other in the forest, using the odor as trail markers; (2) it could delineate the extent of the range, indicating to others that the terrain is occupied, which may attract or repel the visitor according to the circumstances; (3) and it could communicate specific information to others using the range, such as the identity of the individual, the amount of time that has elapsed since it passed, and, in the case of a tigress, whether or not she is in heat. Leyhausen and Wolff (1959) suggested that olfactory markings also help to prevent encounters, functioning somewhat like railway signals: "Fresh mark = section closed, going on implies the danger of a hostile encounter. Less fresh mark = proceed with caution. Old mark = go ahead. The individual, before passing such a mark, regularly covers it with its own thus 'closing the section.'"

The tiger makes no attempt to cover its feces, in contrast to the house cat, and the compact pieces of hair, bone splinters, and other items remain clearly visible. Although a tiger may defecate anywhere, it has a distinct preference for the central grassy strip of the forest roads or the grass immediately bordering them; the hard-packed bare soil of the road is rarely used.

During the first half of the year, when the soil was hard and dry, I noted that there were occasional claw marks around the feces, but

I paid these scant attention. With the onset of the monsoon, when the ground became soft, the scratch marks were suddenly conspicuous. The grass was often torn away, leaving a bare spot consisting of two parallel grooves 12 to 18 inches long, each as wide or slightly wider than a tiger's paw (Plate 23). Frequently the animal urinated rather than defecated on the scratch marks, and occasionally it did neither. One tigress, for example, made five scrapes in three miles of travel without depositing anything on them. When making a scrape, the tiger scratches the soil some two to twenty times with the unsheathed claws of its hindpaws, moving its legs alternately backward, and then either walks away or squats to defecate or urinate. The amount of feces on a scrape is often quite small when compared with the size of a normal bowel movement, giving the impression that the animal has squeezed out a small token to mark the site.

Concentrations of scrapes occurred in certain parts of the range in contrast to others that were not heavily used. One forest road, frequented by at least three adults, was a favored site, as was the top of a ridge where the road dropped into the valley to the south. Watershed divides are also preferred by the puma for depositing its feces, according to Young and Goldman (1946). The feces are covered with soil, making mounds three to five inches high. The number of mounds in a small area may total a dozen in eight square feet.

Scrapes are associated with feces primarily during the damp or wet time of the year, and their frequency declines as the ground dries: between June 21 and October 31, 89 feces were found (100 percent with scrape); between November 1 and 30, 40 feces (85 percent with scrape); and between December 1 and 31, 70 feces (63 percent with scrape). Dung beetles remove the feces or cover them with soil within a few hours after deposit during the monsoon, but the scrape remains as a conspicuous signal on the wet ground. During the dry season, on the other hand, when the beetles are not active, the feces remain visible for several months, and the scrapes, if any, are barely discernible in the dry soil. The feces and scrapes both appear to have communicatory functions, the former providing visual and olfactory cues to other tigers and the latter only visual ones. But the two systems of marking complement rather than duplicate each other, the prominence of each depending on the season.

Scraping and spraying with scent are sometimes used in conjunction, each pattern supplementing and reinforcing the other. For example, a male tiger walked one mile down a road in thirty minutes, ignoring the car which followed him at a distance of 150 to 300 feet, and repeatedly marked the edge of the forest track:

Time	Behavior
1630 hours	Returns to road after having been discovered by us hiding beneath a clump of bamboo.
1632	Squirts scent.
1635	Scratches with his hindpaws 14 times, then urinates.
1636	Sniffs the ground and grimaces with tongue hanging out.
1641–42	Walks slowly as he watches 2 gaur standing 250 feet away in the forest.
1645	Squirts scent.
1647	Squirts scent.
1648	Squirts scent, then scratches ground once with each hindpaw.
1649	Squirts scent.
1651	Squirts scent, then scratches twice with each hindpaw.
1652	Scratches about 12 times, then defecates a small amount of soil and a number of tapeworm segments.
1653	Squirts scent.
1654	Leaves the road and, as he passes through a thicket, apparently squirts scent once.
1655	Squirts scent.
1657	Squirts scent.
1658	Squirts scent.
1700	Turns off the road, squirts scents once, and disappears.

The role of olfaction in the communication between tigers provides an interesting sidelight on a hotly debated issue among hunters. The tiger's sense of smell is usually said to be either poor (Smythies, 1942; Brander, 1923; Champion, 1933; Baikov, 1936) or practically absent (Anderson, 1961; Powell, 1957). Contradicting these authors are Baker (1890), Peacock (1933), and Corbett (1957), who maintained that the tiger has a fine sense of smell. The fact that the tiger uses scent as a means of signaling certainly indicates that its powers of olfaction are good.

Claw marks on trees are another visual signal of possible communicatory value. Tigers were on two occasions seen to rake their claws down a tree trunk, leaving scars in the bark. This action sharpens the claws by peeling off "any thin strips or laminae from the surface that have become loosened or desquamated and are ready to flake off, either on the top of the claw or along the sides and thickened margins" (Wynne-Edwards, 1962). Darwin (1845, quoted in Wynne-Edwards, 1962) noted this behavior in jaguars: "One day, when hunting on the banks of the Uruguay, I was shown certain trees, to which these animals constantly recur for the purpose, as it is said, of sharpening their claws. I saw three well-known trees; in front the bark was worn smooth, as if by the breast of the animal, and on each side there were scratches, or rather grooves, extending in an oblique line nearly a yard in length. The scars were of different ages." Although Champion (1933) and others have also reported seeing trees that had been repeatedly lacerated by tigers, none were found at Kanha, and this method of marking was not an important means of signaling there.

Vocalizations

Tigers vocalize infrequently. A number of different calls, probably comprising most sounds in the animals' vocal repertoire, were noted at Kanha, but some, such as the "cat yowl" of a shot animal (Burton, 1948) and the discordant concert of courting cats described by Forsyth (1889), were not heard.

Purring. According to Leyhausen (1956) and Denis (1964), the *Pantherinae* are unable to purr. On one occasion I watched a tigress as she lay on her back while her cubs climbed playfully all over her. She emitted a purring sound repeatedly. Powell (1957) heard purring in a similar situation.

Prusten. When tigers approach each other in a friendly fashion, they often utter "a gentle puffing sound by expelling air in rapidly repeated jets through the nostrils" (Pocock, 1939). Leyhausen (1956) termed this sound *prusten.* Brander (1923) heard it in the wild, and Burton (1948) and Morris (1953) described noises which are probably the same vocalization. I heard a soft, grunting sound on several occasions when two adults or an adult and a cub came together, and this may have been *prusten.* A tigress in the London zoo made a similar sound as she approached the keeper — appearing to blow air out between slightly parted lips as well as through the nostrils — then emitted a moaning miaow and rubbed her head and body against the bars. Another tigress, which I observed in a private enclosure near London, behaved in similar fashion except that she failed to vocalize. *Prusten* appears to be analagous to the purring of house cats in that both are used to indicate friendliness when two animals approach each other. *Prusten* does not occur in the lion, jaguar, and leopard (Leyhausen, 1950).

Pooking. Perhaps no sound of the tiger has puzzled hunters more

PLATE 26.—A tigress feeds on a buffalo kill, one of her four cubs beside her (November 16, 1964).

PLATE 27.—A tigress attempts to cover the remains of her kill by sweeping earth and grass over it with a forepaw (July 25, 1964).

PLATE 28.—A tigress sits near her kill while one of her cubs, eight months old, stands at the edge of the high grass (July 25, 1964).

PLATE 29.—While the tigress pulls the buffalo down by the rump, her large cub bites and claws at a hindleg.

PLATE 30.—A tigress hides behind a small bush after spotting the investigator, the pattern of her coat making her almost invisible (June 21, 1964).

than pooking because of the remarkable resemblance of this vocalization to the alarm call of the sambar. It is a loud, clear "pok," somewhat flatter in tone and lacking the resonance of the deer call; it is given once or several times in succession. Burton (1933), Anderson (1954), Peacock (1933), and others hypothesized that a pooking tiger mimics the alarm note of the sambar in order to attract and capture the deer, but Brander (1923) and Champion (1927) thought it a sex call. The vocalization has been reported in a number of specific circumstances:

1. By a captive while ejecting urine (Boswell, 1957).
2. "Just after a tiger had relieved nature" (Champion, 1927).
3. While walking near kill (Powell, 1957).
4. Just before approaching kill (Anderson, 1954).
5. When disturbed at kill by man (Brander, 1923).
6. On seeing a man sitting in a tree (Perry, 1964).
7. By a male, accompanied by a female, when noting a person climb a tree in the distance (Lewis, 1940).
8. When shot at or disturbed on the kill (Pollock, 1896).
9. When approaching a kill already occupied by another tiger (this study).
10. By a male (?) tiger in response to roar of a tigress at a kill about a quarter-mile away (this study).
11. By a male tiger when approached by a cub as he lay 20 feet from kill (this study).

In these eleven instances, the vocalization is most commonly elicited near a kill, with the animal appearing to draw attention to itself by pooking as it becomes aware that it is approaching, or being approached by, a tiger or a man. This suggests that the sound serves to advertise the animal's presence and prevent sudden encounters. The fact that pooking has also been reported in conjunction with scent-marking and "relieving nature," both advertisement devices, lends support to this contention.

Grunting. A tigress with small cubs at heel often emits a number of soft to rasping grunts — growly ur-ur-ur or bru-bru-bru — apparently a sound which stimulates the young to follow her. Once, when a tigress grunted as she left a kill, her four cubs immediately fell into line behind her. On another occasion, as a tigress rested by a kill, one of her cubs drifted away through the high grass. She raised herself, grunted once, and the cub abruptly reversed its direction and came to her. One cub followed a male tiger briefly in response to his grunting. A tigress was heard to grunt when approaching a male tiger, but the sound may have been elicited by her cubs which were also in the vicinity.

Miaowing. One cub, about six weeks old, miaowed softly when its mother and siblings moved from sight, the call apparently indicating distress. Another cub, four months old, uttered one plaintive miaow while facing its sitting mother. On another occasion, a year-old cub sat by a kill, wrinkled up its nose, and gave several loud meaa with open mouth, sounding much like a house cat although the tone was flatter. No tiger responded directly to the calls, and their significance in the last two instances was unknown. Ognev (1962) stated that males miaow when courting, as do females (Leyhausen, 1960).

Woofing. A startled tiger emits a "woof," according to Pocock (1939) and Powell (1957). I heard a sound which fits this description once when one cub suddenly slapped another at a kill.

Moaning and roaring. Moans and roars are lumped into one category because the sounds represent variations in intensity of the same basic vocalization. A muffled moaning and groaning — a-a-a-m-m, u-u-u-u — is produced if the tiger fails to open its mouth when calling or does so only partially. This vocalization of low intensity is audible for only a few hundred feet to about a quarter mile. The roar is a resonant and rolling a-a-u-u-u or a-o-o-o-nh, produced by expelling the air through the open mouth while progressively closing it. The volume of this two-toned sound is quite startling and impressive when heard at close range, carrying a great distance in the stillness of the night, as far as two miles according to Powell (1957). Captive tigers usually walk while they roar (Leyhausen, 1950), and this is also true for the most part in the wild. On two occasions, however, I saw a tigress stand while vocalizing. Often a number of successive moans and roars of varying intensity are given.

Tigers moaned in a variety of circumstances, and the calls sounded similar to me regardless of the situation eliciting them. One tigress moaned when I chased her from a kill. Three to four successive moans grading into muffled roars were given by tigers on three occasions after an unsuccessful stalk, just after having been discovered by the deer. Tigresses judged to be in heat frequently moaned and roared in a subdued fashion at irregular intervals as they walked along. This made them conspicuous, and I located them and anticipated their movements several times on the basis of these calls. Powell (1957) noted that tigers moan when suspicious, and Champion (1927) maintained that they moan to keep in contact when hunting together. In all these circumstances, except perhaps the last (the tigers may not necessarily have been hunting), the animal is in some ways excited, and the moan appears to represent a release of tension by vocal means.

Roars are, on the whole, heard rarely, a fact also commented on by Baldwin (1877) and Brander (1923). Two examples illustrate typical situations which elicit roaring and the response of other animals to it. On one occasion, after feeding on a kill for one hour, a tigress walked about a quarter mile away and called a total of 266 times in 75 minutes. She then returned to the kill, now with her cubs, which had joined her. On another occasion, a tigress rested with two of her four cubs beside a kill. Her other cubs were in a thicket on the far bank of a small stream. When a downpour transformed the stream into a torrent, the cubs seemed afraid to cross it. The animals remained separated all afternoon, but at 1900 hours the tigress splashed across the stream, then roared 37 times quite softly and 3 times loudly. Her roars were not answered by the cubs; instead an adult responded in the distance. She led the cubs back to the kill at 2040 hours, having detoured across a bridge. At 2210 hours another tigress suddenly appeared at the kill, having been attracted by the roars.

Roaring is quite prevalent when tigers have killed a large animal such as a buffalo, as noted by Champion (1927). In such situations the tiger gives the impression of trying to draw attention to its ample food supply.

In Manchuria roaring is very prominent during the winter mating period and uncommon at other times of the year (Baikov, 1936; Ognev, 1962). The frequency of calling varied at Kanha with the seasons, being low from March to September, increasing suddenly during the last week of October, and reaching a peak in February. To obtain some measure of the amount of moaning and roaring heard while working in the field during the morning (0500–0900 hours) and afternoon (1500–1900 hours) all instances of it were noted down (see Fig. 14); observations at a kill were not included. The results indicate a peak vocal period during the cool season, which correlates with the time of the year when much of the mating is said to occur.

Forsyth (1889) described the mixture of moaning, roaring, and other sounds of tigers when meeting and apparently mating:

I listened one night to the most remarkable serenade of tigers I ever heard. A peculiar, long wail, like the drawn-out mew of a huge cat, first rose from a river course a few hundred yards below my tent. Presently from a mile or so higher up the river came a deep, tremendous roar, which had

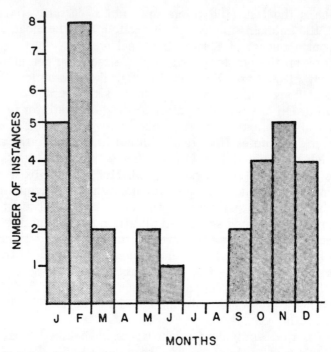

FIG. 14.—Number of instances of tiger moaning and roaring heard each month in 1964 between 0500–0900 and 1500–1900 hours.

scarcely died away ere it was answered from behind the camp by another, pitched yet deeper in tone, startling us from its suddenness and proximity. All three were repeated at short intervals as the three tigers approached each other along the bottom of the deep, dry watercourses, between and above which the camp had been pitched. As they drew together the noises ceased for about a quarter of an hour; and I was dozing off to sleep again, when suddenly arose the most fearful din near to where the tigress had first sounded the love-note to her rival lovers, a din like the caterwauling of midnight cats magnified a hundredfold. Intervals of silence, broken by outbursts of this infernal shrieking and moaning, disturbed our rest for the next hour, dying away gradually as the tigers retired along the bed of the river. In the morning I found all the incidents of a three-volume novel of feline life imprinted on the sand; and marks of blood showed how genuine the combat part of the performance had been.

Tigers also roar during the act of mating, as described by Manteifel (1927, quoted in Ognev, 1962) for a pair at the Moscow zoo:

On gradually becoming accustomed to the male, the tigress touches his long, stiff vibrissae with hers, and if she hears an equine snort [*prusten*] in reply she rapidly relaxes a good deal of her caution. In a few minutes she lies down on her back and begins to wave her paws. The male tiger gazes at her in a surly manner. During mating the female holds her back upward, and the tiger, with a roar like thunder, seizes her neck without piercing the skin with his teeth. . . . Such "love scenes" are repeated many dozen times a day for 5 to 7 days.

Similarly, Baudy (letter, January 21, 1966) wrote about his captive tigers:

The number of daily matings is high. We recorded 17 of them in one single day between one male and one female Bengal. Copulation is short, does not last over 15 to 20 seconds, at the most, with the male letting out a tremendous roar as it reaches climax. Almost at the same time, the male has to get quickly out of the way, as females turn around in a flash to take a swipe at the male.

The evidence indicates that the roar is mainly a long-distance communicatory signal. Cubs respond to the roar of their mother by going to her, which suggests that they recognize her call. The roar may also attract other adults, as when given at a kill or by a female in heat; it may elicit no response; and it may possibly repel. But in every instance the sound draws attention to the animal, making other tigers aware of its presence and location. A tiger sometimes answers a roar, and the repeated calling back and forth, as described by Baikov (1936) and Forsyth (1889), helps the animals to find each other. Occasionally tigers were seen to ignore a distant roar or merely to look in the direction of the sound, but Corbett (1957) and Powell (1957), who used imitation calls to lure tigers to within shooting distance, have shown that the cats sometimes approach silently and investigate the sound. It is possible that the tigers living in a certain area recognize each other's call and respond selectively, depending on the individual giving it.

Growling, snarling, and hissing. Tigers growl, snarl, hiss, and spit when threatening each other as well as when reacting to man. These vocalizations, all apparently expressions of annoyance, may be given interchangeably in a given situation, depending on the intensity of the response. Growling consists of a steady, rolling tone, somewhat resembling a distant motor, and is rarely audible for more than 150 to 200 feet. At a higher level of intensity, the tiger opens its mouth while growling to produce a snarling sound, which can be either quite soft or harsh. Such a snarl may be drawn out, becoming a hiss, or it may end in an abrupt, explosive "tcho." When tigers threaten each other, however, usually in disputes over particular feeding sites, the sounds change in intensity so frequently and grade into one another so readily that categorizing is difficult. An excerpt from my field notes illustrates a situation which elicited much vocalizing:

1825 hours. Two tigresses and 2 cubs feed on a buffalo kill, the former at the rump. The females growl and grumble almost continuously, erupting occasionally into loud snarls as they face each other with open mouth.

1845 hours. The tigresses crouch by the rump, their noses one foot apart, ears folded back, mouths wide open. Each emits a series of harsh, rolling growls; then, as one returns to her meal, the other lies there with exposed canines and continues to growl softly.

1900 hours. One tigress rears up and with a sudden snarl strikes at a cub that has crowded her.

Coughing roar. Attacking tigers emit a short, loud, coughing roar (Pocock, 1939; Locke, 1954; Powell, 1957), often only once but occasionally several times in succession, apparently an indication of anger. After considerable growling and snarling, a tiger sometimes coughed once at another animal in a dispute at a kill. The coughing roar was also directed at vultures and crows; on one occasion, for example, a large male cub rushed twice from some high grass with canines bared and ears laid back, emitting one violent cough as he charged toward some vultures on his kill. A similar sound is used when attacking man. For instance, a tigress which had sat silently with partially open mouth in a patch of dense brush and watched my approach, lunged forward when one hundred twenty feet separated us, coughed twice, and then retreated.

When shot or when fighting with each other, tigers are said to roar "with rage" (Inglis, 1892; Powell, 1957), from all accounts a sound of greater intensity and duration than the coughing roar.

POSTURES AND GESTURES

The most commonly observed interactions between tigers consist of greetings and of minor disputes at kills. Descriptive examples of these and other types of behavior have been given in various contexts, and the purpose here is to comment briefly on a few of these patterns.

The tiger, like the house cat, expresses friendliness by rubbing its face, neck, and occasionally the whole side of its body against the head, neck, and shoulder of another tiger. Sometimes the inter-action is brief, a mere touch of cheeks, but at other times the animal moves its body gently and sinuously against the other, its tail raised vertically or almost so. Sexually receptive cats present in a similar fashion, and the greeting ceremony appears to be derived from this sexual pattern (Leyhausen, 1956). Cubs frequently rubbed themselves against their mother, especially when she returned after a brief absence or when they approached her at a kill. They also greeted the male tiger and each other in this fashion. The behavior was seen only once between adults, probably because courtship and sexual behavior were not seen in the wild. In the one instance, two tigresses and four cubs walked along, one female emitting a low-pitched "ur-ur" call repeatedly. When they stopped, one cub left its mother and walked beneath the other female, rubbing its back on her belly. This tigress then approached the other adult and with a smooth motion glided past her chest, barely touching it.

Tigers behave aggressively in a number of distinct ways, and their gestures are frequently accompanied by vocalizations. In a threat-ening gesture of low intensity, the animal wrinkles its nose and fore-head, alternately bares and covers its canine teeth (Plate 24), and lays the ears back somewhat. The backward movement of the ears is often the first indication that an aggressive action is imminent. An expression of moderate to high intensity includes a partially to wholly open mouth with canines exposed, flattened ears, and much growling and snarling as the cat faces its opponent. Overt attack in the form of slapping with a forepaw or rearing up and swiping with both paws may be included. The movement of the tail also expresses the emotion of the animal, varying from a slight twitching at the tip during a tense situation to violent lashing up and down when highly excited. Serious fights were not observed during the study.

Leyhausen (1960) distinguished between aggressive threat and defensive threat in the facial expressions and body postures of vari-ous cats, presenting excellent diagrams of the two types and the gra-dations in expression between them. In an aggressive threat the mouth is closed, or partially so, the ears are erect and twisted in such a way that the backs almost face forward, displaying the con-spicuous spot which many cats have there, and the pupils are small. In an attitude of defensive threat, on the other hand, the canines may be exposed, the corners of the open mouth pulled back, the ears flattened, and the pupils large. Intermediate expressions contain components of both types. No facial expression corresponding to the aggressive threat was observed in free-living tigers, the features of the defense threat being prevalent even when the animal was attacking.

Leyhausen (1960) suggested that the ear spots in the tiger and some other cats function in intimidation since they are prominent during the attack threat. The conspicuous spots may also have signal value when tigers follow each other through dense vegetation. Except for the white spot on the back of each ear, the pelage of the tiger blends almost completely into its surroundings. In fact, on two occasions I first became aware of a tiger in the grass by noting these markings, and it is possible that they also help tigers, especially cubs, to keep in contact with each other and their mother. In this context, it is interesting to note that in the jungle-dwelling Temminck cat, which lacks prominent ear spots, the underside of the distal third of the tail is a striking white. If the Temminck cat raises its tail to lead its young as the female house cat does, it seems likely that the white tail tip may have signal functions similar to the ear spots of the tiger (Leyhausen, pers. comm.).

A threatened tiger usually steps or jumps aside without assuming a definite submissive posture. On one occasion, however, a tigress rolled partially onto her back when attacked by another female, exposing her abdomen, one paw held limply in the air. One cub also behaved in this fashion when threatened by another cub. The gesture appears to be one of submission.

Behavior of Female and Young

Most observations were made of a tigress with four cubs between March 20, 1964, and March 31, 1965. During this period the cubs grew from the size of setter dogs still fully dependent on their mother, at the age of four months, to semi-independent adolescents nearly as large as the tigress, at the age of sixteen months.

The tigress secretes her newborn cubs in a den, usually a cave or rock overhang (Anderson, 1961; Baikov, 1936), a hollow tree (Bazé, 1957), among dense reeds and bushes (Novikov, 1962), or in some other protected site. The birth weights of three cubs in one litter at the New York Zoological Park were 2 pounds 8 ounces, 2 pounds 9 ounces, and 2 pounds 11 ounces, respectively (Crandall, 1964); three cubs at the National Zoological Park weighed 3 pounds 6 ounces, 3 pounds 8½ ounces, and 4 pounds 1½ ounces, respectively

(J. Eisenberg, pers. comm.). One cub in the first litter opened its eyes on the ninth day after birth, the second on the eleventh day, and the third not until the seventeenth day. On the other hand, "five of our Bengal cubs were born with eyes cracked open, two with eyes fully open and clear without the usual bluish tinge of baby eyes" (Baudy and Baudy, n.d.). The cubs remain in the den for four weeks according to Novikov (1962), for six weeks according to Sanderson (1912), and for eight weeks according to Brander (1923) and Ognev (1962). One tigress at Kanha was followed by four small cubs, each weighing about 10 pounds, estimated to be six to seven weeks old. The tigress provides the young with meat, taking food to the den. Anderson (1961) stated that small cubs are fed on regurgitated meat, behavior which has also been noted in the lion (Adamson, 1960). Baudy (letter, January 21, 1966) noted that his *P. t. tigris* cubs became interested in eating meat at six weeks of age, whereas his *P. t. longipilis* cubs did not reach this stage until ten weeks of age. The cubs leave the den and follow the female to the kill as soon as they are sufficiently mobile. From that time on, the young lack a permanent abode and lead a nomadic life as they move from feeding site to feeding site. Cubs are fully weaned at the age of five to six months (Locke, 1954; Ognev, 1962).

The cubs are wholly dependent on the female until they are about six months old. While she is hunting, they lie quietly hidden in a thicket, a patch of high grass, or an overgrown ravine, waiting for her return. If the tigress has captured some large prey, she leaves it at or near the kill site and leads her cubs to it. Unless disturbed, they remain with the carcass until all meat has been devoured. They often eat up everything in one night, as the following observations made on April 1, when the cubs were about four and a half months old, show:

The tigress stands panting with open mouth on the meadow at 1530 hours, a freshly killed small gaur calf between her spread forelegs. Two hundred feet away at the edge of the forest a gaur cow walks irresolutely back and forth for 5 minutes before disappearing from view. The tigress picks up the calf by the neck and drags it between her forelegs about 300 feet out of sight into a ravine bordered by high grass. She reappears at 1619 hours without her prey and lies down panting. After licking her forepaws, she rears up on a termite mound and looks in several directions before disappearing in the ravine until 1645 hours. Then she strides off through the forest.

I check the kill. The calf lies in the bottom of the ravine, no effort having been made to cover it. There are several deep claw marks on its rump, the neck appears broken, and the nape and base of the skull are severely mauled. It weighs 95 pounds, including about one pound of meat which the tigress has eaten from one thigh.

Soon after dark, at 1905 hours, the tigress arrives with her 4 cubs. They feed intermittently out of sight in the ravine during the night, and the following morning at 0625 hours the tigress and her cubs abandon the site and enter a boulder-strewn thicket near a waterhole about a half mile away. An examination of the feeding area shows that all meat and viscera have been eaten and that only 9½ pounds of bones remain. The tigers leave the thicket at 0948 hours. One cub, apparently startled by our presence, runs off alone in the direction opposite to the one taken by the others. The tigress, followed by 3 cubs, walks 200 feet, stops for about 3 seconds while looking back over her shoulder at her straying cub 500 feet away, and continues on. The cub then runs after its family, all moving from sight at 0955 hours.

A large prey animal may provide food for several days, and the animals camp, so to speak, by the carcass until the last scrap has been devoured. A typical instance of this is condensed from my field notes:

During the night of March 16–17 a tigress killed an adult gaur bull in a ravine. I happened to be walking near the site at 0600 hours on March 17, but when a tigress growled at me, I detoured around the area and thus failed to find the kill. The carcass was discovered on March 19. By then the whole hindquarters had been eaten, but the front half of the animal was intact; a government official cut the head off as a trophy. I tied the remains to a clump of bamboo and watched them from the cover of a tree trunk 120 feet away. When by 1820 hours the tigers had not appeared, I left the site, returning the following morning.

At 0630 hours the tigress stands by the kill and tears off pieces of flesh with lateral jerks of the head or with vigorous pulls. At times she crouches or lies down and cuts the meat and skin with her carnassial teeth before tearing pieces off and bolting them down. The 4 cubs lie in the grass 60 feet away; they are about 4 months old and weigh some 50 pounds each. At 0657 hours they join the female. While one cub grabs a piece of skin and jerks it vigorously back and forth in an attempt to tear it off, the tigress paws the soil first with one and then with the other forepaw as if to cover the remains.

Suddenly the female turns and walks steadily up the ravine, emitting one soft grunt as she does so. The cubs scamper after her in single file. She lies down in the grass 110 feet from the kill while the cubs play alone or together near her. Some wander around exploring their environment, sniffing at grass stalks and peering over the edge of the creek bank, and others stalk carefully through the undergrowth as if sensing some prey. One reaches up the trunk of a small tree and rakes its claws down the bark;

it then tries to climb up and, with much scrambling, reaches a height of 2 feet before sliding down. Another cub creeps through the grass, belly to the ground, carefully lifting a foot at a time, and leaps into the air to land on its forepaws, perhaps having stalked an insect. Occasionally 2 or 3 cubs race in single file up and down a path that leads into the ravine. One cub crouches low, and when another bumbles by it leaps out of hiding and grabs the rump of its victim with unsheathed claws. Once 2 cubs rear up on their hindlegs and grapple with their forepaws while mock-biting each other in the shoulder.

The female rises at 0710 hours and walks toward the cubs. One of them rushes up to her and places its paws on her neck. At 0730 hours she lies down beside the kill but 20 minutes later returns to her cubs, which in the meantime have ceased to play. All move out of sight around a bend in the ravine at 0753 hours and rest there all day.

The tigers are still inactive at 1745 hours. One cub is barely visible in the grass, sleeping on its side with its legs stretched out, only the twitching of its ears revealing its presence. It looks up at 1815 hours, licks its back briefly, yawns, rests its chin on one paw, and then reclines. At 2015 hours the tigress goes to the kill alone. She jerks at the carcass violently, her forelegs stiffly braced, in an attempt to move it to another site; she breaks wind once. For 2 minutes she licks the rib cage, apparently eating the maggots that swarm on the meat. After crunching into the ribs and breaking one off, she holds the bone between her forepaws and gnaws on it. She coughs once, something apparently having lodged in her throat. At 2045 hours she leaves the kill and roars 4 times, followed by about 20 grunts and moans and a final loud roar.

A solitary gaur bull snuffles nearby at 2050 hours, but he senses the tigers and bolts. The female returns to the carcass with her cubs at 2130 hours, and one or more feed until 2320 hours. All rest for half an hour, and then the tigress eats alone for 45 more minutes. After another silent spell, the animals feed off and on from 0230 to 0415 hours. The female growls harshly several times, and there is much breaking wind.

A tiger roars once in the distance at 0330 hours. At 0430 hours the tigress roars twice and is answered by a roar and 15 pooks. Between 0430 and 0620, the tigers rest by the kill. The female then rises, first attempts to drag the carcass away, and finally feeds with the cubs. Several times she emits rolling growls, twice culminating in a harsh "aaarrr" as she jerks her head with exposed canines at a cub beside her. She walks 50 feet from the kill at 0635 hours and sniffs the ground there. One cub rubs its body from shoulder to rump against her foreleg. Back at the kill, she gives an explosive snarly "tcho" at a cub which crowds her. All feeding stops at 0655 hours, and the animals rest beside the kill until 0710 hours, when the cubs go in single file 150 feet up the ravine. They lie down there at 0735 hours and are joined by their mother at 0755 hours.

The male tiger appears suddenly along the bank of the ravine. He passes the remains of the gaur and approaches the tigress and cubs. They rise and watch him. The female steps toward him, and they meet behind a clump of bamboo, only their hindquarters visible to me. They face each other for 3 minutes before the male ambles off without looking back. She follows him 50 feet, squirts scent once, and then returns to her cubs.

The female goes to the kill at 0835 hours and gnaws on a gaur leg. The cubs cluster around her, one climbing over her back. After a brief snack, she rises abruptly and lies down in the shade 30 feet away, where she is joined by the cubs. At 0850 hours she charges 20 feet at several crows which sit in the branches above the carcass. The young move out of sight at 0900 hours, but the tigress is restless, finally settling down at 1030 hours. At 1655 she is still reclining, her hindquarters in a pool. Every so often she swishes her tail up, showering herself with water. She rises at 1712 hours and looks at the gaur bones and the few scraps of skin; she glances to the right, then to the left, checks a few bones 50 feet away, and apparently having decided that nothing edible is left, walks steadily into the forest, leaving her cubs behind.

A prolonged period of play among the cubs, as described above, was seen on only one other occasion, in the evening of May 31:

The tigress rests with her 4 cubs in a shallow ravine near the remains of a chital buck at 1835 hours. The cubs are 110 feet from her, and when she approaches them, all bound up and crowd around her. One places its forepaws on her neck, but she bares her teeth, shakes her head, and emits several deep growls. She lies down, first on her side and then on her back with all 4 feet in the air. A cub lies by her, a second cub chews on the ear of the first one, and a third cub rolls onto its side and claws at the grass; the fourth cub, a male, worms itself close to the female, reaches out with one paw, and strokes her head; he then holds her head between both paws and licks it. One cub rises and rubs the top of its head against the tigress' chin. Another young comes up, flops on its side, and strokes the head of the female with a forepaw. When she turns on her side, a cub drapes itself over her neck. She purrs with open mouth. Two cubs wrestle, one mock-biting the other's head. The female rests once more on her back, now with a cub lying across her face gnawing on an ear.

It is dusky at 1915 hours. Two cubs lie near the tigress. One steps over her body. When another one follows, she cuffs it lightly with a downward swing of her paw. A third cub crouches in the grass and suddenly rushes at another cub 15 feet away; they wrestle. Two cubs face each other, rear up on their hindlegs, and swat with their paws; then 3 of them wrestle vigorously. One bumps into the tigress, receiving several light cuffs in return.

A sloth bear bumbles by 300 feet away at 1935 hours without noticing the tigers, which look up alertly. When the bear moves from sight, the cubs continue to play. I leave at 1945 hours because of darkness.

When disturbed by man, a tigress and her cubs sometimes flee together, but at other times they scatter, with the female seemingly not very solicitous of them. One tigress trailed by four six-week-old cubs fled with the arrival of a busload of shouting tourists. Three cubs kept up with her, but the fourth one lagged behind, lost sight of the others, and three minutes later still wandered around looking for its family. On another occasion several tourists stood on the bank of a ravine overlooking a patch of grass 200 feet away, where a tigress with her six-and-a-half-month-old cubs lay hidden by a buffalo kill. The tigress ran out of the grass, stopped conspicuously on the open slope, and then slowly walked away. Two minutes later a cub broke cover, and then the others emerged singly, each fleeing in a different direction. The behavior of the tigress suggested that she had attempted to draw attention to herself and away from the cubs. Another instance showed this more clearly. On October 27, when the cubs were eleven months old, the tigress killed a calf in a patch of shrubby trees adjacent to the Kanha village. Some fifty men entered the thicket with much shouting and other noise in order to drive the cats away. The tigress fled with one cub, two others apparently crept away, and the fourth one hid itself in some undergrowth. We followed the tigress and her cub on the back of an elephant across a neck of the meadow into the forest. Both entered a small thicket. The cub sneaked away in a crouched position when the elephant was sixty feet away, but the tigress remained until we advanced to within thirty feet. Then she walked slowly into the open, her face in a soundless snarl; she left at a leisurely pace in a direction ninety degrees away from the one taken by the cub. Her speed did not increase when a villager on foot threw an axe at her from a distance of sixty feet, and we followed her slowly. When we were temporarily out of sight behind a low hill, she evidently broke into a run, and on topping the rise, we saw her just disappearing in the distance.

The cubs showed their first signs of independence when they were six and a half months old. The male cub of the litter was seen alone on May 28 as he stalked around a grassy swale, and he was still in the same locality thirteen hours later; however, on May 31 he was back with his family. On June 26, at 0730 hours, the tigress and one cub rested in a grove of trees while the other 3 cubs traced the edge of a ravine for a quarter mile in single file until they came to the remains of a barasingha hind, their kill of the previous night. Finding nothing left to eat, they rejoined their mother. At 0830 hours the tigers were seen one mile away as they moved into the forest.

In mid-October, when the cubs were eleven months old, the male of the litter, who then weighed about two hundred pounds and was considerably larger than his female siblings, became semi-independent and occasionally began to hunt on his own. At 1040 hours on October 17, for example, he snatched a pig one hundred ten feet from the nearest village hut, carrying his victim off by the back of the neck. The female cubs, on the other hand, still seemed to be wholly dependent on the tigress for food. This partial break-up of the family unit appeared to be correlated with the tigress' difficulty in securing enough prey to satisfy her four large young. Because of the relative ease of killing livestock, she frequently hovered around the village. The cubs accompanied her on some of the nightly forays for cattle, to my knowledge the first times that they hunted with their mother. The depredation on the livestock was so frequent and persistent during the latter part of October that the villagers removed most of the cattle from the area for several months.

Sanderson (1912) found that "two cubs born near Morley in November 1875, first began to hunt for themselves in the following June. . . . They still, however, remained with the tigress. They had considerable difficulty at this age in killing even old cattle single-handed, and they scratched them greatly in their attempts. Nor did they attack loose cattle — only such as we picketed for them." When one of the cubs, a female, was shot on July 29, it weighed 118 pounds. Smythies (1942) noted that the male cub leaves the family at the age of twelve months. One male cub observed by Corbett (1957) was supposedly abandoned by his mother at the age of twelve months and he survived by killing peafowl, pigs, barking deer, and chital. Burton (1933) stated that cubs begin to hunt at seventeen months of age. These observations agree in general with my data from Kanha.

In order to observe the behavior of the cubs when twelve months old, three successive buffalo were tethered out between November 13 and 17. The tigress killed one buffalo on the morning of November 14 (see Attacking and Killing, p. 289), but she broke the rope with which the animal was tied and dragged the carcass into a thicket. By the following morning the three female cubs had joined her, but the male cub failed to appear not only on that day but also on the following days, attesting to his independent life. Another tigress with a nine month old cub, a male, joined the others at the site, making a total of two tigresses and four cubs around the carcass.

A second buffalo was tied to a stump at the edge of a thicket near a small ravine at 1655 hours on November 15. To describe the details of interaction between the two tiger families as well as other aspects of behavior, particularly the killing techniques employed by the relatively inexperienced young, my field notes are presented in condensed form:

The buffalo is lying down but he suddenly jumps up at 1800 hours and looks toward the high grass 15 feet away. A cub sits there, and 30 feet farther back is another cub. Four minutes later the buffalo reclines again and chews his cud. At 1807 hours one cub walks to within 6 feet of the buffalo, which gets to its feet. As the cub circles toward the rump, a second cub rushes in from the buffalo's right side, bites it in the abdominal wall, and pulls. The other cub lunges in at the same time and grabs the buffalo by the left hindleg just above the hock. The combined attack causes the buffalo to topple. As it falls onto its right side, the tigress steps swiftly from the grass, reaches over the animal's neck, and grasps the throat, giving a sharp pull. She lies down holding the throat until 1810 hours; she then rises, jerks at the neck, and lies again. The cubs merely circle the downed animal. One cub touches the nose of the tigress with its nose, but she jerks her head back. At 1817 hours, 3 minutes after the death of the buffalo, the tigress releases her hold and sits up.

The second tigress steps from the grass, and the one which has just killed the buffalo lies down and strokes the air with a forepaw, her face in a snarl. She then rises and attempts to haul the buffalo away. At 1825 hours both females begin to eat at the rump. They growl and snarl almost continuously; at 1920 hours the second tigress suddenly rises and disappears in the grass. There is a noticeable lessening of tension. This tigress is not seen again that night, but her male cub remains.

The 3 female cubs feed while the tigress sits and licks her chest and legs. The male cub appears for the first time but returns to the high grass when the tigress growls at him. He comes up again 5 minutes later, however, and eats, mingling freely with the cubs of the other litter.

One or 2 cubs feed at a time until 2015 hours; then all rest. The female rises, and a cub rubs its face against hers. She tries to pull the kill away before eating once more. One cub stands 10 feet from the carcass and paws earth toward it 10 times. The tigress ceases to eat at 2150 hours and growls softly when the male cub walks up. Not deterred, the cub feeds until 2210 hours and then scrapes dirt a total of 22 times, as if attempting to cover up the carcass.

Most animals lie around, some on the side, others on the back. Occasionally a cub ambles around. One eats from 2350 to 2420 hours. After that, the kill lies deserted until 0420 hours. At that time another cub feeds, and then the tigress snacks briefly. A cub flops on its side by the kill with an audible sigh, but 5 minutes later it eats some more. At 0505 hours the 3 female cubs congregate by the kill, but the male cub has left, probably to join his mother nearby. The female and the cubs snack a little, rest, meander into the ravine apparently to drink, stretch out in the morning sun, lick their paws, and feed some more, rarely staying in one spot or doing the same thing for more than a few minutes. One cub rubs its face against that of the female; she then licks its rump, and the two touch noses again.

As the sun grows warmer, the cats become less and less active. The tigress rests on her side breathing heavily, her tail and ears twitching occasionally. At 1315 hours the female and one cub eat for 13 minutes, rubbing faces together beforehand and afterward. At 1530 hours a cub picks up a piece of skin but does not eat it; a cub snacks briefly at 1542 hours, a second one at 1650 hours. Otherwise the tigers remain inactive. I leave the blind at 1715 hours. Only the head and neck of the buffalo remain uneaten, and the edible parts are finished up that night.

A third buffalo is tied out at the site at 0700 hours. Within a few minutes a cub appears 15 feet from the bait and crouches down, the distal part of its tail flicking. The buffalo stares at the tiger with lowered head and, when the cub approaches to within 10 feet, charges. The cub jumps back. Three cubs have assembled by 0828 hours, and the buffalo snorts and charges each time one of them ventures to within 10 feet. At 0914 hours the tigress strides in the direction of the ravine. At 0924 hours, while the buffalo is facing a cub, the tigress advances in a crouching run, lunges in, and grabs one hindleg with her teeth just above the hockjoint, twisting her head sharply to the side. At the same time she swats the other leg with a paw. The combined twist and slap tumble the buffalo onto its side. Still holding the animal by the leg, she drags it backward while two cubs rush in beside her and claw and bite seemingly at random. The female releases her grip and steps back. The buffalo struggles to its feet as one cub rakes the top of its rump with the claws, wheels around, and charges at the tigress. She circles him briefly with the 2 cubs but suddenly departs. The cubs lie down nearby. The buffalo has only superficial wounds; he feeds and rests the remainder of the morning paying no obvious attention to the tigers in the vicinity.

Three cubs approach the buffalo again at 1325 hours, one of them jumping back with a snarl when charged. The tigress sits nearby, and the young join her. At 1410 hours a cub darts in, attempting to grab a hindleg of the buffalo, but retreats rapidly when he spins around with a lowered horns. The tigress stands waiting in a semicrouch as the cubs encircle the buffalo and jump in and dodge back one at a time. Twice she steps closer but retreats again. Finally after 5 minutes she lunges in and bites the animal in the right hindleg, using the same technique to throw it down as earlier. She switches her grip to the upper thigh and drags the buffalo backward. Then she crouches in an attempt to hold him down while the cubs swarm all over him, biting and clawing the hindquarters, belly, and back. One cub straddles the back and repeatedly bites into the hump. The buffalo tries to

*rise, but the tigress merely places both of her paws on its rump and pulls
him back down. At 1421 hours she releases her hold, watches briefly (Plates
25 and 29), and then walks away. The buffalo struggles up, and the cubs
fall off. One cub rears and claws the side, then vaults up on the back while
the others pull and tear at the hindquarters. The buffalo collapses. Five
minutes later the tigress returns, jerks the animal by a hindleg so vigorously
that the stump to which it is tethered breaks off, and drags it 20 feet. Three
cubs begin to eat at the rump; one cub grabs the buffalo's nose and is almost
gored.*

*The second tigress has been watching the proceedings for 10 minutes
without taking part, but her cub has participated in the final phases of the
attack. She moves from sight, but the other tigress remains and licks the
bleeding wounds of the buffalo. One cub coughs and swats another one.
At 1500 hours the female drags the buffalo almost out of sight into some
high grass.*

*The tigers are still satiated from the meal of the previous night, and only
a tigress still feeds at 1525 hours. When the second tigress returns to the
kill, a female cub greets her with a face rub. She inadvertently steps on a
reclining cub, which rears up with a snarl and swats at her. Two cubs lie
beside the kill and stroke each other's shoulders with a paw, then nuzzle
noses. At 1615 hours, the kill has been pulled from sight. I leave the blind.
The carcass is dragged 500 feet away the following night and abandoned
on November 19, all meat having by then been devoured.*

The behavior of the tigress when attacking the third buffalo was
of note. In contrast to her usual efficient method of pulling livestock
down and strangling the animals by grabbing their throats (see
Attacking and Killing, p. 289), she merely threw the buffalo off its
feet and then retreated, permitting the cubs to attack on their own.
She made no attempt to kill in either attack. This suggests that the
tigress provided the cubs with the opportunity to practice the techniques of killing. The cubs, although twelve months old, obviously
had little or no previous experience in dispatching such a large animal. They were reasonably adept in pulling it down, but they failed
to kill efficiently, largely confining their attack to biting and clawing
around the rump, back, and belly rather than grasping the throat.

The killing efficiency of the cubs had not increased appreciably
by late December, as a series of observations at a kill illustrates:

*A bait is tied out at 1700 hours. At 1745 hours a langur calls persistently,
indicating the proximity of a predator, but no tiger appears. Finally at
1950 hours the tigress approaches in a crouching run, grabs the bull by a
hindleg, and with a violent backward jerk, topples it. Her 4 cubs, including
the large male cub, attack immediately. The tigress releases her hold on the
leg and departs for the night. Two cubs bite the animal in the back of*

the neck, and two tear at the hindquarters. One young reaches between the horns in an attempt to bite the neck. The male cub begins to feed alone at the rump of the still live animal; the other cubs tear at the forequarters. When one of his sisters approaches him, the male cub growls and raises a paw; at 2035 hours another cub tries to feed on the rump with him, but he growls and the intruding cub returns to its feeding site at the neck. The male cub is temporarily satiated at 2055 hours and lies down 10 feet from the kill. Another cub immediately takes his place at the rump.

One cub is still eating at 2350 hours. A free-ranging domestic elephant walks to within 30 feet of the kill before the cub backs into the grass. The elephant jerks forward as if to charge when the tiger approaches the carcass again. After venturing to within 15 feet, the elephant retreats and stands by a tree 40 feet from the kill. The cub resumes its meal, while the elephant breaks numerous branches from a tree. It holds the broken end of each branch in its mouth, wraps its trunk around the leafy portion, and rips the foliage off, dropping everything on a pile as if covering something. The elephant continues stripping branches for 15 minutes, afterward remaining in the vicinity until 0100 hours.

At 2403 hours the male cub reclines beside the kill, and at 2435 hours he growls once and takes his former place at the rump; the cub that was in his spot retreats, its face in a snarl. When at 0145 hours the male cub leaves the carcass, another cub takes his place. At 0337 hours the kill lies unused for the first time that night. One cub eats again at 0445 hours, but soon afterward all retreat into dense cover, where they stay apparently without their mother the whole day and the following night.

These and other observations indicated that the four cubs had a rank order, dominance being primarily asserted when claiming a certain position at the kill. The rump was the most favored feeding site, a spot usually taken by the tigress. But when she was not present, or when she was not actively feeding, the male cub tended to appropriate this location. Rank appeared to be largely based on size, with the result that the smallest of the young was occasionally not able to eat until one of its larger siblings vacated a place. When the meat supply is ample, rank is of little consequence to the animal, but if the prey is small, as is often the case, only the dominant individual may obtain a substantial meal. In March, 1965, for example, a pig weighing about fifty pounds was tied out as bait. The male cub killed the pig and ate while the three female cubs waited beside the carcass without being permitted to take a bite. Twice a cub attempted to eat, but the male coughed and growled. After having eaten steadily for 100 minutes, the male allowed a sister to join him; when he was satiated 10 minutes later and departed, only scraps remained for the others. A rank order has also been reported in litters of house cats (Leyhausen, 1960).

Aggressive interactions between the tigress and her cubs and between the cubs were relatively infrequent, if the crowded conditions when feeding are taken into consideration. For instance, the tigress coughed only once and growled six times at a cub during a whole night at a kill when the young were four months old. Twelve months later, in a similar situation, only two coughs on the part of the female were heard. During one night when the cubs were thirteen months old and the tigress was not with them the only audible aggressive interactions consisted of one cough and four growls. Three months later only one cough was heard under similar circumstances.

When in March, 1965, the cubs were sixteen months old, their relations with the tigress had grown quite tenuous. The male cub was now nearly as large as his mother, and his sisters were only somewhat smaller than he. The composition of the tiger family changed constantly as either the male cub or the tigress left to lead a solitary existence, as shown by the following observations of the members of the family that participated in the killing and eating of several baits that were tied out at the same spot.

March 13–14. The whole family devoured a buffalo.

March 17–18. The male cub attacked a sick buffalo alone in the evening, pulling it down by the rump and starting to eat without attempting to kill it. At 0715 hours the tigress arrived at the kill site, perhaps attracted by the circling vultures. She chased the vultures off but departed without feeding.

March 18–19. The 4 cubs ate a pig.

March 20–21. The male cub ate alone on a buffalo dead from disease.

March 21–22. All four cubs attacked a buffalo at 1845 hours. They pulled it down and began to feed without killing it. They ate sporadically until 0830 hours, then remained around the kill all day, some partially submerged in a muddy pool nearby. The male cub ate from 1445 to 1515 hours. The 4 cubs devoured the rest of the buffalo the following night and were still in the area on March 24.

March 27–28. The male cub attacked the buffalo alone at 1915 hours. The tigress arrived at 2006 hours with the 3 female cubs. She left alone during the night.

March 28–29. The male cub killed a buffalo efficiently (see Attacking and Killing, p. 289) and was joined immediately afterward by his sisters. The tigress checked in briefly during the night and departed again.

March 29–30.   The male cub dispatched another buffalo and fed on it with the other cubs. The young were still together on March 31, when the male cub killed another buffalo.

At the age of sixteen months the male cub was capable of killing a buffalo almost as expertly as the tigress. He had been hunting on his own then for about five months. The female cubs, on the other hand, were quite inefficient, apparently because they still depended on the tigress to provide them with food, and had had little experience in killing prey alone. But even when the female cubs had the opportunity to attack tethered baits, they did not always do so. On four occasions, the male cub dispatched an animal alone while his siblings watched, taking no part in the killing although they readily joined in the eating. Leyhausen (1960) has noted that a rank order in sibling cats may prevent a subordinate animal from killing effectively or even attempting to attack while the dominant one is present. Three lion cubs about two years old were observed while having considerable difficulty in killing a wildebeest (Anon., 1963). While a female cub grabbed the antelope by the nose, a male and another female attacked the rump, finally toppling the animal after ten minutes.

Although the social bond between the tigress and her cubs was growing progressively looser, their association undoubtedly continued for several months after the study was terminated on the last day of March, 1965. The male cub probably became fully independent by about eighteen to twenty months of age, whereas the female cubs most likely remained attached to the tigress for an additional three to four months. The weakening of the social bond was apparently not caused by an increased level of aggression between the tigress and her cubs but rather by a seeming inclination on the part of each animal to lead a solitary life as soon as it was able to do so. A shortage of food appeared to have initiated the break-up, with the male cub becoming semi-independent first. The observations in March, however, showed that the male cub and particularly the tigress were often alone in spite of an abundant and readily available supply of meat, indicating that the search for food was not the only basis for their solitary existence.

Food Habits and Hunting, Killing, and Feeding Behavior

The quest for food occupies a large part of the tiger's life. Whether it is actively hunting, feeding, or resting satiated beside the remains of its kill, much of its daily activity revolves around its food supply.

FOOD HABITS

The tiger preys on whatever animals it can catch, including birds, reptiles, amphibians, fish, and even some invertebrates, but mammals — in particular hoofed ones — make up the bulk of its diet. In India the most common wild prey consists of chital, sambar, barasingha, hog deer, barking deer, nilgai, pig, and gaur. Rhinocerous calves and wild buffalo are taken in the Kaziranga Sanctuary (C. Chakravarty, pers. comm.). Pig, Manchurian wapiti, moose, musk deer, roe deer, and sika deer are preyed on in the Soviet Far East (Abramov, 1962), and pigs appear to be the tiger's chief source of food in central Asia (Novikov, 1962; Ognev, 1962).

Livestock has assumed an important role in providing the cat with prey in many areas. Horses (M. Taylor, 1956), donkeys, camels (Novikov, 1962), goats (Anderson, 1954), and even elephants (Sanderson, 1912; Bazé, 1957) are killed and eaten. At Kanha a tiger broke into our shed and removed a sheep, and the local domestic pigs suffered frequent losses. With the drastic decline of India's wildlife, the tigers in most forests subsist at present partly to wholly on cattle and buffalo; in fact, it is likely that these two domestic animals are the chief source of food of the country's tiger population.

Tigers that prey on cattle are generally perfectly well known to the cowherds and others who resort to their neighbourhood. They seldom molest men, and are often driven away from their prey, after killing it, by the unarmed herds. Frequently they are known by particular names; and they really seem in many cases to live among the villagers and their herds much like a semi-domesticated animal, though, from a mutual consent to avoid direct interviews as much as possible, they are chiefly known by their tracks in the river beds and by their depredations on the cattle (Forsyth, 1889).

Tigers prey readily on carnivores, including each other on occasion. Sloth bear, black bear, and brown bear sometimes become victims (Baldwin, 1877; Burton, 1936; Littledale, 1889; Campbell, 1894; Abramov, 1962). In Manchuria, tigers seem to be partial to dogs and wolves (Novikov, 1962), as well as to lynx and badger (Abramov, 1962). Tigers and leopards appear to avoid each other; at least Anderson (1961) and Smythies (1942) noted that leopards tend to be abundant where tigers are scarce and vice versa, an observation which agrees with my limited experience at Kanha. Allen (1960) and Biscoe (1895) found a leopard which had been killed by a tiger, and Anderson (1954) discovered the partially devoured remains of a leopard which had died in a similar encounter. On the other hand, Khan (1936) related an interesting episode in which a male leopard and a tigress remained together for several days and fed on three different baits, the male killing two of them and the female one, until both were shot. Cannibalism, with one tiger killing and eating another, has been reported by Sanderson (1912) and Brander (1923); two recently shot tigers were partly eaten by several others (J. Bombay Nat. Hist. Soc., 1948).

Tigers seem to catch rodents infrequently, with the exception of porcupines, which by all accounts are favored prey. On one occasion at Kanha a tigress sat in some tall grass with neck craned and ears cocked, watching or listening intently. Suddenly she leaped four feet into the air and pounced on something, presumably a rat or mouse, without catching it. In China tigers eat pangolins (Caldwell, 1925).

At Kanha, langur monkeys are commonly captured by tigers. One of these cats passed the village carrying a langur but dropped it and fled when several persons shouted. The monkey was a female with a small infant clinging unhurt to her chest. Tewary told me of seeing a tiger feed on a rhesus monkey in another part of the state.

Although man is the most easily obtainable source of food throughout the tiger's range, he is for unknown reasons rarely eaten. Those tigers that have turned to man for part or all of their nourishment probably picked up the habit for one of several reasons: (1) they were unable to catch their usual prey because of some disability, such as a gunshot wound or porcupine quills in the paws and face (Corbett, 1957; Powell, 1957); (2) they lacked other food in the area (Turner, 1959); (3) they acquired the habit from their mother (Anderson, 1954); (4) they killed a man inadvertently, tasted the meat, and apparently found it to their liking (Corbett, 1957); and (5) they first scavenged on unburied human corpses, later transferring their attention to living prey (M. Taylor, 1956).

Although man-eating tigers have occurred throughout the species' geographic range, they are rare in most areas, with, for instance, none having been reported from the Soviet Far East since 1917 (Abramov, 1962). Corbett (1957) and Anderson (1954), among others, made the man-eaters of India famous, and at one time apparently more of them thrived there than in any other country. In the year 1902 a total of 1,046 persons were listed by the government as having been killed by tigers (as well as 23,166 by snakes), according to Berg (1936). Man-eaters were uncommon in some parts, like southern India (Sanderson, 1912; O'Brien, 1944), but fairly prevalent in others, the Kumaon hills of Uttar Pradesh, the Chanda District of Maharashtra, the Sunderbans, and the Mandla District of Madhya Pradesh, the last being particularly well known for this dietary habit of the tiger. Today the cats are shot before their depredation on man becomes extensive. The swamp forest of the Sunderbans is one of the very few remaining places in India where tigers frequently kill people for food. "The toll of human life by the man-eating tigers of the Sunderbans has been heavy during the year — the figure being twenty. . . . The victims of man-eaters are mostly honey-collectors who go about in search of honey combs in very small parties" (Rao, 1961).

"Man-eaters have always been numerous in Mandla," commented Forsyth (1889) about the district in which Kanha Park lies. "Over large areas in Bengal the villagers had to surround their habitations with high stockades for their protection. As late as 1856 this practice was not uncommon in some of the more wild parts of the Central Provinces. At that period an average of 200 to 300 villagers were killed every year by tigers in the one district of Mandla in the Central Provinces" (Hewett, 1938). "A few years ago there was a well-known tiger in the Mandla district which took possession of the road, and actually stopped the traffic. . . . It was a merciless highwayman, which infested a well-known portion of the road, and levied toll upon the drivers of the native carts, not by an attack upon their bullocks, but by seizing the driver himself . . ." (Baker, 1890). Man-eaters have become rare in the district in recent years. Only two deaths by tigers have been reported within the present confines of the park since 1935. In 1937 a girl was killed, and in 1946 a night watchman at Kisli was taken (Mehta, n.d.). During the time of the study, one man was bitten in the shoulder as he slept in front of a cattle shed in the village of Bhilwani at the park boundary; the tiger then entered the shed and killed four cows.

Birds form an insignificant part of the tiger's diet. Hazel hens (Abramov, 1962), owls (Ognev, 1962), and peafowl (Allen, 1960) are mentioned in the literature as having been eaten. The peafowl at Kanha were not greatly alarmed by the proximity of a tiger. One cock walked past a tigress at a distance of thirty-five feet; on another occasion, when a tigress suddenly stood up in the grass thirty feet from a cock, the bird merely looked up, then continued to forage. Once a tigress took three long leaps, covering a distance of about thirty feet, and landed on her forepaws in a thicket from which five red jungle fowl males flushed, cackling. Another time, a tigress I had been following left a jungle fowl cock freshly killed in her tracks. Its abdomen was split open, apparently from the impact of the pounce, and feathers had been plucked from the chest, but no part of the bird had been eaten. The male tiger cub clawed his way into our chicken coop on January 1, 1965, and ate all four chickens before he was discovered at 0300 hours. Eggshells, probably from a peafowl, were found in one dropping.

Other tiger food items include lizards (Perry, 1964), snakes (Burton, 1936), turtles (Ognev, 1962; Novikov, 1962), crocodiles (Inglis, 1892), frogs (Caldwell, 1925), and fish (Aramilev, 1959; Ognev, 1962). Among the invertebrates, crabs (Burton, 1936) and locusts (Pocock, 1939) are eaten; and I found winged termite remains in one dropping.

Tigers rarely eat carrion, according to Baldwin (1877) and Champion (1933), but all observations in this study, as well as numerous sources in the literature, indicate that they readily do so. Several cattle and buffalo succumbed from disease at Kanha, and others died from infection several days to several weeks after having been bitten or scratched during unsuccessful attacks by tigers. All such animals were placed out on the meadow and usually discovered and eaten within two to three days by tigers. One cow that had been attacked on October 16 died on November 4 and was buried in a hole five feet deep by villagers. The carcass was covered with about four inches of soil and a mass of thorny branches. A tigress located the body three nights later, perhaps by scent, dug it up, and with her four cubs devoured it.

The tiger is said to eat the spiny durian fruit in southeast Asia (Finn, 1929) and cedar nuts in the Far East (Ognev, 1962). One dropping at Kanha contained *Zizyphus* berries.

In the words of a proverb from south India: "If a tiger is hungry he will at last eat grass" (Perry, 1964). Some grass, bamboo leaves, and other bits of vegetation were found in the majority of tiger droppings, but they had probably been ingested inadvertently, having adhered to the meat. However, a few droppings consisted almost entirely of grass blades. Murie (1944) found that several wolf droppings contained both grass and round worms, and he suggested that the vegetation may act as a scour. One such tiger dropping had tapeworm in it.

Thirteen droppings at Kanha consisted wholly of fine black, micaceous soil. These were found only between October 29 and December 23, 1964, suggesting a seasonal incidence of earth-eating. Powell (1957) also noted that tigers ingest soil.

Quantitative data on the food habits of the tiger in Kanha Park were obtained by collecting and analyzing the contents of 335 droppings in the study area during 1964. Most feces contained the remains of only one prey species, but a few contained two different items, with, for example, porcupine and chital occurring together once. Soil and grass were tallied only if 50 or more percent of the droppings consisted of these foods. The results in Table 50 show

TABLE 50

FREQUENCY OF OCCURRENCE OF FOOD ITEMS IN 335 TIGER FECES
COLLECTED IN THE STUDY AREA, KANHA PARK, IN 1964

FOOD ITEM	FREQUENCY OF OCCURRENCE	
	Number of Feces	Percent
Chital.	175	52.2
Sambar	35	10.4
Barasingha.	29	8.6
Gaur	28	8.3
Langur	21	6.2
Domestic cow	20	5.9
Soil.	13	3.8
Porcupine.	9	2.6
Grass.	8	2.3
Domestic buffalo.	6	1.7
Domestic and wild pig.	3	.8
Frog	1	.3
Eggshell.	1	.3
Termite.	1	.3
Zizyphus fruit	1	.3

that about 79 percent of the droppings contained chital (52 percent), sambar (10 percent), barasingha (9 percent), and gaur (8 percent) remains. Livestock, principally cattle, was noted in about 8 percent of the droppings, and langur monkeys in 6 percent, the rest being miscellaneous items none of which exceeded a frequency of 4 percent. Several such prey species as barking deer, nilgai, mouse deer (Locke, 1954), and jungle fowl, which are known to be pursued, were not evident in the droppings, indicating that they were rarely eaten in the study area. Circumstantial evidence, based on the occurrence of *Taenia pisiformis* in the feces of tigers, suggests that the cats also eat hares, for the intermediate host of this parasite is often a lagomorph (Belding, 1952). For comparison, of 18 droppings collected in Corbett National Park, 55 percent contained chital, 17 percent domestic buffalo, 17 percent hog deer, and 11 percent sambar.

To determine if the percentages of prey in the droppings accurately reflect the relative number of animals killed, the figures can in several instances be compared with the known mortality of several species. It is likely that on the average each pile of droppings represents one prey animal, for even though a tiger may defecate repeatedly after having eaten a large mammal, the chances of collecting more than one or two of these for analysis are slight, and duplications are to some extent offset by the droppings that are not found. For example, an estimated 27 barasingha died in 1964, and 29 tiger droppings and 1 leopard dropping were found with the remains of this deer. A total of 14 domestic cattle were taken in the study area during the year, and their hair appeared in 20 feces; 5 buffalo fell prey, and their remains were noted in 6 feces. The figures for these three species show a fairly close correlation between the actual magnitude of the kill and the frequency of occurrence in the droppings.

It must be emphasized that the results in Table 50 apply only to my small study area, not to the park as a whole. Conditions in the central part of the park were unusual, as has been stressed before, in that a fairly large wildlife population provided the tigers with most of their food and livestock was limited to one small herd of cattle and a few pigs. The range of the resident tigers apparently did not regularly encompass the periphery of the park with its great herds of livestock, for the droppings would probably have provided evidence of this.

A further attempt was made to determine the food habits quantitatively by collecting the lower jaws from kills. A total of 228 were found, 100 of these by De and myself and 128 by villagers. The predator that killed the animal was in most instances unknown, but since wild dogs were very rare and leopards uncommon, and since poachers characteristically removed all the remains of their prey, the great majority of these kills were undoubtedly made by tigers, and the data are treated according to this assumption. None of the prey animals autopsied were heavily parasitized, and there was no evidence that disease, starvation, or old age caused death. The kills found by us in the study area are analyzed separately from those brought in by the villagers from all parts of the park because the uneven distribution of the prey species significantly influences the food habits of the tigers (Table 51). For example, the high percentage of barasingha remains from the study area reflects the concentration of these deer on the Kanha meadow; in addition, barasingha kills are more easily found than those of the forest-dwelling sambar. The results in Table 51 are roughly comparable with the ones in Table 50, but direct comparisons except in very general terms are not possible. Table 51 does not include livestock because animals that died from disease and old age could not be separated from those that were killed by predators. Moreover, the bones of some species are more readily found than others; chital

TABLE 51

NUMBER AND KINDS OF PREDATOR KILLS FOUND IN KANHA PARK

SPECIES	COLLECTED BY DE AND SCHALLER IN STUDY AREA		COLLECTED BY VILLAGERS THROUGHOUT PARK		TOTAL	
	Number	Percent	Number	Percent	Number	Percent
Chital. . . .	38	38.0	60	46.9	98	43.0
Barasingha. .	26	26.0	13	10.2	39	17.1
Sambar . . .	18	18.0	38	29.7	56	24.6
Barking deer.			1	.7	1	.4
Gaur	11	11.0	3	2.3	14	6.1
Blackbuck. .	2	2.0			2	.9
Wild pig. . .	1	1.0	9	7.0	10	4.4
Langur . . .	4	4.0	2	1.6	6	2.6
Porcupine . .			2	1.6	2	.9
Total . .	100	100.0	128	100.0	228	100.0

fawns are so completely eaten that the remains are rarely discovered, whereas the skeletons of adult gaur are quite conspicuous.

The tigers outside the study area subsist chiefly on cattle and buffalo, with wildlife taking a secondary position. To determine the size of the livestock population and the number of animals killed by tigers during the year, a house-to-house census was conducted in four villages during late December, 1964, three of them inside the park but near the periphery (Raunda, Sonph, Kisli) and one at the outside border (Bamni Dadar). A total of 929 head of cattle and buffalo were present in the four villages. Tigers were said to have killed 74 adult cattle, 37 calves, 19 adult buffalo, and 3 buffalo calves, a total of 133 animals during the year. The cattle population at Kanha village varied from 20 to 60, as animals were moved in and out of the area. Of these, 7 adults and 4 calves were killed. The magnitude of the kill suggests that about 10 percent of the livestock population falls prey to tigers each year. On the basis of a mortality figure of similar magnitude in the other villages and an estimate of 2,500 as the total number of animals that frequent the park, it may be concluded that at least 250 head are killed annually by tigers.

Quantitative data on the food habits of the tiger in Russian Manchuria published by Abramov (1962) are presented in Table 52 for comparison with the material from Kanha.

HUNTING AND STALKING

Tigers hunt primarily at night, between dusk and dawn, a time when the wild hoofed animals are most active, too. They usually rest between mid-morning and mid-afternoon, although an animal sometimes hunts throughout the day after what appears to have been an

TABLE 52

"FOOD COMPONENTS" OF THE TIGER IN THE SOVIET FAR EAST
(AFTER ABRAMOV, 1962)

COMMON NAME	SIKHOTA-ALIN RESERVE		PRIMORSK AREA	
	Number of Cases	Percent	Number of Cases	Percent
Wild pig	21	35.7	12	30.0
Manchurian wapiti.	13	22.1	20	50.0
Moose	6	10.1	1	2.5
Brown bear. . . .	5	8.4	2	5.0
Musk deer	8	13.6	1	2.5
Hazel hen.	3	5.1		
Roe deer	2	3.4	1	2.5
Lynx.	1	1.7		
Sika deer.			2	5.0
Badger.			1	2.5

unsuccessful night. Tigers were seen hunting or moving a total of 79 times between dawn and dusk, all but 21 percent of the instances being before 0800 hours and after 1600 hours.

A tiger's usual method of hunting is to walk through its range in search of prey (Plate 20). The forest roads at Kanha were particularly favored as routes, progress along them being easy, silent, and rapid as compared with stalking in the high grass or dry leaf litter of the forest. The bottoms of the numerous dry stream beds were also much used for traveling, probably because the banks provided the cat with cover and there was a good chance of encountering some victim at an isolated water hole.

A tiger in search of prey moves over a considerable amount of terrain in the course of one night. One tiger walked 23 miles in ten hours along a road (Sanderson, 1912), and another was tracked by Locke (1954) for 12 miles. According to Baldwin (1877), tigers frequently travel 10 to 12 miles in a day. On several occasions I followed tracks for 3 to 4 miles before losing them in the forest. To obtain some measure of the tiger's traveling speed, I timed several animals over known distances. One tigress walked .6 mile along a road in eleven minutes, moving at not quite 3 miles per hour; another tigress covered a similar distance at the rate of 2.5 miles per hour. These two speeds closely approximated a tiger's average rate of movement, indicating that when walking steadily a cat can travel at least 30 miles in a twelve-hour night. Ognev (1962) maintained that tigers may travel 50 to 62 miles in a day, a distance which, though possible, is probably of rare occurrence because various forms of activity tend to slow the cat down. One male tiger, for example, marked bushes with scent and attempted to stalk gaur as he walked .8 mile along a road in 41 minutes, a speed of only 1.2 miles per hour. Three other travel speeds of hunting tigers were 1.2, 1.3, and 1.8 miles per hour, respectively. Thus, the average distance covered by a tiger during an unsuccessful night of active hunting is probably 10 to 20 miles.

Hunters have noted that tigers tend to use certain routes more than others. "Like policemen, tigers stick to certain beats . . . ," according to Inglis (1892). Allen (1960) found that one tiger covered his beat about once every ten days, and Anderson (1954) noted that rounds were made once every third to fourth month. Although the Kanha tigers preferred certain routes, particularly some forest roads, almost to the exclusion of others, they were consistent neither in their direction of travel nor in their time schedule. The ranges of the resident tigers were so small that some routes near the Kanha meadow were used several times in one week by the same animal, sometimes on consecutive nights.

Five examples from my field notes illustrate the behavior of a tiger while hunting and stalking its prey (see Leyhausen [1960], for descriptions of stalking in other species of cats):

1) At 1757 hours a male tiger strides out of the forest, crosses a road, skirts a coppice, and angles over a stretch of meadow into a tree-fringed ravine. A langur barks in alarm. The tiger advances up the ravine about 300 feet, enters a patch of adjoining forest where a langur and a chital bark, and moves to the edge of a piece of grassland on which about 60 chital and barasingha graze. From 1812 to 1820 hours he stalks up a shallow grass-covered depression that winds partly across the meadow. Suddenly a chital barks and so does a barasingha, and both crane their necks in the direction of the swale, having sensed the tiger. A barasingha stag advances casually but startles back, barks hoarsely, and together with the whole herd, wheels and runs 100 feet. While at least 20 chital and barasingha bark at him, the male tiger appears 150 feet from the deer, roars softly 3 or 4 times and moves out of sight at 1835 hours.

2) The male tiger sits on a forest road at 0544 hours, then walks along it slowly. He stops 5 times to sniff at a bush or a tuft of grass before spraying the site with scent. At 0605 hours he reaches a slight rise and, in the valley 400 feet ahead, spots about 10 gaur grazing by the banks of a bamboo-bordered ravine. He stands motionless with raised head for 2 minutes staring at the animals. Suddenly he turns off the road and into a bamboo thicket, moving in a semicrouch apparently with the intention of reaching the gaur by stalking up the bottom of the ravine. One gaur standing apart from the others senses the cat, however, snorts loudly, and bolts, followed by the rest of the herd. The tiger jerks erect and the tip of his tail quivers. He then descends briefly into the ravine, cuts back to the road, and moves from sight at 0625 hours.

3) A tigress pads along the meadow's edge just inside the forest at 0745 hours. Six hundred feet ahead of her are 3 barasingha grazing by some tall grass. These suddenly bark in alarm at 0755 hours, facing the forest while doing so. The deer flee when the tigress walks into the open, 80 feet from them. She roars softly twice. On the meadow 600 feet away are 7 other barasingha. On hearing the barking, two does, a fawn, and a stag, in that order, walk in the general direction of the sound, seemingly out of curiosity but obviously alert as they advance with necks stretched forward and ears erect. When 20 feet separates them from a belt of tall grass, the lead doe barks once, and the head of the tigress pops from the vegetation 40 feet away. As the deer wheel and scatter, the stag and fawn dashing one way and the 2 hinds another, the tigress bounds out and rushes after one of the hinds, swiping at the air several times with a forepaw. The deer veers sharply, and the tigress terminates her pursuit abruptly and walks off. The 2 hinds trot after the cat immediately and approach to within 60 feet of her. The other barasingha join the hinds, and the herd then mills around on the trail taken by the tigress. She moves steadily away, disappearing from sight at 0807 hours.

4) A tigress walks along the forest's edge at 0827 hours and stops when she sees a herd of 9 blackbuck grazing 500 feet away on the meadow. She approaches the antelopes in a semicrouch but with head held high as she looks over the top of the grass. Three hundred feet from the blackbuck the tall-grass species give way to a short type which provides no cover. The tigress looks at the deer with forequarters raised but hindquarters lowered, then crouches fully down for 10 seconds, but abruptly changes her mind and rises, apparently having decided that a further stalk is futile. The blackbuck crowd together when they see her. She moves from sight at 0839 hours.

5) About 150 feet from our bungalow is a shallow ravine densely over-

*grown with grass and shrubs. At 1410 hours a chital barks in alarm, and a
doe with a fawn, about 3 months old, bound from the undergrowth into the
open sal forest. The doe trots to one side, but the fawn moves in the opposite direction. About 30 seconds later a tigress appears from the ravine.
She looks at the doe, then the fawn, and at a fast walk turns in the direction
of the latter. The fawn bolts toward the doe past the tigress. Covering 100
feet at an estimated speed of 35 miles per hour, the tigress bounds in pursuit and just out of my sight in a depression pounces on the fawn, which
bleats twice. The doe looks on silently for about 5 seconds from a distance
of about 60 feet, then joins 4 other chital nearby. All move off feeding intermittently.*

These and several other observations indicate that the tiger spots
its prey primarily by sight and at night, probably also by hearing.
I obtained no evidence to suggest that tigers use scent as a means
of locating live prey. A stalking cat orients itself primarily by sight,
sometimes exposing itself in order to determine its position in relation to its intended victim. Corbett (1957) stated that stalks are usually made upwind, but in my experience the conformation of the
terrain and the availability of suitable cover determined the direction of advance. The tiger has to approach to within about thirty
to eighty feet of a fleet-footed prey before a final rush can bring it
into contact with the surprised animal. But if the prey is already
alert, as in the example involving barasingha (3) described above,
even an attack from a distance of 40 feet may be too far to insure
success. Animals on a short-grass meadow, which offers little concealment, are relatively secure from tiger predation, whereas many
are caught along creek beds and in ravines. For example, of 10 killing sites of free-ranging cattle and buffalo, 6 were in creek beds, 3
in sal forest, and one on a meadow; of 19 fresh killing sites of barasingha, chital, and gaur located on and around the Kanha meadow,
11 were along creek beds, 3 in forest, and 5 on the open meadow.
In one of the second group of killings, the tracks clearly showed the
progress of the tigress as she stalked through grass two and a half
feet high to within thirty feet of a barasingha hind; unco-ordinated
hoof marks and blood marked the site where the deer was attacked
and pulled to the ground. On another occasion a barasingha stag
was rushed and killed by the male tiger from a distance of about
twenty feet, the cat having crept up a small gulley almost to within
striking distance. Once a tigress apparently surprised a chital buck
at night after stalking through grass six inches high to within 50
feet or less of him.

Although tigers usually search actively for their prey, they also hunt by secreting themselves along game trails or near water holes, where they wait for an unsuspecting animal; this hunting method is apparently used mostly during the hot season. On one occasion a tigress crouched at 1800 hours in a patch of grass bordering a trail down which gaur traveled almost nightly. She still lay concealed there an hour later when 3 gaur emerged from the forest 250 feet away, having used another route that evening. Tigers also secreted themselves in the grass surrounding pools at the bottom of ravines, and I saw them emerge several times from such a location after having been discovered by deer looking down from the bank.

There are no records of tigers pursuing monkeys and other prey by ascending trees, although they are able to climb. One tigress in the Mandla district clambered eighteen feet up a sal tree and grabbed the leg of a hunter (Hewett, 1938); and Shakespear (1860), Fletcher (1911), Pocock (1939), and others reported seeing tigers in the branches of trees as high as thirty feet above ground in attempts to escape from flood waters, wild dogs, or hunters.

The tiger usually makes no attempt to chase its prey over long distances. Once I observed a tigress as she bounded at full speed after a jackal for nearly a quarter mile but was easily outdistanced. Locke (1954) observed a boar followed by a tiger, both seemingly tired after a long chase. It is unlikely, however, that a tiger is capable of catching most species in this fashion, and the fact that deer approach a visible cat to within a hundred feet on occasion suggests that they are able to assess their degree of danger with some precision.

Little effort is wasted by the tiger in pursuit of prey which has detected it or which is too difficult to stalk successfully, such as blackbuck grazing on the open meadow. The alarm bark of a deer directed at a hidden tiger is apparently a sufficient indication to the cat that further stalking is futile, for it then commonly rises from its place of concealment and walks away, as illustrated in two of the examples cited above.

Champion (1933), Hewett (1938), and others have given the impression that the tiger's method of hunting and stalking is so efficient that it can obtain prey with little difficulty. This is perhaps true of tigers which subsist on livestock, but those at Kanha appeared to expend considerable effort in securing a wild animal. Tracks, feces, and other signs indicated that at least one tiger traversed the Kanha meadow daily. The frequent intense barking by herds of deer further attested to their numerous encounters with tigers. Yet even when the wildlife was concentrated on the meadow — about seven hundred head of hoofed animals in a three-square-mile area in July — relatively few kills were found. Of twelve complete stalks observed, only one was successful. It was common to see tigers in the morning with their bellies very lean, showing that they had not eaten a substantial meal the previous two or three nights. The majority of stalks ended in failure, the cat having been detected primarily by the acute senses of smell and hearing of its prey. Probably at least twenty unsuccessful attempts were made for each animal captured. Similarly, a pack of wolves observed by Mech (1964) made 77 attacks on moose on Isle Royale over a three-year period, but only six animals were killed; in one day the wolf pack chased moose fifteen times without securing a single one.

After an unproductive night of hunting, the tiger rests in some secluded place, preferably near water. One tigress, for example, crossed the meadow at 0750 hours, entered a patch of shady forest, and reclined on her side in some tall grass. She moved sixty feet to the base of another tree three minutes later and remained there until 1630 hours, when she moved off in the direction of a water hole five hundred feet away.

ATTACKING AND KILLING

Hunters have rarely witnessed and still more rarely described the tiger's technique of killing wild prey, and I was able to witness only one successful stalk during the study. One freshly killed chital doe had a lacerated throat, tooth punctures on the lower back (one canine having penetrated a kidney), and claw marks on the chest. A barasingha stag was bitten in the back of the neck as well as the throat, and there were claw marks on both shoulders. A gaur calf was bitten through the nape and base of the skull, and it had claw marks on the rump. These wounds generally reflect the killing technique described by Corbett (1957). He saw about twenty attacks, of which only one, that on a chital doe, involved a head-on charge: "The attacks in the other cases witnessed were made by the killers coming up from behind, or at an angle, and with a single spring or short rush getting hold of their victims with their claws, and then with a lightning-fast movement seizing them by the throat and bringing them to the ground." Hearsey (1932) watched a tiger seize a barasingha and hold it down for about fifteen minutes before releasing its hold.

One adult sambar stag at Kanha was apparently straddled by a tiger and severely lacerated before managing to escape. The wounds healed, leaving large scars on the shoulders, sides, and rump, some of them 12 to 15 inches long and 2 inches wide. There were eleven such scars on his right side and nine on the left. His movements were stiff and slow.

Sanderson (1912) and A. Singh (pers. comm.) found a freshly killed boar bitten through the back of the neck. Butt (1963) observed a tiger as it grabbed the neck of a pig and dragged it from a bamboo thicket. Inglis (1892) watched a tiger as it "alighted clean on the boar's back, inserting his teeth above the shoulders, tearing with his claws and biting out great mouthfuls of flesh." One domestic pig, weighing about fifty pounds and closely resembling a wild one in size and appearance, was tethered out as bait. The male tiger cub approached it to within five feet, took two swipes at its head with a forepaw, and suddenly lunged in, grabbing the pig by the nape and holding it for two minutes until it died. Boars, which may weigh well over two hundred pounds, are dangerous antagonists, and the tiger may have considerable trouble in killing one as this account by Turner (1959) illustrates:

The tiger walked down the bank on to the soft sand, and circled the boar who wheeled to face him. The circling and wheeling continued three or four times until suddenly the tiger charged the boar, striking him with all his might, and, with the greatest agility leaping aside after his blow. The boar met the onslaught by turning dexterously and taking it on the side of the shoulder. In this manner the tiger delivered blow after blow. . . . His blows told their tale, for the boar was dripping with blood from his shoulders downwards. Whenever the boar showed the least tendency to charge, the tiger would step backwards. . . . The tiger, in striking and endeavouring to jump away from the boar, either lost his balance and landed awkwardly, or skidded in the soft sand. Seeing his opportunity, and astonishingly quick to grasp it, the boar charged straight into him, and, burying his razor-edged tushes in the tiger's belly, ripped and ripped again, reinforcing his thrusts to the fullest by his stupendous might and enormous weight.

With the greatest difficulty the tiger succeeded in extricating himself and stood apart. . . . He was disembowelled, with much of his entrails dangling low and heavily from his belly. Slinking towards the bank, with dragging intestines, he ascended it and disappeared in the thorny scrub bordering it . . .

where he was found dead the following morning.

One tigress at Kanha apparently jumped on the back of an adult bull gaur from a stream bank, bit him in the back of the neck, bearing him to the ground, and then grasped his throat, a reconstruction based on the tracks at the site and the tooth marks on the dead animal. One adult female gaur was found shortly after she had died, probably from wounds inflicted by a tiger a few days earlier. The cause of death seemed to be a large septic wound on the dorsal ridge. She had, in addition, a deep tooth puncture on the right side of her throat and on the left side of her chest. There were claw marks on both sides of her rump and on the neck. The evidence suggests that a tiger attacked her persistently and was able to clamber onto her back once before being thrown off. Berg (1936) shows a photograph of a banteng with a healed wound on the hump, probably the result of a tiger's attack. Tigers are also said to hamstring gaur (Brander, 1923; Bazé, 1957; Butt, 1963).

Baikov (1925) reported that Manchurian tigers attack bears from above, by lying in wait on cliffs, and kill them by biting through the neck vertebrae.

The tiger's method of attacking domestic cattle and buffalo is frequently commented upon in the literature, but the accounts are usually incomplete, as, for example, in Burton (1929), or contradictory because the observer was also attempting to shoot the cat at the same time or made only a cursory examination of the dead animal. Baldwin (1877) and Forsyth (1889) stated that animals are usually seized by the nape and pulled to the ground with a wrench that dislocates the neck. On the other hand, Sanderson (1912) and Fletcher (1911) found that cattle are almost invariably grabbed by the throat. According to Inglis (1892), after "delivering the numbing blow with his mighty fore paw, he fastens on the throat of the animal he has felled, and invariably tries to tear open the jugular vein." Brander (1923) and Finn (1929) also mentioned that livestock may be knocked down with the blow of the paw. Anderson (1954) described the method of killing as follows:

In fact, when attacking, the tiger rises up beside its victim, generally places a paw over its shoulder and seizes the beast by the back of the neck or throat, according to its size, pressing the head to the ground. The paw is then used as a lever to cause the victim to topple over itself, while the tiger continues to hold the head down. Thus the weight of the animal's own body is the factor that breaks the neck. . . .

Brander (1923) provided an account of an attack on a free-ranging animal and a general description of the technique used in killing tethered bait:

The tiger sprang up and in three short bounds had seized the neck. The animal had started into motion, but the shock of the tiger's rush immediately rolled them over, and the tiger, hanging on to the neck, twisted the same in the opposite direction to which the body of the animal was revolving. The weight of the revolving body opposed by the twist on the neck in the opposite direction resulted in instant dislocation. . . .

The tiger advances stalking within 20 yards or so of the bait. . . . Two or three long rapid strides are then taken, and dipping its head like lightning under the buffalo's chin, the throat is seized and immediately pulled to the ground. The tiger remains thus pinning the beast's head and neck to the ground. When in this position, the tiger is down on its elbows but the hindquarters remain up. The buffalo struggles to remain standing but presently falls over and in so doing sometimes breaks its own neck, which of course is pinned firmly to the ground all the time. On the other hand, this frequently does not happen, and the two animals simply remain as they are until the buffalo is dead from strangulation and suffocation.

The same tigress at Kanha was observed to kill a tethered buffalo alone on three occasions, and a large male cub was seen to do so on four occasions. Each of the baits was tied by a foreleg or by the neck to a stump or tree to prevent its escape. The killing techniques employed in four of these instances are described in detail below. Attacks by more than one tiger at the same time have already been discussed in the section on female-young behavior.

1) A tigress pads along a forest path at 0712 hours and suddenly sees the buffalo 100 feet away in the high grass. Without breaking her stride, she continues for another 100 feet while looking intently at the animal. She then stands motionless for 3 minutes, her head raised above the grass, watching. Finally she retraces her steps and enters the grass walking very slowly. She approaches the buffalo to within 50 feet, stands, and looks, her body hidden in the grass but her head visible above it. When the buffalo inadvertently faces in her direction, she crouches down, but as soon as it turns aside, she advances, carefully lifting and placing each paw separately.

The buffalo raises its nose and sniffs at 0717 hours, apparently having scented the tigress. It faces in her direction for 43 minutes, and the tigress remains hidden the whole time. She peers briefly above the grass at 0803 hours, only the top of her head showing, then crouches down, actions she repeats several times during the next 10 minutes.

At 0814 hours she suddenly raises her head completely above the grass and bounds forward as the buffalo turns to flee. In 3 leaps she reaches it and places her right paw on its back while biting into the left side just behind the front leg. The combined pull of the paw and the teeth topples the buffalo in the direction of the tigress, and even as it falls, she releases her hold, dodges around its head, and grabs it by the throat. The buffalo then lies on its side, with the cat crouching at right angles holding the throat. Twice she readjusts her hold with a snap. At 0819 hours the buffalo kicks its hindlegs, its last movement. At 0820 hours the tigress jerks the throat twice. Finally at 0823 hours she rises and begins to drag the buffalo away, her teeth having inadvertently cut the rope by which it was tied. With her head held high and her teeth clamped to the throat, she pulls the 400 pound animal slowly alongside her body. Three times she stops and readjusts her hold. After 12 minutes she has dragged the kill into a thicket 150 feet away. There she is joined by one of her female cubs, now one year old, which apparently has accompanied her on the hunt.

2) At 1940 hours the tigress steps from the high grass and grabs the bull by the left hindleg before it has time to turn. She jerks the animal backward so violently that its forequarters collapse. As it struggles to rise, she reaches between the hindlegs, seizes it by the throat, but soon releases her hold to once again pull on a hindleg. When the animal falls over, she dodges around the kicking legs and grabs its throat. Lying on its side, with the tigress facing it in a crouch, it struggles and once manages to lift its head about 2 feet. But the tigress merely raises herself slightly and exerts downward pressure on the neck until the head is back on the ground. Suddenly she loosens her hold somewhat and with the same movement vaults to the other side of her victim so that she now faces the back of its neck. After securing her grip on the throat, she braces her four legs and vigorously jerks the neck several times in her direction, thereby twisting it and audibly snapping the vertebral column. Movement in the animal ceases at 1948 hours. The tigress releases her hold at 1950 hours.

3) The tigress stalks from a shallow ravine at 2006 hours and circles the buffalo slowly at a distance of about 20 feet. When for a moment the animal faces away from her, she lunges in and places her forepaws on its rump. Its hindquarters collapse under the pulling weight, and as it struggles to rise, the tigress straddles its back with the claws of one forepaw dug into each shoulder. She leans down its right side and bites it in the throat. Then, retaining her hold on the throat of the now standing animal, she dismounts on its left side, an action which causes it to fall over. The tigress nimbly jumps back, yet keeps her grip on the throat, and faces the back of the buffalo's neck out of reach of the thrashing hooves. She releases her hold at 2012 hours, the animal having died about 3 minutes earlier.

4) The male tiger cub 16 months old, hides in the grass 30 feet from the buffalo at 1828 hours. Thirty seconds later, when the animal turns its back toward the cub, he dashes in, clambers up on the rump, and bites it in the neck. The buffalo stumbles and falls but dislodges the tiger while struggling to rise. The cub then grabs one of the buffalo's hindlegs with both paws, as if trying to prevent its escape, and bites into the hock joint. Once again the cub scrambles up on the animal's back and grips the nape, his forepaws clutching the shoulders. Holding on firmly, he slides off to one side, his weight pulling the buffalo over. He jumps clear and, as the buffalo hits

the ground, reaches over the back of the neck and bites into the throat. The buffalo struggles, but the tiger retains his hold, either standing, sitting, or half-crouching while doing so. Once the buffalo manages to raise its fore-quarters briefly while the tiger, now facing it, with one forepaw hooked into each shoulder in a seeming attempt to pull it down, continues to grip the throat with his teeth. Finally the tiger just sits, holding the throat up off the ground, the buffalo's nose pointing skyward, until it dies at 1837 hours.

Although the buffaloes were tied, the methods of attack and killing probably approximated those used on free-ranging animals quite closely. Of nine untethered cows and buffalos examined after they had been killed, all had lacerated throats, and two had also been bitten in the nape. Two, and possibly three, seemed to have broken necks. One large domestic bull, which survived after the attacking tigress was driven off by villagers, had been bitten in the right hind-leg, the left front leg, and the abdomen, as well as clawed on the shoulders. The following methods of attack were used by the same tigress, which entered a cattle shed repeatedly at night in late October:

October 16–17   Bit cow above the hock joint and clawed right side of neck before being chased away by villagers.

October 18–19   Carried away one calf, disemboweling it 300 feet from shed and taking the rest of the carcass with her.

October 20–21   Clawed hindleg of a calf, bit it in the back of the neck, but was disturbed by villagers before being able to kill it.

October 25–26   Bit a cow in the back of the neck; bit a calf through the back of the neck, killing it, but was chased away by the villagers. The following morning, at 1030 hours, when the cattle were being driven out to feed, the tigress killed another calf with a bite through the nape and clawed both of its shoulders.

The four examples illustrate not only that several different techniques are used by the tiger in killing large mammals but also that diverse methods are employed by the same tiger in dispatching its prey under very similar conditions. In general, the killing consists of two steps, which, however, may be combined on occasion: (1) the attack, during which the animal is thrown off its feet, and (2) the actual killing, usually by biting into the throat or the back of the neck. During the initial assault, the tiger attempts to approach from the side or behind, avoiding the front where many hoofed animals carry weapons in the form of antlers or horns. The force of the contact may be sufficient to bowl the prey over, but if it is not, the cat bites at the legs, rump, back, neck, or abdomen, depending on the circumstances, while using its weight and the power of its forelegs to cause the animal to topple. If the prey attempts to escape, the tiger uses its hooked claws and teeth to grasp and bite at any convenient part of the body, often the legs and rump. The hindlegs of the tiger tend to remain on the ground during the attack while the forelegs and jaws do the lacerating; no tiger was seen to make a flying leap at its prey, although the cats are able to jump as far as twenty feet (Brander, 1923; Bazé, 1957).

Many authors (Fenton, 1905; Brander, 1923; Corbett, 1957; Bazé, 1957; K. Singh, 1959) maintained that tigers commonly hamstring large prey like cattle and gaur, an action which is said to facilitate the killing. I saw no evidence of hamstringing or definite attempts to do so. Although tigers frequently bit a buffalo in the hindleg, in apparent attempts to pull it off its feet or to prevent its escape, the wounds never incapacitated the animal, and it retained the full use of its leg. In fact, it is possible that many of the so-called hamstrung animals reported in the literature did not have severed tendons in their hindlegs but merely wounds incurred when the tiger attacked them in the manner that has already been described.

Adult tigers give the impression of being very cautious, attacking only when the danger of being injured is minimal. Even domestic buffalo can be dangerous opponents since they have been known to charge tigers and drive them away (Baker, 1890; Allen, 1960); in Madhya Pradesh, for example, a herd of buffalo is sometimes used to drive a wounded tiger from dense cover (Butt, 1963). The response of a tigress to a gaur at Kanha illustrates this caution:

A tigress saw an adult gaur bull 200 feet away. She stopped, looked, advanced 30 feet, and watched alertly while the bull moved along slowly. She then walked 70 feet at an angle toward the bull, which had not yet sensed her, but she suddenly retreated; she lowered herself into a semicrouch as if beginning to stalk, stepped several feet in one direction, then in another, seemingly undecided about her course of action. Finally she left, heading away from the gaur.

After the prey has been thrown off its feet, the tiger characteristically lunges for and grasps the throat, if it has not done so earlier during the attack, the throat being the most vulnerable part of a large animal's body. The hold is retained until the prey dies and usually for several minutes afterward. Death appeared to be due to strangulation in most of the instances observed. The throat hold confers the following additional advantages on a tiger: (1) horns and antlers cannot be used effectively by the prey; (2) the thrashing hooves cannot reach the tiger as long as it remains near the head; and (3) by holding the neck of the prey to the ground, the cat can with relative ease prevent it from righting itself and gaining its feet, an important advantage when handling a gaur, which may weigh seven times as much as the tiger.

Adult cattle, buffalo, and gaur are apparently only rarely killed by a bite through the back of the neck, probably because of the thick bones, the long spinal processes on the cervical vertebrae, and the heavy padding of muscle. Out of a total of 22 large cattle and buffalo checked during or after an attack, none were killed by a bite through the back of the neck. Other prey, however, such as barasingha, chital, pigs, gaur calves, and cattle calves may be successfully attacked in this fashion. Cats, in general, tend to kill by biting their victims through the nape, as described in great detail by Leyhausen (1960, 1965c), and the throat hold as used by the tiger may be a special adaptation for dealing with large prey.

The fact that animals killed by tigers sometimes have broken necks has been noted repeatedly in the literature. In the two instances quoted above (Anderson, 1954; Brander, 1923), the neck appears to have been broken accidentally as the animal fell awkwardly under the impetus of the attack. One buffalo at Kanha pitched forward and apparently dislocated its neck when the male cub vaulted onto its back. However, the broken neck is probably not accidental in all instances, as my one observation in which a tigress twisted the throat backward until the vertebrae snapped suggests.

Occasionally a tiger kills several animals during a prolonged attack. "Silver Hackle" (1929) reported that six chital were struck down by one or two tigers. Sanderson (1912) several times noted four to five, and once fourteen, cattle on the ground after an attack; and one tiger is said to have killed eight cattle at mid-day (Morris, 1946). Forsyth (1889) attributed such behavior to the exuberance of young tigers. It seems likely that in some cases the tiger merely bites and claws at any animal in its vicinity while attempting to catch one in the confusion of a milling herd, as described by Strachan (1933): "A tiger once rushed right through a herd, clawing and biting right and left, but without succeeding in pulling down any beast that had been allowed to feed too near its haunts. Despite the shouts of the man in charge at the time, five were badly injured, three of them eventually dying. . . ." Some livestock is perhaps killed simply because of the ease with which it can be stalked and attacked. Locke (1954) reported a tiger which killed twenty-three cattle over a period of seven weeks without eating them.

BEHAVIOR AT THE KILL

After the prey has been killed, the tiger usually drags or carries it to a secluded place, preferably into a thicket near water. Since much of the prey at Kanha was attacked along ravines with cover readily available, most animals were not taken far from the kill site. Carcasses were rarely moved more than 600 feet before the tiger commenced its meal, but on one occasion a tigress dragged a chital for 1,800 feet before eating, the longest distance noted. A tiger is exceedingly strong, and large kills, such as a 400–500 pound buffalo, which three men find difficult to move, are readily pulled for several hundred feet by the cat. One tiger jumped 15 feet up the bank of a stream while carrying a 150 pound carcass (Smythies, 1942), and another tiger carried a 400 pound bullock for 900 feet (Sanderson, 1912). The cat usually grasps the prey by the neck and drags the carcass between its forelegs or along the side of its body. Anderson (1961) reported that a tiger carried a domestic bull "slung across his back with one hoof trailing along the wet ground. . . ." Small pieces of meat are lifted off the ground and carried in the mouth. One tigress carried the 142 pound forequarters of a cow 600 feet along a stream bed and 100 feet up into a mass of boulders without leaving a drag mark.

The tiger begins to feed, regardless of the time of day, as soon as it has moved the carcass to a suitable locality. On three occasions a tigress first ate for several minutes on her fresh kill and then departed to fetch her cubs. When the kill was a domestic cow or buffalo, the tiger began to eat at the rump in all of the instances observed, although it sometimes started at the neck if another tiger had already occupied the preferred place at the hindquarters. One tigress began to eat the head of a pig rather than the rump. The tiger's carnassial teeth are highly efficient cutting tools, parting the skin of its victim like scissors; with a combination of cutting, pulling, and tearing, the cat rapidly bolts down the meat, skin, and viscera. A feeding tiger either lies, crouches, stands (Plate 26), sits, or rests on its elbows with the rump elevated. The forepaws are little used when eating large prey, although small pieces of meat may be held down with a paw while the cat tears at them. Bones are sometimes gnawed on while propped between the pads of the forepaws.

A tiger eats steadily but rarely for more than one hour before stopping and resting awhile. The longest uninterrupted feeding periods lasted 70, 75, 95, 110, and 145 minutes, respectively, the last instance being that of a tigress which ate, then departed, leaving her large cubs at the kill. After a few minutes to several hours of resting, wandering around, drinking, grooming, and other activities, the tiger returns to the kill and eats some more. The number of major feeding periods, not including brief snacks, of one tigress between the time of killing in the evening and the beginning of the daytime rest period was 1, 3, 3, 4, and 5, respectively; a male cub once ate in one uninterrupted session when the meat supply was limited (a pig) and once in two sessions (Fig. 15). A tiger visiting a kill made by another tiger appears to eat less often than the owner, as shown in Figure 15; for example, in the instances where both female H and the male fed on the kills of female G. The total time spent in actual feeding in the course of a night varied. One tigress (female G) ate for a total of 70, 130, 145, 181, and 191 minutes, respectively, not including cursory gnawing on bone scraps; another tigress (female H) ate for 55 and 90 minutes on the two occasions observed; the male tiger once ate for 35 minutes; and the male cub once ate for 110 minutes and another time for 135 minutes. Thus a tiger seems to require about 1½ to 2½ hours of feeding to become satiated.

A hungry tiger can consume a prodigious amount of food, readily eating the hindquarters of a cow weighing 350–400 pounds during the first night, much of the forequarters during the second night, and the remaining meat during the third and fourth nights. Locke (1954) estimated that a tiger can eat 40 pounds of meat in one meal; Brehm (1918) placed the figure at 66 pounds, Sanderson (1912) at 70 pounds, and Ognev (1962) at 66 to 110 pounds. It was difficult to determine the exact weight of the food consumed by one tiger at Kanha because several animals usually shared a kill. Two tigresses ate 89 pounds from a cow in one night; a tigress with four small cubs devoured 85 pounds from a gaur calf; and a tigress with one small cub ate 40 pounds from a chital. In each of these instances all edible parts of the carcass were eaten, and the tigers could presumably have taken more. When the male tiger killed a barasingha estimated to have weighed 250 pounds, he required three nights to eat the animal, consuming approximately 160 to 175 pounds of meat, or 53 to 58 pounds per day. Only 53 pounds of bones and 65 pounds of rumen contents remained of a buffalo weighing about 320 pounds after two tigresses and four one-year-old cubs ate one night, indicating that about 200 pounds, or 33 pounds per animal, had been devoured. These four cubs ingested about 150 pounds (37 pounds per cub) of a cow the first night and 70 pounds (17.5 pounds per cub) the second night (the kill was weighed after the first night); they gnawed only on bones the third

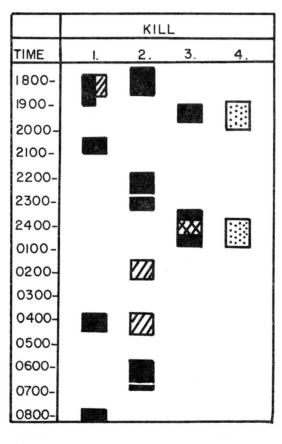

Fig. 15.—The number of tiger feeding periods and amount of time spent eating at four different kills between 1700 and 0800 hours.

night, failing to eat 72 pounds of rumen contents and 46 pounds of bones. During the night of March 27–28, 1965, the tigress and her four cubs ate two buffalo, each weighing about 300 pounds, leaving only scraps of meat and hide as well as the bones and contents of the intestinal tract. At least 50 pounds per animal were eaten. Between November 14 and 19, 1964, two tigresses and four cubs devoured three buffalo, each tiger averaging about 25 pounds of meat per day; between March 13 and 30, 1965, the tigress and four cubs ate numerous baits, averaging 22 pounds of meat per day. These figures indicate that an adult tiger can readily consume 40 to 60 pounds of meat during a night, and probably more in the case of a large male. The amount of food eaten may total as much as one-fifth of the tiger's body weight.

The tiger usually eats up its prey so completely that almost nothing remains for the scavengers. The skin, except on the head and lower part of the legs, is ingested together with the meat. The viscera are also devoured, although Locke (1954) maintained that they are never eaten in Malaya. Occasionally a tiger disembowled a carcass, leaving the digestive tract uneaten near the kill site, but in most instances the stomach and intestines, although not their vegetal contents, were consumed. Bones are also swallowed, particularly the soft ones of young animals. The only remnants of a full-term barasingha fetus were several slivers of long bones and one hoof. The remains of a chital fawn, three months old, were a piece of cranium, three pieces of long bone, one metatarsus, and four bone splinters. The hard, large bones of adult animals are not eaten, although relatively thin parts such as the edge of the scapula, the ends of the ribs, the tip of the sternum, and the nasal bones are commonly bitten off. The horny covering of the hooves is also swallowed.

Instances of the tiger's daily schedule of activity at the kill have been given in the section on female-young behavior. Most feeding takes place at night, but brief snacks may be had at any time of the day. For example, tigers returned to their kill for a full session of feeding at 1825, 1828, 1915, 1930, 2015, and 2025 hours, respectively, at or soon after darkness, and then spent the night in alternately eating and resting (Fig. 15). With the approach of morning, the cat usually tries to drag the carcass into cover. The remains of free-ranging prey are frequently carried to another site, sometimes a considerable distance away. As a result, the bones from the hindquarters of a kill may be in one place and those of the forequarters in another. For instance, one tigress killed a cow in a ravine; after dragging the carcass three hundred feet, she ate the hindquarters, leaving the rumen contents and the bones of the hindlegs and pelvis at the feeding site. The rest of the cow was dragged a half mile over two ridges to the banks of another ravine and concealed there beneath some grass. The tigress reclined partially submerged in a pool two hundred feet away.

Jungle cows and white-backed vultures rapidly strip the meat from any unattended carcass. Since the tiger usually rests near the kill, its presence keeps all but a few crows from descending. If the scavenging birds attempt to feed, the tiger may rush at them to chase them away. One tigress killed a domestic bull and left him in a ravine. When a number of vultures began to feed, the cat stalked to within a hundred feet of them, according to De, who witnessed the event, and with a coughing roar rushed forward. She grabbed an airborne vulture by the neck with her forepaws, dropped it, and then swatted it once, leaving it dead. Half an hour later she attacked the vultures once more, killing one with a sweep of the paw. Strachan (1933) observed similar behavior.

Tigers frequently hide their kill or cover it with debris, especially if they leave its vicinity. The remains of one cow were wedged among some boulders, and those of another cow were almost completely hidden in a narrow erosion gulley overgrown with grass. The tiger may also cover the carcass with leaves, grass, and other material, as noted by Brander (1923) and Powell (1957). When attempting to cover the kill, the tiger faces away from it and scratches vegetation and earth over it with backward strokes of a forepaw (Plate 27). Pocock (1939) and Brander (1923) reported that tigers bite off grass and cover the kill with it. Only one instance of this was noted at Kanha—the forequarters of one buffalo were quite well concealed by grass that apparently had been bitten off. The puma also hides its kills beneath leaves (Young and Goldman, 1946).

The tiger is relatively inactive during the daylight hours, usually resting on its side, belly, or back in a shady spot or even partially submerged in a pool when it is hot. The animal is often quite restless until mid-morning as it meanders around the kill with seeming aimlessness. Occasionally it may lick its chest and forepaws, yawn, rise and stretch by extending its hindlegs and arching its tail, and then recline and roll over; several minutes later it may inspect the kill, tentatively picking up and dropping a bone, and finally rest once more (Plate 28). After being quite torpid during the hot noon hours, the animal becomes active again toward dusk, often going to a water hole to drink at that time. One tigress went to the banks of a stream at 1710 hours and drank steadily for 132 seconds in a crouched position.

When the last edible scraps of a kill have been devoured, the tiger usually leaves the site and either begins to hunt again or rests in another locality. On one occasion a large cub revisited a kill site two days after its family had abandoned the remains. Small-sized prey, such as chital, may be eaten up and remnants left behind in one night, but a large prey, like a gaur, may last for five or more days.

The bones of an abandoned kill are sometimes concentrated in a relatively small area, but at other times they are scattered over several hundred feet of terrain, as illustrated in Figures 16 and 17, both of which are based on kills of barasingha hinds that were eaten up in one night by the same tigress and four cubs.

Response to Man

The tiger's reputation for savagery appears to be largely based on its potential to do harm and on the fact that under certain circumstances, such as when shot and only wounded, it may attack and kill the careless hunter. The fear inspired by the few individuals which turn to man-eating has also contributed to the belief that tigers attack without provocation. Exaggerated accounts by hunters have added to the widespread misconception about the cat's response to man. Shakespear (1860), for example, wrote: "You will on no account whatever move in a jungle infested with tigers without your rifle in your hand and both barrels at full-cock." And one hundred years later Scott (1960) related his experience with a distant tiger:

We were in a lost position, almost a hundred yards from the tree and the safety of the machan. In a few quick bounds the tiger could be among us, sweeping his great paws. It would have to be one shot, and it would have to kill him — dead. Or else we would be. Now, suddenly the three of us had rifles at our shoulders. It was a long shot, at least three hundred yards. I had no scope on the .458, and all I could see clearly was his great head. . . . Now we knew how death in the jungle arrived, silently deadly, without warning. We had been coldly close to it in those few minutes.

On the other hand, persons familiar with tigers all agree that the animals are generally so shy and avoid man so assiduously that they are rarely seen (Champion, 1933; Allen, 1960). A person "is safe anywhere with a walking stick" (Fletcher, 1911). Forsyth (1889), who hunted tigers in Madhya Pradesh when they were still abundant, expressed himself well on this point:

At the outset of one's experience in forest life it is impossible to avoid the belief that the tiger of story is about to show himself at every step one takes in the jungle; and it is not till every effort to meet with him has been used in vain that one realizes how very little danger from tigers attends a mere rambler in the jungles. During ten years of pretty constant roaming about on foot in the most tigerish localities of the Central Provinces, I have only once come across a tiger when I was not out shooting, and only twice more when I was not actually searching for tigers to shoot. In truth, excepting in the very haunts of a known man-eater, there is no danger whatever in traversing any part of the jungles of this, or I believe any other part of India.

In Kanha Park, where tigers are not shot from cars, their usual response to a slowly approaching vehicle is either to walk or trot away or to crouch in an apparent attempt to hide. One tigress, for example, crouched for ten minutes in the grass, watching the car 300 feet away, before rising and walking off into some dense undergrowth. On another occasion a tigress saw the car 150 feet away at 0715 hours. She hid in the grass until 0743 hours, then sat up and looked around briefly; she crouched again but, apparently changing her mind, suddenly walked away. When the car followed her slowly, she sought cover 80 feet from it and waited fifteen minutes before reappearing and departing. On several occasions, the tiger merely stepped into the high grass bordering the road and pressed itself to the ground when the car drew near, and the animal's tawny, black-striped coat blended so well into the surroundings that it was invisible from a distance of fifteen feet. Even a thinly leafed shrub or the low stubble of a burned meadow sometimes broke the outline of the cat's body sufficiently that a casual glance failed to reveal it (Plate 20). Some tigresses, which were presumably in heat, seemed to ignore the car even when it approached to within 40 feet of them.

A person on foot rarely sees a tiger because the animal apparently perceives him first and avoids an encounter by hiding or sneaking away. If surprised by a silent approach, the tiger's usual response is to flee. One tigress bolted when I stepped around the bend of a stream bed and found her resting in the sun 70 feet away. Another tigress growled at me, her ears back and her face in a snarl, from the bank of a ravine at a distance of 80 feet. She then trotted away

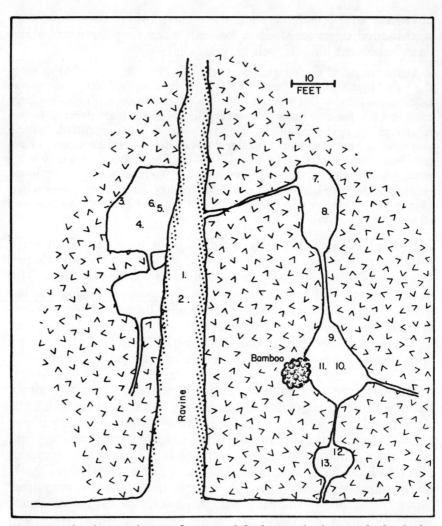

FIG. 16.—Sketch map showing location of the bones of a barasingha hind after a tigress with four cubs killed and ate her during the night of June 28–29. The deer was captured in a small ravine and eaten in the tall grass surrounding it, leaving the grass trampled down in spots (white areas). (1) kill site, (2) rumen contents, (3) hindleg, (4) front leg, (5) hindleg, (6) scapula, (7) skull, (8) four cervical vertebrae, (9) rib cage and some loose ribs, (10) pelvis with some articulated lumbar and sacral vertebrae, (11) several thoracic and lumbar vertebrae, (12) front leg, and (13) scapula. All leg bones were articulated.

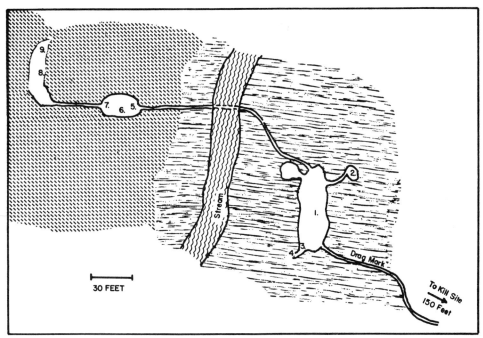

Fig. 17.—Sketch map showing location of the scattered bones of a barasingha hind after a tigress with four cubs (same animals as in Fig. 16) killed and ate her during the night of August 23–24. The kill was dragged from an area of short grass into some tall grass (irregular lines) bordering a stream. The deer was partially eaten there, the grass being trampled down in the process (white area), then dragged across the stream into a patch of sal forest (dashed lines) where the rest was consumed. (1) rumen contents, (2) bone splinters of foetus, (3) hindleg, (4) scapula, (5) pelvis with sacral vertebrae, (6) lumbar vertebrae, (7) hindleg, (8) head and several cervical vertebrae, and (9) front leg, scattered ribs, and thoracic vertebrae. The leg bones were articulated. One front leg and one scapula were not found.

and hid in a thicket nearby. The tiger's disinclination to attack a person was further demonstrated on two occasions. One evening I sat with my back to a rock at the top of a ridge, watching the remains of a cow in the valley 200 feet below. When one fallen leaf rustled, I cautiously raised myself and looked over the rock. A tigress stood with craned neck 10 feet away; but she merely turned and departed at a fast walk. Another time I silently approached a large, slanting boulder in a bamboo grove without noting the large female tiger cub, fourteen months old, asleep on it. When the tiger looked over the edge of the rock, our faces were 3 to 4 feet apart. It emitted a growling roar, and I leaped aside, then backed away hurriedly and quietly for 100 feet. It jumped off the rock and bounded toward me apparently out of curiosity, and I ascended a tree to a height of 15 feet and sat down. The tiger reclined 75 feet away, watching. Ten minutes later, a large male cub arrived and rested 60 feet away without sensing me. His mouth was partially open, and the tip of the tongue moved in and out as he panted in the heat. After a few minutes I said in a conversational tone "Hello there." The male cub looked slowly around. When his eyes focused on me, he growled once and fled. The female cub remained, however, and she was joined by her two sisters, all of which then watched me. After half an hour in the tree, I shouted once at the tigers, and they scampered off.

A tiger on a kill usually retreats silently or with a low growl or snarl when a person is still 100 to 150 feet away, but sometimes it does so with some hesitation and show of aggression. Once I inadvertently surprised a tigress on a kill. She spotted me at 80 feet, backed away snarling loudly, and then in a semicrouch ran 60 feet into a thicket, from where she watched me partially hidden behind a screen of branches. On another occasion I followed the drag mark of a cow kill for 800 feet through the forest to a patch of tall grass where about 25 crows fed on the remains, usually an indication that the tiger has departed. Feeling uneasy, I waited 60 feet from the kill. Three minutes later a tigress coughed once within 10 feet of the carcass, then departed with a growl.

The most vigorous response of a tiger to my presence was shown by a female with one small cub. After following the drag mark of her kill 1,000 feet over a ridge and through a dry stream bed, I sat down on a boulder at the edge of a patch of tall grass surrounded by bamboo, a site where I suspected the tiger to be. Within one minute a low, continuous growling commenced in the grass. The tigress rose 120 feet away and pulled the corners of her mouth back in a snarl several times. Suddenly she bounded 50 feet toward me, emitting two coughing roars. She then retreated 70 feet and for 20 minutes crouched, only part of her face showing; finally she departed with her cub.

Except for an occasional glance or a snarl in response to a sudden noise, the three resident adults and the five cubs tended to ignore flashlights and various mechanical sounds in a blind near their kill as long as it was dark. However, the animals were obviously more nervous during the day, approaching the kill cautiously and retreating with little provocation. Blinds were used at six different localities and varied in construction from permanent park structures of wood and cement, to flimsy ones of grass and foliage, to movable ones (that is, a car); yet the responses of the tigers were not noticeably different. One tigress and four cubs grew so used to the presence of persons around the kill after having been fed five head of livestock that they merely retreated about 100 feet in the grass while I walked back and forth to the blind, either alone or accompanied by another person, and they readily attacked baits and fed from the kill during the day. The tigress in particular became very bold and in one instance returned to her kill and dragged it away as I stood 45 feet from it. These tigers had probably never been shot at or otherwise harmed, a fact which undoubtedly accounted for the readiness with which they adapted to man's presence.

In general, my findings agree closely with those of Corbett (1957), who wrote: "Tigers, except when wounded or when man-eaters, are on the whole very good-tempered. . . . Occasionally a tiger will object to too close an approach to its cubs or to a kill that it is guarding. The objection invariably takes the form of growling, and if this does not prove effective it is followed by short rushes accompanied by terrifying roars. If these warnings are disregarded, the blame for any injury inflicted rests entirely with the intruder."

CHAPTER 10

OTHER PREDATORS

A few notes on several rare to uncommon carnivores in the park are included in this section. Observations on these species have not been expanded with published information, since it is readily available in any of the standard works on Indian mammals.

Leopard

There were no resident leopards in the study area. With the exception of prolonged observations on one animal in July, I saw them there only four times, but tracks and kills indicated that the Kanha meadow was visited by transients sporadically throughout the year. A measure of the scarcity of the leopard around the Kanha meadow was the fact that during the monsoon months from June to August, when spoor can easily be seen in the soft earth, I found only five fresh sets of tracks whereas those of tigers were noted daily. According to the local forest rangers, leopards are fairly common around the numerous villages at the periphery and outside the park, where they prey extensively on livestock.

Two observations on the leopard illustrate certain aspects of behavior:

1) During the night of July 9–10, a leopard entered our shed and carried off a lamb weighing about 30 pounds, leaving a goat untouched. In hopes of observing the behavior of the leopard at a kill, I tied the goat to a tree the following evening about 35 feet from the porch on which I slept. At 2355 hours I heard a choked bleat and a thump. The beam of my flashlight revealed the goat on its side and a medium-sized male leopard, weighing an estimated 100 pounds, sitting in a hunched position with his canines clamped into the animal's throat. The goat kicked and arched its body sporad-

ically. The leopard crouched down on three occasions and with a quick snap readjusted his grip, then sat up again. The goat died after 5 minutes, but the leopard retained his hold for 5 additional minutes. During the following 20 minutes he pulled at the body of the goat, attempting to drag it away, but finally, he licked the bloody throat twice and began to feed. Leopards characteristically start to eat at the abdomen between the rib cage and pelvis (Baker, 1890; Butt, 1963; Inglis, 1892), differing in this respect from the tiger, which usually begins at the rump. The leopard cut through the body wall with his carnassial teeth, alternately biting and tearing off pieces of muscle. After a sizable hole had been made, he pulled out and devoured a piece of the liver. The stomach and intestines were dragged 5 feet from the carcass but not eaten. At 0100 hours the leopard lay down 25 feet from the kill and rested until almost 0200 hours. Then, after feeding for 15 minutes, he disappeared until 0350 hours when he returned for another 10 minutes of snacking. At 0400 hours he left, having devoured the testes, kidneys, liver, one lung, all meat on the inside of the femurs and pelvis, and also all skin and muscle between pelvis and rib cage. I covered up the remains at dawn.

The following evening, shortly after 1900 hours, the leopard returned and attempted to drag the body away without success. He left and did not return until 2400 hours. At that time he ate for 30 minutes; he then interrupted his meal for 10 minutes before feeding a little more, primarily on the hindlegs, rib cage, and heart. He moved from sight at 1250 hours and remained away until 0420 hours. He was nervous after his return, growling several times, apparently because a male tiger was on a barasingha kill about a quarter mile away.

On the third night, the leopard arrived at 2140 hours and ate until 2210 hours with interruptions to circle briefly around the kill. He then rested nearby until about 0100, when he fed some more. From the alarm calls of chital, it appeared that he spent the rest of the night prowling around in the vicinity, although between 0440 hours and 0505 he visited the kill twice more. He was obviously nervous, as he growled and looked over his shoulder several times toward the meadow. All meat, except the head and one foreleg, was now devoured.

During the fourth night, 2 adult jackals with 2 full-grown young came to the remains, but less than 10 minutes later, at 2030 hours, one jackal emitted several loud piercing yips, and three of them fled. The leopard had crept up to a young male weighing 12 pounds, grabbed it with his paws, three of his claws slicing through the body wall on each side, and bitten it through the back of the head, as a later autopsy showed. Ignoring the dead jackal, the leopard ate for a few minutes on the goat and departed.

Initially the goat weighed 72 pounds, of which the leopard ate 39 pounds, or 54 percent of the total, the rest being intestinal tract (16 pounds), bones and head (16 pounds), and a few miscellane-

TABLE 53

AMOUNT OF TIME SPENT IN EATING AND TOTAL NUMBER
OF POUNDS CONSUMED BY A LEOPARD DURING FOUR
CONSECUTIVE NIGHTS, JULY 9–13, 1964, AT A GOAT KILL

Night	Number of Minutes Feeding	Total Number of Pounds Eaten
1	60	17.0
2	40	9.5
3	65	10.5
4	20±	2.0
Total	185±	39.0

ous scraps. The amount consumed each night and the time spent at the kill are summarized in Table 53.

2) On May 14, at 0840 hours, I followed a herd of about 15 foraging chital through a fairly dense patch of forest. The animals were 120 feet ahead of me when 3 of them suddenly bolted off to one side and the others rushed ahead. No alarm calls were given, but one emitted a drawn-out, high-pitched bleat. I waited one minute, then advanced cautiously. A leopard left its kill — a chital fawn weighing 56 pounds. The cat had apparently crouched by a log and pounced on the fawn, biting it through the back of the neck, one canine severing a jugular vein. The leopard failed to return to its kill during the daylight hours, and that night a tigress appropriated the carcass.

Chital and langur monkeys appeared to be the main prey species of the leopard in the study area. De discovered the site where a leopard had dragged a partially eaten adult chital 100 feet to a tree and then hauled the remains up into the branches 25 feet above ground. Direct evidence for predation on langurs was difficult to find, because almost the whole animal was eaten. Once I came across the stomach of a freshly killed langur, the cat apparently having removed the rest of the carcass to another site; on another occasion all that remained of a langur was the stomach, some hair, and part of the cranium. Twenty-two leopard droppings collected in the study area contained the following prey items, expressed as percent of occurrence: chital, 59 percent; langur, 27 percent; porcupine, 9 percent; sambar, 9 percent; and barasingha, 4.5 percent. The proglottids of a tapeworm (*Taenia pisiformis*, [Bloch, 1780]) were found in one dropping. Three droppings were checked for ova of parasites, and *Diphyllobothrium* sp. was noted in one, *Taenia* sp. in another, and *Paragonimus*, sp. in all three.

Man is eaten occasionally, but on the whole does not contribute significantly to the leopard's diet. Three persons were killed in 1961 by leopards, one at Sonph in the park, and two at Khatiya bordering the park. No further deaths were reported from the area until August 2, 1964, when a leopard entered a hut at Khatiya at night and carried off a child. During the night of August 4–5 presumably the same leopard attacked a sleeping boy in a house at Sonph, over five miles from Khatiya, lacerating his scalp and pulling one eye from the socket. Chased off, the cat apparently returned to Khatiya, for a man was killed there during the night of August 5–6. In January, 1965, a man was killed at Bhilwani at the periphery of the park, and in late February another child was taken in Khatiya. During the night of March 10–11, a man sleeping in the doorway of his hut in Kisli was severely mauled in the face. A week later a leopard killed a cow in the same village; a visiting hunter waited by the carcass and shot the cat at 2030 hours on March 19, when it returned to its kill. It was a male, 6 feet 9 inches long and weighed 97 pounds. Twenty-eight ticks, *Haemaphysalis leachii*, were found in his pelage. His right lower canine was missing, his mandible showed evidence of having been infected, and there was a small hole in his frontal bone, which, together with several bare spots on his skin, indicated that he had once received a shotgun charge in his face. This animal was presumed responsible for the attacks in the area during the preceding eight months. On August 27, 1965, however, another leopard mauled a man at Khatiya and was killed with axes by the villagers.

Jungle Cat

Jungle cats, which are the size of house cats, are potential predators on chital fawns. Although fairly common in the park, they were infrequently seen except during the cool season, when they congregated on the meadow apparently while mating. All of the 27 droppings collected contained the hair and bones of rats and mice and in two instances also the remains of a lizard.

Sloth Bear

The sloth bear is a medium-sized bear, weighing about 200 pounds, with a long, shaggy, black coat and a white crescent of hair on the chest. The animal was uncommon in the park, and I encountered solitary individuals on only seven occasions. Remaining in the hills for most of the year, the bears came down into the valleys primarily during the hot season when several kinds of fruit ripened there. They were almost wholly nocturnal, and the usual sign of their presence in the area was a crater in the road bed some thirty inches deep that had been excavated by a bear to expose and eat the subterranean termites.

A total of 92 droppings were collected during the year, except from August to October, when there was no sign of the bears around the Kanha meadow. Thirty-six (38 percent) of the droppings consisted wholly of the exoskeletons of termites and some ants together with a great deal of earth. The other droppings were composed of fruit remnants such as seeds and peelings, the kinds varying with the seasons. Figs (*Ficus*) were important as a food from March to May, with 16 percent of the droppings containing seeds of this fruit, and *Cordia myxa* was noted in 26 percent of the droppings, mostly during May and June. Other fruits in season included *Zizyphus jujuba* in December and January, wild mango in May and June, *Syzygium cumini* in June and July, and dried seeds of *Cassia fistula* in April, July, and December. Although fruit is an important part of the bear's diet from April to June, termites are its staple food for much of the year. Champion (1933) and Sanderson (1912) noted that sloth bears may scavenge on tiger and other kills, but no evidence for this was found at Kanha.

Striped Hyena

There were no resident hyenas in the study area, and I found only three sets of their tracks on the Kanha meadow during the year. A few hyenas frequented the vicinity of the villages at the periphery of the park, where for fifty minutes I observed one feeding on a cow killed by a tiger.

Wild Dog

Wild dogs were once so common in Kanha Park that in 1947 the forest department placed a bounty on them because they were suspected of killing too many deer. Khajuria (1963), Gee (1964), and others described encounters with this species in the park. For unexplained reasons, however, the wild dog population had declined drastically before the beginning of my study, and I neither saw the animals nor found any sign of their presence. About eight dogs pursued a chital fawn into Kisli village on August 28, the only definite record for the park during 1964.

Bengal Fox

A fox chased a chital doe in the park according to Gee (1964). Only one fox was seen in the area during the study.

Jackal

The two pairs of jackals that inhabited the Kanha meadow rarely left the vicinity of the village to venture into the forest. One female gave birth in about February and raised four pups; the second female had young in April or May and also reared four young. One pup was killed by a leopard and another by village dog. The adult jackals were usually seen singly or in pairs, sometimes accompanied by their young, as they trotted along the meadow roads.

Jackal feces were collected and analyzed throughout the year. Of 138 droppings examined, two-thirds contained the hair and bones of rats and mice (Table 54). Expressed as percent of volume eaten, the contribution of rodents to the jackal's diet was perhaps as much as 80 percent. No attempt was made to identify the rodent remains, but the following species are found in the park: *Rattus blanfordi* (Thomas), *Rattus rattus narbadai* (Hinton), *Rattus rattus rufescens* (Gray), *Golunda ellioti ellioti* (J. Gray), *Mus booduga booduga* (J. Gray), *Mus musculus homoorus* (Hodgson), and *Vandelenria oleracea oleracea* (Bennett). Jackals caught hares occasionally, although they were uncommon in 1964. There are other small mammals in the area, such as musk shrew, palm squirrel, mouse deer, and Madras tree shrew, but these species were not found in the droppings. Our domestic chickens were favorite prey of the jackals, and they also appear to catch such wild birds as jungle bush quail. Minnow-like fish are common in the creeks, and these were either caught or scavenged, as indicated by scales in the droppings, but the total amount of food from this source was small. The remains of reptiles, most frequently lizards, were surprisingly prevalent in the feces. The most common lizards at Kanha are *Calotes versicolor, Mabuya dissimilis, Mabuya macularia, Mabuya carinata, Lygosoma maculatum,* and *Riopa albopunctata.* One dropping contained a small piece of unidentified snake, perhaps *Natrix stolata* or *Elaphe helena.*

One jackal was observed as it chased a chital fawn, and a free-ranging domestic lamb was discovered that had been severely lacer-

TABLE 54

FREQUENCY OF OCCURRENCE OF FOOD ITEMS IN 138 JACKAL FECES
FROM THE KANHA MEADOW

Type of Food	Number of Occurrence	Percent of Occurrence
Rat and mouse	94	68.1
Reptile	16	11.6
Bird	13	9.4
Fish	11	8.0
Hare	3	2.2
Chital	3	2.2
Domestic cattle	2	1.4
Insect (grasshopper, ant)	2	1.4
Langur	1	.7
Zizyphus fruit	24	17.4
Garbage (rice, maize, etc.)	9	6.5
Grass and grass seeds	4	2.9
Unidentified seeds	1	.7

ated by the animals. However, the remains of ungulates, both domestic and wild, were present in only about 4 percent of the feces, a figure which probably represents scavenged food rather than prey killed by the jackals themselves. Jackals ate from tiger kills less frequently than anticipated. During March, 1965, for example, when a total of eleven head of livestock were fed to tigers at the same locality over a period of two weeks, no jackal was seen to visit the carcasses. On one occasion five jackals spotted a number of crows low in the bushes 150 feet away, an obvious sign that a fresh kill was nearby. The jackals milled around briefly, then left the area. At Kanha, where tigers usually rest in the vicinity of their kill, the jackals may have learned to avoid such potentially dangerous sites. Strachan (1933) reported that a tiger killed a jackal at a carcass, and I saw a tigress chase one. Jackals approached a kill closely on five occasions, but they were so nervous that twice they ate nothing before fleeing.

One jackal, killed by a leopard while it was scavenging on a goat, had some goat meat, maize kernels, and the fruit of *Syzygium cumini* in its stomach.

Vegetable matter in substantial amounts was found in over 25 percent of the feces, principally *Zizyphus* fruit and village garbage (Table 54).

Python

A few *Python molurus* are said to occur in the park, but I failed to see any. Corbett (1957) encountered pythons which had swallowed chital and barking deer.

CHAPTER 11

THE EFFECT OF PREDATION

ON THE PREY POPULATIONS

IN KANHA PARK

Although several kinds of predators occur in Kanha Park, the tiger is the only one which exerts a considerable influence on the populations of hoofed animals. But to what extent does the tiger prey not only on the various species but also on the age and sex classes within those species? How often does the tiger kill? What is the size of its daily food intake? What is the total effect of predation on the populations of prey? In short, what is the interrelationship of the tiger and its prey in Kanha Park? Although answers to these and other questions cannot be given after a study of only one year, even tentative conclusions are valuable as a basis for further work and as a means of placing the local predator-prey relations into perspective. Such information is particularly needed for Kanha Park, where in recent years the government has shown its concern over the apparent increase of tigers and the concomitant decrease in the number of deer. A direct cause and effect has been assumed by some members of the forest department. Added to this are the complaints of some local inhabitants who for economic and other reasons resent the depredation by tigers of their herds of livestock. As a result a reduction in the number of tigers has been contemplated. Kanha Park is one of the few legally protected areas in India that harbors a fair number of both tigers and wild hoofed animals, and in view of the virtual extirpation of the wildlife over much of the sub-continent, the park is assuming increasing importance as an area large enough and remote enough to assure the perpetuation of a sample of the country's fauna. The problem, then, is to determine how many tigers the park can adequately support.

316

Predation is frequently said to be selective. Errington (1946), for instance, stated that "the large-sized wild ungulates suffer from sub-human predation chiefly when immature, aged, crippled, starved, sick, or isolated from their fellows." Studies on wolves in North America have tended to support this contention, although the results have by no means been consistent. Murie (1944) found that wolves in Mount McKinley National Park, Alaska, preyed mainly on the young, old, and diseased Dall sheep. "Because of the limited survival of lambs during some winters, it appears that the predation on lambs is the most important limiting factor in stabilizing sheep numbers. Furthermore, it was found that the sheep preyed upon, other than lambs, were generally old or diseased and therefore already doomed to an early death." In a study of wolves preying on moose on Isle Royale, Allen and Mech (1963) noted that 20 of 68 winter kills involved animals less than one year old and that all others, with one exception, were over six years old. Furthermore, 45 percent of the moose killed as adults had one or more disabilities, such as a bone infection or heavy parasitism. Similarly, Olson (1938) found that the majority of deer and moose killed by wolves in Minnesota were old and diseased, and Crisler (1956) observed that wolves in Alaska found it difficult to catch healthy adult caribou. Borg (1962) noted that of 156 roe deer killed in Sweden by such predators as dog and lynx, 54.5 percent were diseased. On the other hand, Stenlund (1955), working on wolf predation in Minnesota, stated that, of the adult deer killed, "only two, or 7 percent, were considered old; all others were in the prime of life." Burkholder (1959) examined 14 adult caribou killed by wolves in Alaska, and all appeared to be in prime condition; of 7 moose kills, one was a yearling and the others were calves.

The wolves' method of hunting, as described by Murie (1944), Crisler (1956), Burkholder (1959), and others, consists largely of running the prey down, a technique contrasting sharply with the stalking and rushing practiced by most cats. Very little quantitative information on predation by the big cats has been published. Hibben (1937) examined eleven deer killed by puma and found all of them crippled, diseased, or otherwise in poor condition. Wright (1960) collected the remains of one hundred fifty lion kills in Kenya and Tanzania:

The main food supply of the lion in the region studied was wildebeeste, zebra, and Thomson's gazelle. These three made up 74 percent of all lion kills. Adult wildebeeste in the prime of life and in old age were the age classes taken, and most of them were in good condition. This was different in the zebra, where immatures and old animals were the age classes found in the kill sample. Thomson's gazelles were mainly adult animals, with a distinct preponderance of males. The age classes of all prey killed by lions showed that immature and young prime animals were to prime and past prime animals as 24:76.

In order to determine whether tiger predation is selective or whether it affects all animals equally, the kills of hoofed animals were aged by means of the eruption and wear of the premolar and

TABLE 55

AGE CLASSES OF WILD UNGULATES KILLED BY PREDATORS AT KANHA PARK, BASED ON THE ERUPTION AND WEAR OF THE PREMOLAR AND MOLAR TEETH IN THE LOWER JAW

Age Class	Characteristics
I	Milk premolars erupting to fully erupted. First molar partially to almost wholly erupted. Second molar sometimes starting to erupt through gum.
II.	First molar fully erupted. Second molar erupting to almost wholly erupted. Third molar sometimes barely visible to partially erupted.
III	Milk premolars replaced by permanent premolars toward latter part of age class. First and second molars fully erupted and third molar erupting to erupted except for the posterior cusp.
IV	All permanent teeth fully grown. Lingual crest of molars sharp; wear on posterior cusp of third molar slight.
V	Lingual crest of first molar blunt and dentine of crest as wide as or wider than the bordering enamel. Posterior cusp of third molar concave on the occlusal surface.
VI	Wear moderate to heavy on second and third premolars. Lingual crests worn down on first molar and partly off second molar. Dentine of lingual crest of all molars broader than the enamel.
VII	Wear heavy on second and third premolars. Infundibulum on first molar fine line or chevron or barely worn away.
VIII.	Infundibulum worn away on first molar and heavily worn on second molar. The first molar sometimes worn toward the gum line on the buccal side.
IX	Infundibulum absent from all molars except for occasional remnant on third molar. Molars often worn close to or down to gum line on the buccal side.

molar teeth in the lower jaw. In the absence of animals of known age, nine different classes based on relative age were established (Table 55). The criteria used in distinguishing the nine classes are based on the work of Dahlberg and Guettinger (1956), Robinette *et al.* (1957), and Thompson (1958) on *Odocoileus* deer. These arbitrary age classes can be used to compare the percentage of animals killed in each class within a species but not necessarily between species, for the time of tooth eruption varies, for example, between chital and gaur, and the rate of tooth wear may well be affected by the food habits. A major bias in using kills as a means of determining the extent of predation is that the remains of young animals, particularly those in age class I, are rarely found, since they are usually almost wholly eaten.

The pattern of tooth eruption in the chital appears to correspond more closely to the mule deer than to the white-tailed deer, as summarized by Mosby (1963). For example, in one spike buck in velvet, estimated to be 15 months old, the second molar was half erupted but the third molar was not yet visible; in another spike buck, judged to be 17 months old, the third molar was just erupting. This suggests that the chital in class I are less than 10 months old, in class II about 10 to 18 months old, and in class III about 18 to 26 months old. Thus, class I comprises fawns, and classes II and III mostly yearlings. The majority of animals in class IV are young adults around 2½ years old. Classes V, VI, and VII are prime adults; class VIII consists of animals perhaps somewhat past their prime, and class IX, aged deer. The high turnover in the population suggests that few chital live longer than 10 years in the wild, although captives have been known to survive for 20 to 22 years (Crandall, 1964; Simon, 1943b).

Chital fawns are poorly represented among the kills (Table 56), but it was estimated that about 48 percent of them fall prey during the first year of life (see Chital, Population Dynamics, p. 40). Mortality is, therefore, greater in class I than at any other age. Yearling bucks comprise about 35 percent of the yearling and adult buck population (see Table 19), and the percent of yearling does is probably of similar magnitude. Of 94 yearling and adult kills found, only about 19 percent were yearlings (classes II and III), or slightly more than half as many as the expected 35 percent. Classes IV to VII, the young and prime adults, comprise 54 percent of the 94 yearling and adult kills found, with a marked peak (22 percent) in the last class; and 27 percent of the kills fall into the two oldest classes. The data indicate that chital of every age are taken by tigers and other predators, including prime animals not suffering from disease, starvation, or other disabilities, but that predation is heaviest on the fawns and probably lowest on yearlings and adults in the younger classes. Of the 10 kills Negi and I found in Corbett Park, 2 belonged to class II, 3 to class VI, 2 to class VII, and one each to classes III, V, and VIII.

The pattern of tooth eruption in the barasingha and sambar appears to be roughly similar to the one described for the wapiti by Quimby and Gaab (1957). One barasingha spike, estimated to be 16 months old, had his second molar half erupted, but the third molar was not yet visible (class II); another yearling, about 22 to 23 months old, had his second molar fully erupted and the third molar barely erupted (class III). Classes IV to VII comprise, as in the chital, young to prime adults. Class VII corresponds to an eight-year-old wapiti pictured by Quimby and Gaab (1957), and class

TABLE 56

NUMBER OF PREDATOR KILLS IN EACH AGE CLASS OF THREE SPECIES OF DEER AND GAUR AT KANHA PARK

AGE CLASS	CHITAL		BARASINGHA		SAMBAR		GAUR	
	Number	Percent	Number	Percent	Number	Percent	Number	Percent
I . . .	4	4.1	4	10.3	3	5.4	6	42.9
II . . .	10	10.2	3	7.7	1	1.8	1	7.1
III. . .	8	8.2	4	10.3	7	12.5	1	7.1
IV . . .	7	7.1	7	17.9	2	3.5	1	7.1
V . . .	14	14.3	5	12.8	3	5.4	1	7.1
VI. . .	9	9.2	4	10.3	6	10.7	2	14.3
VII . .	21	21.4	7	17.9	14	25.0	1	7.1
VIII . .	16	16.3	5	12.8	14	25.0	1	7.1
IX . . .	9	9.2			6	10.7		
Total	98	100.0	39	100.0	56	100.0	14	99.8

VIII to a nine-year-old animal. It is likely that the barasingha and sambar have a longer average life span than the chital. Barasingha have survived 23 years in captivity, and sambar 24 years (Crandall, 1964). Murie (1951) reported that a tagged free-ranging wapiti was 25 years old when shot by a hunter. Predation on the barasingha appears to affect all classes equally (Table 56), with young and prime adults being taken as readily as the older animals. The small size of the population and the poor annual increment of fawns probably caused by disease (see Barasingha, Population Dynamics, p. 101) have undoubtedly affected these results.

The sambar revealed a pattern of mortality similar to the one shown by chital (Table 56). Mortality was estimated to be about 50 percent in the fawn population (see Sambar, Population Dynamics, p. 135), but kills of young were rarely found; half of the kills belonged to classes VII and VIII.

In the domestic ox, the first molar is erupted by the age of 6 months; the average age of eruption of the second molar is 1 to 1½ years and of the third molar 2 to 2½ years (Sisson, 1930). Since the gaur probably show a roughly comparable development, class I comprises calves up to one year of age, and classes II and III yearlings, with a few adults up to an age of 2½ years. Of 14 gaur kills found, 43 percent belonged to class I, most of these less than about 4 months old, and the others were scattered fairly evenly among the remaining classes (Table 56). Thus the gaur is similar to the three species of deer in that a large percentage of young fall prey, but it differs strikingly in that the adult members of the population are killed infrequently.

Of 10 wild pig jaws obtained, all were adults belonging to classes IV to VII.

These data show that predation is not confined to the young, old, sick, and surplus animals, but that prime ones are also readily taken. However, the largest proportion of deaths occur among the young, which can probably be traced in part to their inexperience in detecting and avoiding predators. The extent of mortality among yearlings and adults depends largely on the species, with, for example, adult gaur being such formidable opponents that tigers attack them infrequently; adult deer, on the other hand, are commonly taken. Fewer adults in the younger age classes of chital and sambar appear to fall prey than in the older classes (VII and VIII), but whether this is actually the case or whether the statistic merely reflects a different time interval between each of the relative age classes could not be determined. It must also be emphasized that even those animals that were classified on the basis of tooth wear as somewhat aged (VII and VIII) were most likely in good physical condition at the time of death, fully able to reproduce, having presumably reached only about half of their physiological life span as determined by the longevity of the species in zoos. Only a few animals in class IX showed such heavy wear on their molars that they could be classified as very aged. No dental malformations, necrosis, or other kinds of bone disease were noted at Kanha in contrast to their frequent occurrence in North American ungulates (Murie, 1944; Murie, 1951).

Selection operates on somewhat different levels depending on the predator involved. In eluding a wolf, which often pursues its victim over a fairly long distance, speed, strength, and endurance are important attributes for survival. But to escape from a tiger, which usually stalks its prey in dense cover and attacks from close range, good senses of hearing and particularly of smell, coupled with speed of reaction and agility, appear to be the main attributes for success. Since the acuity of the senses and the rapidity of response probably do not diminish appreciably in deer and other prey until advanced age, unless the animals are physically in poor condition, various other factors may contribute importantly to their vulnerability. For instance, the preferred habitat of a species as well as the seasonal change in the density of the cover affects the degree of predation. The blackbuck, which tended to remain on the short-grass meadow where the big cats found it difficult to approach undetected, lost only one fawn in over fifteen months. The precise date of death of ten barasingha killed by tigers was determined in 1964. Only three of these deaths occurred between January and June, when the animals spent much time on the burned parts of the meadow, but seven were caught in the three months between July and September, when the grass had grown high again. The fact that the hinds were in advanced stages of pregnancy also contributed to the high death rate during these months because the animals seemed to have lost some of their agility. Four out of the five hinds fell prey at that time, and all were in their prime. This stresses the fact that although tiger predation undoubtedly culls the less fit animals from the population, leaving the vigorous ones to propagate, a considerable percentage of healthy, prime animals are also killed, having increased their vulnerability by frequenting certain habitats, by being pregnant, and perhaps by other means.

The possibility of selective predation on the sexes is also of importance in the dynamics of the prey populations. Klein and Olson (1960) analyzed the data from 63 white-tailed deer killed by wolves, as presented by Stenlund (1955), and found that the ratio of adult bucks to adult does was 125:100. Female deer probably predominated in the population, indicating that proportionally more males than females were killed. Wright (1960) sexed 49 animals killed by lions, noting that 29 were male and 20 were female, but since neither the species of prey nor the composition of the prey population is given, the data have little significance. A total of 46 yearling and adult chital, barasingha, and sambar kills were sexed at Kanha. More females than males were killed among chital and barasingha (Table 57). Since females also outnumbered the males in the population, males did not fall prey more readily than females, as they did in the study quoted by Klein and Olson (1960). In fact the reverse may be true, since slightly more females were taken than would have been expected from the population ratio. Although this conclusion is based on a small sample of kills, the figures are corroborated to some extent by information collected by the forest department. A total of 96 chital kills were reported by villagers to the local foresters between 1960 and 1963. Of these 30 were bucks and 66 were does, a ratio of 45:100. In my experience the villagers sometimes made mistakes in identifying the sex and even the species of kills found, but the results are probably indicative. Of 9 chital kills sexed in Corbett Park, 6 were male and 3 were female. Predation must be responsible to a large extent for the unbalanced adult sex ratios in the living popu-

TABLE 57

Sex of Yearling and Adult Deer Kills Found in Kanha Park

Species	Number Sexed	Males : 100 Females Killed		Males : 100 Females in Population	
Chital	18	50	: 100	71	: 100
Barasingha	17	70	: 100	90	: 100
Sambar	11	120	: 100	30	: 100
Total	46				

lations, since it is the chief form of mortality, but the kills found do not account for the low proportion of males. The kill sample of the barasingha is probably biased because some solitary stags roam widely and their remains are less likely to be located than those which die around the Kanha meadow. The disproportionate sex ratio of adult chital is perhaps due to a higher death rate of male fawns than female fawns, if it is assumed that the kill sample is not biased and the sex ratio is equal at birth.

More male than female sambar kills were found in spite of the fact that hinds outnumbered stags 3:1 in the population (Table 57). Of 20 sambar kills reported by the villagers, the ratio of males to females was 100:100. These data suggest that the highly disproportionate sex ratio of adult sambar may be due to selective predation on adult males and possibly also on male fawns.

To determine the effect of tiger predation on the prey populations as a whole, a number of other points need to be discussed, especially the amount of food required by a tiger in the course of a year. Various authors have estimated the frequency of killing by tigers. Eardley-Wilmot (1910) reported that a tiger kills one sizable animal like a cow once a week, but Forsyth (1889) placed the figure at once every 5 days, Baker (1890) at 4 days, Brander (1923) at 4 to 5 days, and Baldwin (1877) and Anderson (1954) at 3 to 4 days. The range of variation of these estimates is from 52 to 122 animals per year. It was not possible to determine the frequency with which tigers captured free-ranging prey at Kanha, because consecutive kills by the same animal were rarely found. On one occasion, a tigress with four cubs killed a yearling chital buck during the night of May 30–31. No prey was secured the following night, but at 2000 hours on June 1, the same tigress attacked a buffalo which had strayed from the village. The tigers consumed this animal by the morning of June 3, having killed twice in 4 days. The same tigress and cubs caught and ate one barasingha hind during the night of June 28–29 and a barasingha stag during the night of June 30–July 1, two kills in 3 nights. The frequency of killing obviously depends on the size and species of the prey, on the number of tigers eating from the remains, and on other factors, making estimates of food consumption based solely on the number of animals killed of slight value.

The amount of meat eaten by a tiger in the course of a night or even over a period of days may be prodigious (see Tiger, Behavior at the Kill, p. 297), but the number of pounds ingested in a short time give little indication of the animal's need on a long-term basis. The tiger can adapt to a feast or famine regime. For example, Sanderson (1912) noted that a trapped tiger showed no discomfort after a fast of ten days. The bobcat is able to maintain its physical condition on widely varying quantities of food intake, and its use of the consumed energy is probably relatively constant (Golley *et al.*, 1965), facts undoubtedly also true for the tiger. Wright (1960) calculated that the average annual kill per lion consists of 36.5 prey animals and that a lion weighing 350 pounds kills 45 pounds of food per day, about twice as much as required. Data from zoos provide an indication of the amount of meat needed to keep a tiger in healthy condition. Two adult males, each weighing about 500 pounds, received an average of 11 pounds of horse meat per day; two tigresses received 7.5 and 9 pounds, respectively, the differing amounts being determined by their size (Crandall, 1964). According to E. Lang (pers. comm.), a 300 pound tiger in the Basel zoo is fed about 9 to 11 pounds of meat per day. In the National Zoological Park adult males receive an average of 15 to 17 pounds of meat per day and adult females 10 pounds (J. Eisenberg, pers. comm.). Albritton (1954) presented average figures of 10 pounds of meat per day for a female and 14 pounds for a male. Although free-living tigers are on the whole more active than captives, they also spend a great deal of time in resting and feeding, periods when their energy output is not appreciably higher than in zoos. The food requirement of the average adult tiger at Kanha, where prey is plentiful and ranges relatively small, is probably on the order of 12 to 15 pounds per day, somewhat lower than the 15 to 20 pounds estimated earlier (Schaller, 1965). At this rate of consumption, a tiger uses 4,380 to 5,475 pounds of meat per year.

However, parts of each kill are inedible, primarily the rumen contents and the bones, and the tiger has to kill more in terms of weight than the amount actually eaten. For example, the remains of one chital buck, which initially weighed about 130 pounds, consisted of 14 pounds of rumen contents, 18 pounds of bones, and 3 pounds of other scraps, or 27 percent of the total weight of the deer. The inedible parts of a domestic animal weigh, relative to size, more than those of a wild one, comprising an estimated 30 to 40 percent in a cow or buffalo. Most of the tiger's food in the study area consisted of wild prey, and an average of 70 percent of the total weight of each animal was probably consumed. Thus, an adult tiger has to kill about 6,257 to 7,821 pounds of prey per year. Novikov (1962) estimated that a tiger needs 30 animals, each weighing 100 kilograms per year, or 6,600 pounds, a figure which agrees closely with mine. The amount represents, of course, a minimum and presumes that the tiger devours all edible parts of the carcass, which is sometimes not the case. If the tiger is disturbed by man and forced to leave its kill, vultures consume the remains; and in areas where the cats are commonly shot at while feeding, they often fail to return for a second meal. It is likely that tigers in some localities kill twice as much as they need, especially if their prey consists of livestock near villages. At Kanha, where they are relatively undisturbed except by villagers scavenging kills, the figures of about 6,300 to 7,800 pounds per year probably reflect fairly accurately the amount killed.

In order to compute the total poundage of prey taken in the study area during 1964, an estimate of the number of tigers is necessary. One male tiger and one tigress were full-time residents. An additional two tigresses used the area sporadically, as did a number of transients (and an occasional leopard), for varying lengths of time; the amount of prey killed by these animals probably equalled about that taken by two to two and a half resident ones. There were also five cubs which were small at the beginning of the year but large at the end of it. Each cub needed perhaps, on the average, half as much meat as an adult. Based on these estimates, the study area supported the equivalent of six and a half to seven adult tigers, which required a total of 40,670 to 54,747 pounds of prey in 1964.

A rough estimate of the amount of prey actually killed can be computed for each species from the known population size, the percent of annual mortality, and the weight of the animals, as presented in earlier chapters (Table 58). The chital and gaur apparently increased slightly in number, and the adult mortality figures of 24 and 10 percent, respectively, which are based on a presumed stable population, are too high. An estimated 20 and 5 percent mortality, as used in Table 58, are believed to be more accurate. The livestock was killed around the village or tied out by me as bait. Many of these animals were small, averaging less in weight than the figures used in Table 43. The results in Table 58 show that the predators killed an estimated 43,825 pounds of wild prey of four species and 6,800 pounds of cattle and buffalo, for a total of 50,625 pounds. These animals provided the bulk of the tiger's diet, and such occasional items as langur, porcupine, pig, and barking deer contributed at most a few hundred pounds to the yearly total. The poundage of animal life killed by the predators is roughly similar to the estimated food requirements of the tigers. It should be kept in mind that predation by man is included in the computations, and although the amount of poaching in the study area during 1964 was not great, the total number of animals taken by this method probably amounted to a few thousand pounds.

What was the actual effect of the predation on the wildlife populations in the study area? As already pointed out, the chital and gaur were thought to have increased slightly, the sambar were presumed to have remained stable, and the barasingha declined drastically as a result of predation on a small localized population with poor annual recruitment. All evidence indicates that the tiger was the main factor limiting the growth of the populations of these species. Tigers also killed about 6,800 pounds of livestock. In the absence of cattle or buffalo, predation pressure on the wild prey would either have increased somewhat, removing a larger percentage of the annual increment, or the number of tigers in the area would have decreased. Between December 20, 1963, and March 31, 1965, for example, a total of 16 cattle, 14 buffalo, and 8 pigs were captured by tigers near the village or tied out as bait. Of these a tigress with four cubs killed or participated in the eating of at least 12 cattle, 13 buffalo, and 2 pigs, enough food to support one tiger for a year. This livestock undoubtedly contributed to the female's suc-

TABLE 58

Estimated Number and Weight of Four Wild and Two Domestic Prey Species Eaten by Predators in the Kanha Park Study Area during 1964

Species	Young				Yearlings and Adults				Total Weight Of Young, Yearlings, and Adults in Pounds
	Estimated Percent Mortality	Estimated Number Taken by Predators	Average Weight in Pounds	Total Weight in Pounds	Estimated Percent Mortality	Estimated Number Taken by Predators	Average Weight in Pounds	Total Weight in Pounds	
Chital	48	115	50	5,750	20	85	125	10,625	16,375
Barasingha					33	27	350	9,450	9,450
Sambar	50	15	100	1,500	13	6	400	2,400	3,900
Gaur.	50	25	200	5,000	5	7	1,300	9,100	14,100
Total				12,250				31,575	43,825
Domestic cattle. . . .		3	150	450		11	350	3,850	4,300
Domestic buffalo . . .						5	500	2,500	2,500
Total				450				6,350	6,800
Grand total									50,625

cess in raising four cubs; in the absence of this easily available prey one or more cubs would probably have succumbed (see Tiger, Population Dynamics, p. 227), decreasing the predator pressure in the area. The data emphasize two important points: (1) that during 1964 the predator and wild prey populations in the study area were almost in balance, and (2) that livestock constitutes important buffer species. Each point needs elaboration.

The populations of all species except the barasingha remained stable or increased slightly, indicating that in spite of the heavy predator pressure a small annual surplus survived. Most predation was by tigers, with man probably removing only a small proportion of the estimated 44,000 pounds of wildlife. An increase in predation of perhaps as little as 15 percent might have been sufficient to wipe out this surplus, preventing an increase or even causing a decrease in the size of the populations. During 1963 and in earlier years, most species in the park declined (Table 2) even though livestock was available as prey and there appeared to be fewer tigers. All evidence indicates that the general decline in the years prior to 1964 was predominantly due to poaching, the prey populations being unable to maintain themselves under the combined heavy predation by man and tiger. How many tigers can the study area support? This, of course, depends to a large extent on the size of the prey populations. Under conditions existing in 1964, there appeared to be as many tigers as the wild prey could adequately support and still show a slight annual increase. The elimination of poaching would speed up the rate of increase, and this in turn would ultimately enable more tigers to inhabit the area.

The tigers in the study area subsisted for the most part on wildlife; only about one-seventh of the total amount killed was livestock. But even this small percentage served to deflect some of the tiger predation from the wild prey and also to compensate to some extent for the deer lost to poachers. In other areas of the park, where the wildlife has been drastically reduced by excessive hunting, the livestock is largely responsible for supporting the tigers. It was estimated that about 250 head of cattle and buffalo fall prey within the park each year, enough to maintain ten tigers. From the standpoint of tiger conservation, it makes no difference whether the prey consists of cattle or wildlife, and the careless way in which livestock is tended shows the lack of concern on the part of most local people that their animals may be killed. On the other hand, from the standpoint of habitat conservation and the maintenance of the park as a sanctuary devoted to the perpetuation of wildlife, the live-stock should ideally be eliminated and the wild hoofed animals be permitted to increase until they once again become the tiger's prin-cipal food throughout the area. However, the sudden eviction of all livestock would pose a management problem because the cattle and buffalo are buffer species, maintaining the tigers at an artificially high population level. "As prey increase the predators follow and in some cases consume enough prey to cause a decline of prey. Then predators decline till they no longer can hold the prey in check and the prey again increase. . . . But if a buffer is present the preda-tors can turn to it when the prey become scarce and thus the predators remain and are ready when the prey begins to increase. The buffer thus may keep the predators on hand to check the in-crease of the prey and thereby the predators may hold down the prey population" (Davis, 1957). Thus, a sudden removal of all livestock from the park would probably increase the predator pressure on the wildlife, possibly preventing its increase, and it might also cause a partial shift of the tiger population into the for-ests surrounding the park. A gradual reduction, culminating in com-plete withdrawal of the livestock, coupled with strict enforcement against poaching, would circumvent this problem.

Although the tiger has a strong depressive influence on the num-ber of wild hoofed animals, another point needs consideration. Popu-lations of animals, both predator and prey, are largely self-limited in that if individuals fail to die from one cause they frequently succumb to another. "A great deal of predation is without truly depressive influence," wrote Errington (1946):

In the sense that victims of one agency simply miss becoming victims of another, many types of loss — including loss from predation — are at least partly intercompensatory in net population effect. Regardless of the count-less individuals or the large percentages of population that may annually be killed by predators, predation looks ineffective as a limiting factor to the extent that intraspecific self-limiting mechanisms basically determine popu-lation levels maintained by the prey.

Wynne-Edwards (1962) elaborated on this concept when he wrote:

Predation is not in its own right a density-dependent process, independent-ly capable of controlling a prey population from outside: the "cooperation" of the prey population, in insuring that its surplus members are specially vulnerable to predators through the operation of the social machine, is almost sure to be the indispensable condition underlying whatever density-dependent, homeostatic influence predation may be found to have.

These comments are only partially applicable to Kanha in that they concern only natural predation, excluding that of man, on large, healthy prey populations. But they do emphasize the concept that predation by carnivores on hoofed animals is usually not sufficient to keep them in check and that their ultimate population level is often determined by such other means as disease and habitat conditions.

The tiger population also appears to be self-limited, with perhaps a social spacing mechanism keeping the number of animals in a particular area relatively constant regardless of the abundance of prey. This was evident at Kanha when the wild prey concentrated during the hot season but there was no increase in the number of tigers; on the other hand, the presence of livestock as a buffer at the periphery of the park may have affected the behavior of the tigers. However, it seems likely that there is a density level based on intraspecific intolerance which maintains the tiger population at or near an optimum both in relation to the food resources and independent of them. When the population density exceeds the optimum, reproduction may decline or stop, as was probably the case with the wolves on Isle Royale (Mech, 1964), females may abandon their cubs, litters may be smaller, and fewer young may survive to adulthood, as reported for the lion (Guggisberg, 1961). It is possible that serious strife between individuals at kills and the occasional propensity of males to devour cubs are extreme manifestations of intolerance when the local population is too high, and such behavior therefore may represent a social means of controlling the abundance of the species.

India's wildlife has reached a critical stage in its survival, and the country is fortunate in possessing a sanctuary like Kanha Park, where a remnant of the peninsular fauna still exists in fair number. The park is large enough and ecologically varied enough to support a considerable wildlife population on a permanent basis, especially since the forests surrounding it provide a buffer zone between the park and the heavily cultivated parts of the district. As a potential tourist attraction the tiger has few equals among animals. And the park as a whole can provide future generations with a view of how their country once looked before the forests were overexploited for timber and overgrazed by livestock and before much of the wildlife fell to the poacher's gun. The park can also become a study area unaffected by man's influence where the interrelationships between species and many other ecological problems can be investigated. A national park represents a specialized form of land use in which,

ideally, the native flora and fauna are permitted to exist undisturbed by man. This in particular should apply to the predators,
which have aroused the antipathy of man for centuries and have as a
result been needlessly persecuted on the slightest pretext. Certain
management practices in a park are sometimes necessary, and these
should of course be based on a thorough study of the situation and
be directed at the principal and not the superficial cause of a problem.
The evidence presented in this report, for example, indicates that
poaching and not tiger predation has been the general cause of the
decline of the wildlife in the park. The most effective means of
managing the tiger is obviously to manage the prey, which in turn
means (1) curtailing the activity of poachers, and (2) limiting
and gradually eliminating all livestock from within the boundaries
of the park. Only after these two tasks have been accomplished, and
all forms of wildlife have been substantially increased, will the park
be able to fulfill its unique potential as a living museum and natural
laboratory. Above all, Kanha Park is part of India's cultural heritage, a heritage in many ways more important than the Taj Mahal
and the temples of Khajuraho, because, unlike these structures
formed by the hands of man, once destroyed it can never be replaced.

APPENDIX A

Common and scientific names of wild mammals and birds mentioned in the text.

Mammals

Order Marsupialia
    Virginia opossum   *Didelphis virginiana*

Order Insectivora
    Musk shrew   *Suncus murinus*

Order Chiroptera
    Flying fox   *Pteropus giganteus*

Order Primata
    Madras tree shrew   *Anathana ellioti*
    Rhesus monkey   *Macaca mulatta*
    Common langur   *Presbytis entellus*

Order Pholidota
    Pangolin   *Manis* sp.

Order Lagomorpha
    Indian hare   *Lepus nigricollis*

Order Rodentia
    Palm squirrel   *Funambulus palmarum*
    Indian porcupine   *Hystrix indica*
    Muskrat   *Ondatra zibethica*

Order Carnivora
    Wolf   *Canis lupus*
    Asiatic jackal   *Canis aureus*
    Indian wild dog   *Cuon alpinus*
    Bengal fox   *Vulpes bengalensis*
    Black bear   *Selenarctos thibetanus*
    Brown bear   *Ursus arctos*
    Sloth bear   *Melursus ursinus*

Striped hyena	*Hyaena hyaena*
Badger	*Meles meles*
Grey mongoose	*Herpestes edwardsi*
Temminck cat	*Profelis aurata*
Jungle cat	*Felis chaus*
Bobcat	*Lynx rufus*
Lynx	*Lynx lynx*
Cheetah	*Acinonyx jubatus*
Puma	*Felis concolor*
Snow leopard	*Panthera uncia*
Jaguar	*Panthera onca*
Lion	*Panthera leo*
Tiger	*Panthera tigris*
Leopard	*Panthera pardus*

Order Proboscidea
Indian elephant	*Elephas maximus*

Order Perissodactyla
Zebra	*Equus burchelli*
Great Indian rhinoceros	*Rhinoceros unicornis*

Order Artiodactyla
Wild pig	*Sus scrofa*
Vicuna	*Vicugna vicugna*
Mouse deer	*Tragulus meminna*
Musk deer	*Moschus moschiferus*
Barking deer	*Muntiacus muntjak*
Roe deer	*Capreolus capreolus*
Chital	*Axis axis*
Hog deer	*Axis porcinus*
Caribou	*Rangifer arcticus*
Reindeer	*Rangifer tarandus*
White-tailed deer	*Odocoileus virginianus*
Black-tailed deer	*Odocoileus hemionus columbianus*
Mule deer	*Odocoileus hemionus hemionus*
Moose	*Alces alces*
Sambar	*Cervus unicolor*
Barasingha	*Cervus duvauceli*
Wapiti	*Cervus canadensis*
Red deer	*Cervus elaphus*
Kashmir stag	*Cervus elaphus hanglu*
Manchurian wapiti	*Cervus elaphus xanthopygus*
Nilgai	*Boselaphus tragocamelus*
Four-horned antelope	*Tetracerus quadricornis*
American bison	*Bison bison*
Yak	*Bos grunniens*

Kouprey	*Bos sauveli*
Banteng	*Bos banteng*
Gaur	*Bos gaurus*
Water buffalo	*Bubalus bubalis*
Uganda kob	*Adenota kob*
Wildebeest	*Gorgon taurinus*
Waterbuck	*Kobus defassa* and *K. ellipsiprimnus*
Thomson gazelle	*Gazella thomsoni*
Grant gazelle	*Gazella granti*
Indian gazelle	*Gazella gazella*
Blackbuck	*Antilope cervicapra*
Impala	*Aepyceros melampus*
Springbuck	*Antidorcas marsupialis*
Chamois	*Rupicapra rupicapra*
Mountain goat	*Oreamnos americanus*
Serow	*Capricornis sumatraensis*
Takin	*Budorcas taxicolor*
Markhor	*Capra falconeri*
Ibex	*Capra ibex*
Tahr	*Hemitragus jemlahicus*
Bharal	*Pseudois nayaur*
Urial	*Ovis orientalis*
Stone's sheep	*Ovis dalli stonei*
Dall sheep	*Ovis dalli dalli*

Birds

King vulture	*Torgos calvus*
White-backed vulture	*Gyps bengalensis*
Red-wattled lapwing	*Vanellus indicus*
Jungle fowl	*Gallus gallus*
Jungle bush quail	*Perdicula asiatica*
Peafowl	*Pavo cristatus*
Hazel hen	*Tetrastes bonasia*
Ring dove	*Streptopelia decaocto*
Green barbet	*Megalaima zeylanica*
Brainfever bird	*Cuculus varius*
Common mynah	*Acridotheres tristis*
Black drongo	*Dicrurus adsimilis*
Jungle babbler	*Turdoides striatus*
Jungle crow	*Corvus macrohynchos*

REFERENCES CITED

ABRAMOV, V.
1962. A contribution to the biology of the Amur tiger, *Panthera tigris longipilis* (Fitzinger, 1868). Vestn. Cesk. Spolecnosti Zool., **26**:189–203.

ADAMSON, G.
1964. Observations on lions in Serengeti National Park. East Afr. Wildl. J., **2**:160–61.

ADAMSON, J.
1960. Born free. London.
1961. Living free. London.

AFLALO, F.
1904. The sportsman's book for India. London.

ALBRITTON, E. (ed.)
1954. Standard values in nutrition and metabolism. Philadelphia.

ALI, S.
1927. The Moghul emperors of India as naturalists and sportsmen. J. Bombay Nat. Hist. Soc., **31**(4):833–61.
1953. Hyderabad State, pp. 82–89. *In* The preservation of wild life in India: A compilation. Edited by R. Burton. Bangalore.

ALLEE, W.
1952. Dominance and hierarchy in societies of vertebrates. Colloq. Int. Cent. Nat. Rech. Sci., **34**:157–81.

ALLEN, D., and Mech, D.
1963. Wolves versus moose on Isle Royale. Nat. Geogr. Mag., **123**(2)200–219.

ALLEN, H.
1960. The lonely tiger. London.

ALTMANN, M.
1956. Patterns of herd behavior in free-ranging elk of Wyoming, *Cervus canadensis nelsoni*. Zoologica, **41**(2):65–71.
1959. Group dynamics in Wyoming moose during the rutting season. J. Mammal., **40**(3):420–24.

1960. The role of juvenile elk and moose in the social dynamics of their species. Zoologica, **45**(4):35–39.

AMOROSO, E., and JEWELL, P.
1963. The exploitation of the milk-ejection reflex by primitive peoples. Occas. Pap. No. 18, Roy. Anth. Inst., pp. 126–37.

AMOROSO, E., and MARSHALL, F.
1956. External factors in sexual periodicity, pp. 707–831. *In* Marshall's physiology of reproduction. Edited by A. Parkes. London.

ANDERSON, K.
1954. Nine man-eaters and one rogue. London.
1961. The call of the maneater. London.

ANON.
1956. With gun and rod in India. New Delhi.
1961. One hundred years of Indian forestry. Vol. II: The forests. Dehra Dun.
1962. National council of applied economic research; techno-economic survey of West Bengal. New Delhi.
1963. Amateur killers. Animals, **1**(10):22–23.
1964a. Mammals in danger of extinction. Oryx, **7**(5):226–28.
1964b. Notes and comments. Oryx, **7**(4):147–48.
1965a. News in brief. Oryx, **8**(2):116.
1965b. Poison for Indian tigers and leopards. Oryx, **8**(2):75.
1965c. Zwanzigjährige Tigerin. Das Tier, **5**(3):30.

ANTHONY, H.
1929. Horns and antlers: Their occurrence, development and function in the mammalia. New York Zool. Soc. Bull., **32**:2–33.

ANSELL, W.
1960. The breeding of some larger mammals in Northern Rhodesia. Proc. Zool. Soc. London, **134**:251–73.

ANTONIUS, O.
1932. Beobachtungen an Rindern in Schönbrunn. Zool. Garten, **5**(7):178–91.

ARAMILEV, I.
1959. Beyond the Ural Mountains. London.

ASDELL, S.
1946. Patterns of mammalian reproduction. Ithaca.
1964. Patterns of mammalian reproduction. 2d ed. Ithaca.

BACKHAUS, D.
1958. Beitrag zur Ethologie der Paarung einiger Antilopen. Zuchthygiene, **2**:281–93.

BAIKOV, N.
1925. The Manchurian tiger. London.
1936. Big game hunting in Manchuria. London.

BAKER, S.
> 1890.   Wild beasts and their ways. London.

BALDWIN, J.
> 1877.   The large and small game of Bengal and the northwestern provinces of India. London.

BAUDY, R., and BAUDY, C.
> n.d.   Hand-raising of large felines. Mimeographed manuscript from the Animals Training Center, Florida. 3 pp.

BAZÉ, W.
> 1957.   Tiger! Tiger! London.

BEDFORD, DUKE OF, and MARSHALL, F.
> 1942.   On the incidence of the breeding season in mammals after transference to a new latitude. Proc. Roy. Soc. London, Ser. B, **130**:396–99.

BELDING, D.
> 1952.   Textbook of clinical parasitology. New York.

BERG, B.
> 1936.   Tiger und Mensch. Berlin.

BHADIAN, C.
> 1934.   Notes on the swamp deer (*Rucervus duvaucelli*) in Assam. J. Bombay Nat. Hist. Soc., **37**(2):485–86.

BISCOE, W.
> 1895.   A tiger killing a panther. J. Bombay Nat. Hist. Soc., **9**(4):490.

BLANFORD, W.
> 1888–91.   The fauna of British India: Mammalia. London.

BORG, K.
> 1962.   Predation on roe deer in Sweden. J. Wildl. Mgmt., **26**(2):133–36.

BOSWELL, K.
> 1957.   "Scent trails" and "pooking" in tiger. J. Bombay Nat. Hist. Soc., **54**(2):452–54.

BOURLIÈRE, F.
> 1963.   Observations on the ecology of some large African mammals, pp. 43–54. *In* African ecology and human evolution. Edited by F. Howell and F. Bourlière. Viking Fund Publ. Anthr. No. 36. New York.

BRANDER, A.
> 1923.   Wild animals in Central India. London.
> 1953.   The Central Provinces (Madhya Pradesh), pp. 46–51. *In* The preservation of wild life in India: A compilation. Edited by R. Burton. Bangalore.

BREHM, A.
> 1918.   Brehms Tierleben. Vol. IV: Die Säugetiere. Leipzig.

BROOKS, A.
1961. A study of the Thomson's gazelle (*Gazella thomsonii* Günther) in Tanganyika. Colonial Research Publ. No. 25. London.

BROWN, C.
1936. Rearing wild animals in captivity, and gestation periods. J. Mammal., **17**(1):10–13.

BUDDEN, J.
1921. Black buck v. motor. J. Bombay Nat. Hist. Soc. **27**(4):939.

BUECHNER, H., and SCHLOETH, R.
1965. Ceremonial mating behavior in Uganda kob (*Adenota kob thomasi* Neumann). Z. f. Tierpsych., **22**(2):209–25.

BURKHOLDER, B.
1959. Movements and behavior of a wolf pack in Alaska. J. Wildl. Mgmt., **23**(1):1–11.

BURNETT, J.
1959. Increase of swamp deer (*Cervus duvauceli* Cuv.) in the Kaziranga Sanctuary, Assam. J. Bombay Nat. Hist. Soc., **56**(2):318–19.

BURTON, R.
1929. The tiger's method of making a "kill." J. Bombay Nat. Hist. Soc., **33**(4):974–76.
1933. The book of the tiger. Boston.
1936. The tiger hunters. London.
1940. The Indian wild dog. J. Bombay Nat. Hist. Soc., **41**(4):691–715.
1948. "Death cry" of tiger. J. Bombay Nat. Hist. Soc., **48**(1):176–78.
1950. Rabies in tiger—two proved instances. J. Bombay Nat. Hist. Soc., **49**(3):538–41.
1952. A history of shikar in India. J. Bombay Nat. Hist. Soc., **50**(4):845–69.

BUTT, J.
1963. Shikar. London.

CALDWELL, H.
1925. Blue tiger. London.

CAMPBELL, T.
1894. A tiger eating a bear. J. Bombay Nat. Hist. Soc., **9**(1):101.

CHAMPION, F.
1927. With a camera in tiger-land. London.
1933. The jungle in sunlight and shadow. London.
1953. The United Provinces (Uttar Pradesh), pp. 63–68. *In* The preservation of wild life in India: A compilation. Edited by R. Burton. Bangalore.

CHAMPION, H.
1938. A preliminary survey of forest types of India and Burma. Ind. For. Rec. (N.S.), **1**.

CLUTTON-BROCK, J.
1965. Excavations at Langhnaj: 1944–63. Part II: The fauna. Deccan College Building Centenary and Silver Jubilee Series No. 27. Poona.

COLLIAS, N.
1944. Aggressive behavior among vertebrate animals. Physiol. Zool., **17**:83–123.

COMBER, E.
1904. Breeding seasons of big game. J. Bombay Nat. Hist. Soc., **16**(1):176–79.

CONNELL, W.
1944. Wild dogs attacking a tiger. J. Bombay Nat. Hist. Soc., **44**(3):468–70.

COOCH BEHAR, MAHARAJAH OF.
1908. Thirty-seven years of big game shooting. Bombay.

COOPER, J.
1942. An exploratory study on African lions. Comp. Psychol. Monogr., **17**(7):1–48.

CORBETT, G.
1892. A tiger attacking elephants. J. Bombay Nat. Hist. Soc., **7**(1):192.

CORBETT, J.
1957. Man-eaters of India. London.

COWAN, I.
1956. Life and times of the coast black-tailed deer, pp. 523–617. *In* The deer of North America. Edited by W. Taylor. Washington, D.C.

COWAN, I., and GEIST, V.
1961. Aggressive behaviour in deer of the genus *Odocoileus*. J. Mammal., **42**(4):522–26.

CRANDALL, L.
1964. The management of wild mammals in captivity. Chicago.

CRISLER, L.
1956. Observations of wolves hunting caribou. J. Mammal. **37**(3):337–46.

DAHLBERG, B., and GUETTINGER, R.
1956. The white-tailed deer in Wisconsin. Techn. Wildl. Bull. No. 14. Wisconsin Conservation Department, Madison.

DANG, H.
1962. The future of the tiger. The Cheetal, **5**(1):46–47.
1964a. The Himalayan wild life research project – first project report. The Cheetal, **7**(1):24–29.
1964b. A natural sanctuary in the Himalaya:Nanda Devi and the Rishiganga Basin. The Cheetal, **7**(1):34–42.

1964c. Wild life in open country. I: The black buck. The Cheetal, **7**(1):20–24.

DARLING, F.
1937.   A herd of red deer. London.

DASMANN, R., and MOSSMAN, A.
1962.   Reproduction in some ungulates in southern Rhodesia. J. Mammal., **43**(4):533–37.

DASMANN, R., and TABER, R.
1956.   Behavior of Columbian black-tailed deer with reference to population ecology. J. Mammal., **37**(2):143–64.

DAVAR, S.
1938.   Cause of sore neck in sambar. J. Bombay Nat. Hist. Soc., **40**(1):118–22.

DAVIS, D.
1957.   The use of food as a buffer in a predator-prey system. J. Mammal., **38**(4):466–72.

DENIS, A.
1964.   Cats of the world. London.

DHARMAKUMARSINHJI, K.
1959.   A field guide to big game census in India. Indian Board for Wild Life, Leaflet No. 2, New Delhi.

DITMARS, R.
1919.   Our oldest specimens. Bull. New York Zool. Soc., **22**(3):60–65.

DOLLMAN, G., and BURLACE, J.
1935.   Rowland Ward's records of big game. London.

EARDLEY-WILMOT, S.
1910.   Forest life and sport in India. London.

ECKSTEIN, P., and ZUCKERMAN, S.
1956.   The oestrous cycle in the mammalia, pp. 226–396. *In* Marshall's physiology of reproduction. Edited by A. Parkes. London.

EINARSEN, A.
1956.   Life of the mule deer, pp. 363–429. *In* The deer of North America. Edited by W. Taylor. Washington, D.C.

ELLERMAN, J., and MORRISON-SCOTT, T.
1951.   Checklist of Palaearctic and Indian mammals, 1758 to 1946. British Museum, London.

ERRINGTON, P.
1946.   Predation and vertebrate populations. Quart. Rev. of Biol., **21**(2):144–77; (3):221–45.

ESPMARK, Y.
1964a. Rutting behavior in reindeer (*Rangifer tarandus* L.). Animal Behaviour, **12**(1):159–63.
1964b. Studies in dominance-subordination relationship in a group of semi-domestic reindeer (*Rangifer tarandus* L.). Animal Behaviour, **12**(4):420–26.

ETKIN, W.
    1954.   Social behavior of the male blackbuck under zoo conditions.
            Anat. Record, **120**(3): Abstract No. 81.

EVANS, G.
    1912.   Big game shooting in Upper Burma. London.

FAHIMUDDIN, M.
    1963.   Animal production in Bihar. Bombay.

FENTON, L.
    1905.   Tigers hamstringing their prey before killing. J. Bombay Nat.
            Hist. Soc., **16**(4):756.

FINN, F.
    1929.   Sterndale's mammalia of India. Calcutta.

FLEROV, K.
    1960.   Fauna of U.S.S.R.: Musk deer and deer. Israel Program for
            Scientific Translations, Washington, D.C.

FLETCHER, F.
    1911.   Sport on the Nilgiris and in Wynaad. London.

FLOWER, S.
    1931.   Contributions to our knowledge of the duration of life in verte-
            brate animals. V: Mammals. Proc. Zool. Soc. London, pp.
            145–234.

FOENANDER, E.
    1952.   Big game of Malaya. London.

FORSYTH, J.
    1889.   The highlands of Central India. London.

FORSYTH, W.
    1911.   The number of cubs in a tiger's litter. J. Bombay Nat. Hist. Soc.,
            20(4):1148.

FUCHS, S.
    1960.   The Gond and Bhumia of Eastern Mandla. Bombay.

FULLER, W.
    1960.   Behaviour and social organization of the wild bison of Wood
            Buffalo National Park, Canada. Arctic, **13**(1):2–19.

GEE, E.
    1937.   Strange behaviour of a tigress. J. Bombay Nat. Hist. Soc.,
            39(3):614.
    1953.   The life history of the great Indian one-horned rhinoceros
            (*Rhinoceros unicornis* Linn.). J. Bombay Nat. Hist. Soc.,
            51(2):341–48.
    1961.   Wild life sanctuaries in India. Department of Tourism, New
            Delhi.
    1962a. The present status of four rare animals in India. The Cheetal,
            4(2):29–33.
    1962b. The management of India's wild life sanctuaries and national
            parks. Part IV. J. Bombay Nat. Hist. Soc., **59**(2):453–85.

1963.   Report on a brief survey of the wild life resources of Nepal, including the rhinoceros. Oryx, **7**(2–3):67–76.

1964.   The wild life of India. London.

GEIST, V.

1963.   On the behaviour of the North American moose (*Alces alces andersoni* Peterson, 1950). Behaviour, **20**(3–4):377–416.

1964*a*.   On the rutting behavior of the mountain goat. J. Mammal., **45**(4):551–68.

1964*b*.   Social mechanisms involved in habitat retention of Stone's sheep (*Ovis dalli stonei*). Am. Zool., **4**(3): Abstract.

GILBERT, R.

1888.   Notes on sambhur and sambhur stalking. J. Bombay Nat. Hist. Soc., **3**(4):224–32.

1889.   Notes on man-eating tigers. J. Bombay Nat. Hist. Soc., **4**(3):195–206.

GOLLEY, F., PETRIDES, G., RAUBER, E., and JENKINS, J.

1965.   Food intake and assimilation by bobcats under laboratory conditions. J. Wildl. Mgmt., **29**(3):442–47.

GORDON-CUMMING, R.

1872.   Wild men and wild beasts. London.

GRAF, W.

1956.   Territorialism in deer. J. Mammal., **37**(2):165–70.

GUGGISBERG, C.

1961.   Simba. London.

GUPTA, A.

1959.   Tigers at high altitudes. J. Bengal Nat. Hist. Soc., **29**(1–2):55–56.

GUPTA, K., and VERMA, N.

1949.   Rinderpest in wild ruminants. Indian J. Vet. Sci. and Animal Husbandry, **19**(3):219–24.

HAFEZ, E., and SCHEIN, M.

1962.   The behaviour of cattle, pp. 247–96. *In* The behaviour of domestic animals. Edited by E. Hafez. Baltimore.

HANLEY, P.

1961.   Tiger trails in Assam. London.

HAYES, F., GERARD, W., SHOTTS, E., and DILLS, G.

1960.   Further serologic studies of brucellosis in white-tailed deer of the southeastern United States. J. Am. Vet. Med. Assoc., **137**(3):190–91.

HEAPE, W.

1901.   The "sexual seasons" of mammals and the relation of the "prooestrum" to menstruation. Quart. J. Microscop. Sci., **44**:1–70.

HEARSEY, L.

1932.   Tiger killing swamp deer or Gond (*Rucervus duvaucelli*). J. Bombay Nat. Hist. Soc., **35**(4):885–86.

HEDIGER, H.
1952. Beiträge zur Säugetiere-Soziologie. Colloq. Int. Cent. Nat. Rech. Sci., **34**:297–320.
1955. Studies of the psychology and behaviour of captive animals in zoos and circuses. London.

HEWETT, J.
1938. Jungle trails in northern India. London.

HIBBEN, F.
1937. A preliminary study of the mountain lion. Univ. New Mexico Bull. No. 318. 59 pp.

HIGGINS, J.
1935. The game birds and animals of Manipur State with notes on their numbers, migration, and habits. J. Bombay Nat. Hist. Soc., **37**(2):298–309.

HINGORANI, B.
1962. Annual progress report of forest administration in the wild life preservation organization for the year 1961–62. Manuscript with forest department, Uttar Pradesh.

HITESHI, H.
1947. The "watching" attitude of the cheetal or spotted deer (*Axis axis* Erxl.). J. Bombay Nat. Hist. Soc., **47**(2):376–77.

HODGSON, B.
1847. On various genera of the ruminants. J. Asiat. Soc. Bengal, **16**:685.

HORNADAY, W.
1885. Two years in the jungle. New York.

HUBBACK, T.
1937. The Malayan gaur or seladang. J. Mammal., **18**(3):267–79.

HUXLEY, J.
1961. The conservation of wild life and natural habitats in Central and East Africa. UNESCO, Paris.

INGLIS, J.
1892. Tent life in tigerland and sport and work on the Nepaul frontier. London.

INVERARITY, J.
1888. Unscientific notes on the tiger. J. Bombay Nat. Hist. Soc., **3**(3):143–54.
1889. The Indian bison, with some notes on stalking him. J. Bombay Nat. Hist. Soc., **4**(4):294–310.
1895. The cheetul or spotted deer. J. Bombay Nat. Hist. Soc., **9**(4):481–85.

JARVIS, C. (ed.).
1965. The international zoo yearbook. Vol. V. London.

JARVIS, C. and MORRIS, D. (eds.).
1962. The international zoo yearbook. Vol. III. London.
1963. The international zoo yearbook. Vol. IV. London.

JERDON, T.
  1874.   The mammals of India. London.
JOURNAL OF THE BOMBAY NATURAL HISTORY SOCIETY, EDITORS OF.
  1921.   Sore neck in sambar. **27**(4):937–38.
  1948.   A tale of many tigers. **48**(1):175–76.
  1960.   How many young does a chital have? **57**(3):653–54.
KAISER, M., and HOOGSTRAAL, H.
  1964.   The *Hyalomma* ticks (*Ixodoidea, Ixodidae*) of Pakistan, India, and Ceylon, with keys to subgenera and species. Acarologia, **6**(2):257–86.
KENDREW, W.
  1961.   The climates of continents. Oxford.
KENNETH, J.
  1953.   Gestation periods. Tech. Comm. No. 5, Commonwealth Bureau of Animal Breeding and Genetics, Edinburgh.
KHAJURIA, H.
  1963.   The wild dog (*Cuon alpinus* [Pallas]) and the tiger (*Panthera tigris* [Linn.]). J. Bombay Nat. Hist. Soc., **60**(2):448–49.
KHAN, I.
  1936.   Association between a leopard and a tigress. J. Bombay Nat. Hist. Soc., **39**(1):155–56.
KILEY-WORTHINGTON, M.
  1965.   The waterbuck (*Kobus defassa* Ruppel 1835 and *K. ellipsiprimnus* Ogilby 1833) in East Africa — spatial distribution: A study of the sexual behaviour. Mammalia, **29**(2):177–210.
KINLOCH, A.
  1892.   Large game shooting in Thibet, the Himalayas, northern and central India. Calcutta.
KIRK, G.
  1966.   Lob-nor Tiger ausgerottet. Das Tier, **6**(2):46.
KLEIN, D., and OLSON, S.
  1960.   Natural mortality patterns of deer in southeast Alaska. J. Wildl. Mgmt., **24**(1):80–88.
KOFORD, C.
  1957.   The vicuna and the puna. Ecol. Monogr., **27**:153–219.
KRISHNAN, M.
  1959.   The Mudumalai wild life sanctuary. Madras State Forest Department, Madras.
LENT, P.
  1965.   Rutting behaviour in a barren-ground caribou population. Animal Behaviour,**13**(2–3):259–64.
LEOPOLD, A., RINEY, T., MC CAIN, R., and TEVIS, L.
  1951.   The Jawbone deer herd. Calif. Dept. Nat. Resources, Div. Fish and Game, Bull. No. 4.

LEWIS, E.
1940. The "sambar" call of the tiger and its explanation. J. Bombay Nat. Hist. Soc., **41**(4):889–90.

LEYHAUSEN, P.
1950. Beobachtungen an Löwen-Tiger-Bastarden mit einigen Bemerkungen zur Systematik der Grosskatzen. Z. f. Tierpsych., **7**(1):48–83.
1956. Das Verhalten der Katzen (*Felidae*). Handbuch der Zool., **8**(10):1–34.
1960. Verhaltensstudien an Katzen. Berlin.
1965a. The communal organization of solitary mammals. Symp. Zool. Soc. London, **14**:249–63.
1965b. The sane community — a density problem? Discovery. September. Unpaginated reprint.
1965c. Über die Funktion der relativen Stimmungshierarchie. Z. f. Tierpsych., **22**(4):412–94.

LEYHAUSEN, P., and WOLFF, R.
1959. Das Revier einer Hauskatze. Z. f. Tierpsych., **16**(6):666–70.

LINSDALE, J., and TOMICH, P.
1953. A herd of mule deer. Berkeley, Calif.

LITTLEDALE, H.
1889. Bears being eaten by tigers. J. Bombay Nat. Hist. Soc., **4**(4):316.

LIVINGSTON, H., PAYNE, W., and FRIEND, M.
1962. Urea excretion in ruminants. Nature, **194**(4833):1057–58.

LOCKE, A.
1954. The tigers of Trengganu. London.

LONGHURST, W., LEOPOLD, A., and DASMANN, R.
1952. A survey of California deer herds: Their ranges and management problems. Calif. Dept. Nat. Resources, Div. Fish and Game, Bull. No. 6.

LYDEKKER, R.
1893. Horns and hoofs. London.
1898. The deer of all lands. London.
1913–16. Catalogue of ungulate mammals in the British Museum. 5 vols. London.
1924. The game animals of India, Burma, Malaya, and Tibet. London.

MAA, T.
1965. A synopsis of the *Lipopteninae* (*Diptera: Hippoboscidae*). J. Med. Ent., **2**(3):233–48.

McCABE, R., and LEOPOLD, A.
1951. Breeding season of the Sonora white-tailed deer. J. Wildl. Mgmt., **15**(4):433–34.

McHugh, T.
  1958.   Social behavior of the American buffalo (*Bison bison bison*).
         Zoologica, **43**(1):1–40.
Marshall, F.
  1937.   On the change over in the oestrous cycle in animals after
         transference across the equator. . . . Proc. Roy. Soc. London,
         Ser. B, **122**:413–28.
Matthes, H.
  1962.   Verbreitung der Säugetiere in der Vorzeit. Handbuch der Zool.,
         11(1):1–198.
Mech, L.
  1964.   My three years among timber wolves. Nature and Science,
         1(8):3–6.
Mehta, J.
  n. d.   Working plan for Mandla division, 1949–50 to 1963–64. Forest
         Department, Madhya Pradesh.
Meinertzhagen, R.
  1939.   Some weights and measurements of large mammals. Proc. Zool.
         Soc. London, **108**:433–40.
Milroy, A.
  1953.   Assam, pp. 59–62. *In* The preservation of wild life in India: A
         compilation. Edited R. Burton. Bangalore.
Mitchell, C., Hoogstraal, H., Schaller, G., and Spillett, J.
  1966.   Ectoparasites from mammals in Kanha National Park, Madhya
         Pradesh, India, and their potential disease relationships. J.
         Med. Ent., **3**(2):113–24.
Mitchell, C., and Nadchatram, M.
  1966.   Seven new species of chiggers from central India, with a re-
         description of *Leptotrombidium* (L.) *pelta* (Womersley, 1952)
         (*Acarina: Trombiculidae*). J. Med. Ent., **3**(1):1–17.
Morris, R.
  1927.   A tigress with 5 cubs. J. Bombay Nat. Hist. Soc., **31**(3):810–11.
  1937a. Close seasons for big game — are they beneficial? J. Bombay
         Nat. Hist. Soc., **39**(3):621–22.
  1937b. A very large sambar stag. J. Bombay Nat. Hist. Soc., **39**(2):390.
  1938.   "Stamping grounds" and "sore neck" in sambar. J. Bombay Nat.
         Hist. Soc., **40**(3):560–61.
  1946.   Destruction of cattle by tiger en masse. J. Bombay Nat. Hist.
         Soc., **46**(4):714.
  1947.   Weight of bull bison. J. Bombay Nat. Hist. Soc., **47**(1):153.
  1953.   Unrecorded sounds made by tiger and wild dog. J. Bombay
         Nat. Hist. Soc., **51**(2):494–95.
  1948.   Sambar sore neck. J. Bombay Nat. Hist. Soc., **47**(4):729–30.
Mosby, H.
  1963.   Wildlife investigational techniques. Wildlife Society, Blacks-
         burg, Virginia.

MOYNIHAN, M.
  1955. Remarks on the original sources of displays. Auk, **72**(3):240–46.

MURIE, A.
  1944. The wolves of Mount McKinley. U.S. Dept. Int., Natl. Park Serv. Fauna Ser. No. 5, Washington, D.C.

MURIE, O.
  1951. The elk of North America. Washington, D.C.

NATH, B.
  n.d. Interim working plan report for the Kanha National Park. Forest Department, Madhya Pradesh.

NICHOLS, L.
  1960. Ecology of the *Axis* deer. Job completion report, September 1, 1957, to September 1, 1960. Mimeographed manuscripts from the Division of Fish and Game. Hawaii.

NOVIKOV, G.
  1962. Carnivorous mammals of the fauna of the U.S.S.R. Israel Program for Scientific Translations, Washington, D.C.

O'BRIEN, E.
  1944. Where man-eating tigers occur. J. Bombay Nat. Hist. Soc., **45**(1):231–32.

OGILVIE, C.
  1953. The behavior of seladang (*Bibos gaurus*). Oryx, **2**:167–69.

OGNEV, S.
  1962. Mammals of U.S.S.R. and adjacent countries. Vol. III: Carnivora. Israel Program for Scientific Translations, Washington, D.C.

OLSON, S.
  1938. A study in predatory relationship with particular reference to the wolf. Sci. Monthly, **46**:323–36.

PEACOCK, E.
  1933. A game-book for Burma and adjoining territories. London.

PERRY, R.
  1964. The world of the tiger. London.

POCOCK, R.
  1910. On the specialized cutaneous glands of ruminants. Proc. Zool. Soc. London, pp. 840–986.
  1912. On antler-growth in the *Cervidae*, with special reference to *Elaphurus* and *Odocoilus* (*Dorcelaphus*). Proc. Zool. Soc. London, pp. 773–83.
  1929. Tigers. J. Bombay Nat. Hist. Soc., **33**(3):505–41.
  1939. The fauna of British India: Mammalia. London.

POLLOCK, F.
  1896. Fifty years reminiscences of India. London.

POLLOCK, F. and THOM, W.
  1900. Wild sports of Burma and Assam. London.

POWELL, A.
    1957.   Call of the tiger. London.
    1964.   The gaur or Indian bison. J. Bengal Nat. Hist. Soc.,
           32(2):73–80.

PRAKASH, I.
    1960.   Shikar in Rajasthan. The Cheetal, 2(2):68–72.

PRATER, S.
    1934.   The wild animals of the Indian empire. Madras.
    1940.   The number of tigers shot in reserved forest in India and
           Burma during the year 1937–1938. J. Bombay Nat. Hist. Soc.,
           41(4):881–89.
    1945.   Breeding habits of swamp deer (*Rucervus duvaucelli*) in As-
           sam. J. Bombay Nat. Hist. Soc., 45(3):415–16.
    1948.   The book of Indian animals. Bombay Natural History Society,
           Bombay.

PRUITT, W.
    1954.   Rutting behavior of the whitetail deer (*Odocoileus virgin-
           ianus*). J. Mammal., 35(1):129–30.
    1960.   Behavior of the barren-ground caribou. Biol. Pap. Univ.
           Alaska, No. 3.

PURI, G.
    1960.   Indian forest ecology. 2 vols. New Delhi.

QUIMBY, D., and GAAB, J.
    1957.   Mandibular dentition as an age indicator in Rocky Mountain
           elk. J. Wildl. Mgmt., 24(4):435–51.

RANDHAWA, M.
    1958.   Agriculture and animal husbandry in India. New Delhi.

RAO, S.
    1957.   History of our knowledge of the Indian fauna through the
           ages. J. Bombay Nat. Hist. Soc., 54(2):251–80.

RAO, V.
    1961.   Annual report on wild life preservation in West Bengal for the
           year 1958–59. West Bengal Government Press, Alipore.

REED, T.
    1959.   Report on the National Zoological Park for the year ended
           June 30, 1958. Smithsonian Institution Report for 1958, pp.
           140–79.

RICE, W.
    1857.   Tiger-shooting in India. London.

RICHARDSON, W.
    1890.   Tiger cubs. J. Bombay Nat. Hist. Soc., 5(2):191.

RIPLEY, S., and the EDITORS OF LIFE.
    1964.   The land and wildlife of tropical Asia. New York.

ROBERTSON, F.
    1936.   Our forests. Allahabad.

ROBINETTE, W., GASHWILER, J., LOW, J., and JONES, D.
1957. Differential mortality by sex and age among mule deer. J. Wildl. Mgmt., **21**(1):1–16.

ROBINETTE, W., GASHWILER, J., and MORRIS, O.
1961. Notes on cougar productivity and life history. J. Mammal., **42**(2):204–17.

ROBINETTE, W., JONES, D., ROGERS, G., and GASHWILER, J.
1957. Notes on tooth development and wear for Rocky Mountain mule deer. J. Wildl. Mgmt., **21**(2):134–53.

RODON, G.
1897. Leopard versus chital; pig versus leopard. J. Bombay Nat. Hist. Soc., **11**(1):158–59.

ROOKE, E.
1908. Wild animals and birds of Bastar. Unpublished manuscript in files of Bombay Natural History Society.

ROWLAND, B.
1963. The Ajanta caves. Fontana UNESCO art book.

RUSSELL, C.
1900. Bullet and shot in Indian forest, plain and hill. London.

SADLEIR, R.
1966. Notes on reproduction in the larger felidae, pp. 184–87. *In* The international zoo yearbook. Vol. VI. Edited by C. Jarvis. London.

SANDERSON, G.
1912. Thirteen years among the wild beasts of India. Edinburgh.

SANKHALA, K.,
1964. Wildlife sanctuaries of Rajasthan. J. Bombay Nat. Hist. Soc., **61**(1):1–8.

SCHALLER, G.
1964. Notes on the behaviour of the peafowl. Newsletter for Bird-watchers (Bombay), **4**(9):1–3.
1965. My year with the tigers. Life, **58**(25):60–66.

SCHALLER, G., and DE, R.
1964. The shedding of antlers by cheetal deer. The Cheetal, **7**(1):15–17.

SCHALLER, G., and SPILLETT, J.
1966. The status of the big game species in the Keoladeo Ghana Sanctuary, Rajasthan. The Cheetal, **8**(2):12–16.

SCHEIN, M., and FOHRMAN, M.
1955. Social dominance relationships in a herd of dairy cattle. Brit. J. Animal Behav., **3**:45–55.

SCHLOETH, R.
1958a. Cycle annuel et comportement social du taurau de Camargue. Mammalia, **22**(1):121–39.

1958b. Über die Mutter-Kind-Beziehungen beim halbwilden Camargue-Rind. Säugetierkundliche Mitteilungen, **6**(4):145–50.

1961. Das Sozialleben des Camargue-Rindes. Z. f. Tierpsych., **18**(5):574–627.

SCLATER, P.

1863. Record of the period of gestation of certain ruminants which bred in the Society's gardens. Proc. Zool. Soc. London, pp. 230–31.

SCOTT, J.

1960. Forests of the night. London.

SEVERINGHAUS, C., and CHEATUM, E.

1956. Life and times of the white-tailed deer, pp. 57–186. *In* The deer of North America. Edited by W. Taylor. Washington, D.C.

SHAH, K., SCHALLER, G., FLYGER, V., and HERMAN, C.

1965. Antibodies to Myxovirus Parainfluenza 3 in sera of wild deer. Bull. Wildl. Disease Assoc., **1**:31–32.

SHAKESPEAR, H.

1860. Wild sports of India. London.

SHULL, E.

1962. Gestation period of the fourhorned antelope *Tetracerus quadricornis* (Blainville). J. Bombay Nat. Hist. Soc., **59**(3):945–47.

"SILVER HACKLE."

1929. Indian jungle lore and the rifle. Calcutta.

SIMON, E.

1943a. Breeding season of the Indian sambar (*Rusa unicolor*, Kerr.). J. Bombay Nat. Hist. Soc., **44**(1):118–19.

1943b. Life span of some wild animals in captivity. J. Bombay Nat. Hist. Soc., **44**(1):117–18.

SIMPSON, G.

1945. Principles of classification and classification of mammals. Bull. Am. Mus. Nat. Hist. No. 85. New York.

SINGH, B.

1958. Working plan for the Haldwani forest division, western circle, Uttar Pradesh, 1956–57 to 1965–66. Allahabad.

SINGH, K.

1959. The tiger of Rajasthan. London.

SINGH, P.

1959. The old Dholpur Sanctuary. The Cheetal, **1**(2):3–6.

SINGH, Y.

1963. The cause — as before. The Cheetal, **6**(1):34–44.

SISSON, S.

1930. The anatomy of domestic animals. Philadelphia.

SKOOG, R.

1956. Range, movements, populations, and food habits of the Steese-Fortymile caribou herd. Master's thesis, University of Alaska.

SMEETON, M.
　1961.　A taste of the hills. London.
SMYTHIES, E.
　1942.　Big game shooting in Nepal. Calcutta.
SRIVASTAVA, S.
　1957.　Working plan for the Kalagargh forest division, western circle, Uttar Pradesh, 1955–56 to 1969–70. Allahabad.
STANFORD, J.
　1951.　Crab-eating chital. J. Bombay Nat. Hist. Soc., **50**(2):398–99.
STEBBING, E.
　1911.　Jungle by-ways in India. London.
　1912.　Game sanctuaries and game protection in India. Proc. Zool. Soc. London, pp. 23–55.
STENLUND, M.
　1955.　A field study of the timber wolf (*Canis lupus*) on the Superior National Forest, Minnesota. Minn. Dept. Cons. Tech. Bull. No. 4.
STERNDALE, R.
　1884.　Natural history of Indian mammals. London.
STEVENSON-HAMILTON, J.
　1954.　Wild life in South Africa. London.
STEWART, A.
　1928.　Tiger and other game. London.
STOCKLEY, C.
　1928.　Big game shooting in the Indian empire. London.
STOCKLEY, V.
　1913.　Big game shooting in India, Burma, and Somaliland. London.
STOREY, H.
　1907.　Hunting and shooting in Ceylon. London.
STRACEY, P.
　1961.　The future of the tiger. The Cheetal, **3**(2):29–32.
STRACHAN, A.
　1933.　Mauled by a tiger. London.
TABER, R., and DASMANN, R.
　1954.　A sex difference in mortality in young Columbian black-tailed deer. J. Wildl. Mgmt., **18**(3):309–15.
　1958.　The black-tailed deer of the chaparral. Cal. Dept. Nat. Resources, Div. Fish and Game, Bull. No. 8.
TAIBEL, A.
　1937.　*L'Antilope cervicapra*: Osservazioni sul gruppo in allevamento presso la Stazione sperimentale di Avicultura di Rovigo. Rassegna Faunistica (Roma), **4**:3–19.
TALBOT, L.
　1960.　A look at threatened species. Fauna Preservation Society, London.

TALBOT, L., and TALBOT, M.
    1963. The wildebeest in Western Masailand, East Africa. Wildl.
          Monogr. No. 12.
TAYLOR, M.
    1956. The tiger's claw. London.
TAYLOR, W. (ed.).
    1956. The deer of North America. Washington, D. C.
THOM, W.
    1937. The Malayan or Burmese sambar (*Rusa unicolor equinus*).
          J. Bombay Nat. Hist. Soc., **39**(2):309–19.
THOMAS, J., ROBINSON, R., and MARBURGER, R.
    1965. Social behavior in a white-tailed deer herd containing hypo-
          gonadal males. J. Mammal., **46**(2):314–27.
THOMPSON, D.
    1958. Field techniques for sexing and ageing game animals. Special
          Wildl. Report No. 1, Wisconsin Conservation Department,
          Madison.
TOOGOOD, C.
    1936. Number of cubs in a tigress litter. J. Bombay Nat. Hist. Soc.,
          39(1):158.
    1937. Curious behaviour of bison (*Bibos gaurus* H. Sm.). J. Bombay
          Nat. Hist. Soc., **39**(4):852–53.
TURNER, J.
    1959. Man-eaters and memories. London.
VENKATARAMANY, P.
    1961. Handbook of Indian forest statistics, 1957–1958. Forest Re-
          search Institute, Dehra Dun.
WALLACE, L.
    1945. The effect of diet on fetal development. J. Physiol.,
          104(1):34–35.
WALTHER, F.
    1958. Zum Kampf und Paarungsverhalten einiger Antilopen. Z. f.
          Tierpsych., **15**(3):340–80.
    1960. Beobachtungen zum Sozialverhalten der Sasin. Jahrb. G. v.
          Opel-Freigehege f. Tierforschung, **2**:64–78.
    1964. Einige Verhaltensbeobachtungen an Thomsongazellen (*Ga-*
          zella thomsoni Günther, 1884) im Ngorongoro-Krater. Z. f.
          Tierpsych., **21**(7):870–90.
    1965. Verhaltensstudien an der Grantgazelle (*Gazella granti* Brooke,
          1872) im Ngorongoro-Krater. Z. f. Tierpsych., **22**(2):167–208.
WARD, R.
    1922. Records of big game. London.
WHARTON, C.
    1957. An ecological study of the kouprey, *Novibos sauveli* (Urbain).
          Monogr. Inst. Sci. Technol. (Manila), No. 5.

WISLOCKI, G.
  1943. Studies on the growth of deer antlers. II: Seasonal changes in the male reproductive tract of Virginia deer (*Odocoileus virginianus borealis*), pp. 631–47. *In* Essays in biology. Berkeley, Calif.
WISLOCKI, G., AUB, J., and WALDO, C.
  1947. The effects of gonadectomy and the administration of testosterone propionate on the growth of the antlers in male and female deer. Endocrinology, **40**:202–24.
WRIGHT, B.
  1960. Predation on big game in East Africa. J. Wildl. Mgmt., **24**(1):1–15.
WRIGHT, M.
  1930. Season of shedding and growth of antlers in swamp deer (*Rucervus Duvaucelli*) in Assam. J. Bombay Nat. Hist. Soc., **34**(1):236.
WYNNE-EDWARDS, V.
  1962. Animal dispersion in relation to social behaviour. Edinburgh.
YOUNG, S., and GOLDMAN, E.
  1946. The puma, mysterious American cat. New York.
ZUCKERMAN, S.
  1953. The breeding season of mammals in captivity. Proc. Zool. Soc. London, **122**(1):827–950.

ACKNOWLEDGMENTS

This investigation was supported by Public Health Service Grant No. H. 26.6114 from the National Institutes of Health to the Johns Hopkins Center for Medical Research and Training, Baltimore and Calcutta. The study was undertaken while I was a research associate at the Johns Hopkins University and a member of the Center for Medical Research and Training, and it was directed by Drs. F. Bang and C. Southwick, to whom I am indebted for advice and assistance. Several members of the program furthered certain aspects of my work considerably. Mr. J. Spillett worked with me for brief periods in Kanha National Park and in the Keoladeo Ghana Sanctuary, generously contributing his data as well as making the task of gathering mine more enjoyable. Mr. C. Mitchell collected and identified many of the mammalian ectoparasites, particularly the mites, from Kanha Park. Dr. G. Schad identified the ova of parasites in tiger and leopard feces and during a visit to Kanha Park made a representative collection of amphibians and reptiles. Dr. K. Shah analyzed blood sera for antibodies. Dr. C. Wallace, Mr. N. Alim, and Mrs. G. Dutt handled many of the local administrative details in Calcutta. The help of these and other members of the program is gratefully acknowledged.

The project was affiliated locally with the University of Calcutta, and I would like to thank Dr. J. L. Bhaduri for his interest in the work.

The observations on the chital deer in the Calcutta Zoological Garden were made possible with the generous permission and assistance of Superintendent R. K. Lahiri. Mr. B. Goswami and particularly Mr. A. Ghosh collected data on the deer during my absence from Calcutta.

Mr. R. C. De, a graduate student from the University of Calcutta, ably assisted me at Kanha Park for six months, contributing cheerfully to all aspects of the work. I am indebted to him for many observations in this report. I also wish to express my gratitude to Mr. Madhu Khati, who, though nominally my chauffeur, was invaluable as a general assistant without whose calm and efficient presence the work would have progressed far less smoothly.

I owe a great debt to Mr. E. P. Gee of Shillong, Assam, who first suggested Kanha Park to me as a possible study site, who facilitated my work everywhere, and who consistently gave me useful advice, information, and encouragement.

I am extremely grateful to the government of Madhya Pradesh and the state forest department for permission to live in Kanha Park and for renting me tourist accommodations there. The staff of the forest department offered unfailing courtesy and assistance, and I would particularly like to thank former Secretary to the Government S. Verma, Chief Conservator of Forests K. Mishra, Divisional Forest Officers B. Tewary and S. Shrivastava, Superintendent of Parks V. Singh, Working Plan Officer B. Nath, and Ranger Gahelot.

I also acknowledge with pleasure the help of the Bombay Natural History Society, particularly Mr. J. Daniel and Mr. R. Grubh, with whom I spent ten profitable and pleasant days in censusing wild buffalo, and Mr. Z. Futehally, who received me cordially in Bombay.

While conducting wildlife surveys in a number of states I was hospitably received and greatly aided by numerous persons: in West Bengal by Divisional Forest Officer M. Sarkar, who accompanied me on a visit to the Sunderbans; in Uttar Pradesh by Chief Wild Life Warden D. Misra, who made my work in Corbett Park and in other areas possible, by Mr. A. Singh of Palia Kalan, who generously boarded me for a week while I studied the deer near his farm, by Mr. N. Singh also of Palia Kalan, who loaned me four elephants with which to census barasingha, and by Mr. H. Dang, the editor of *The Cheetal*, who shared his knowledge of wildlife with me and in many other ways was of assistance; in Rajasthan by Deputy Conservator of Forests K. Sankhala, Divisional Forest Officer H. Gupta, and Assistant Conservator of Forests D. Govil, who greatly facilitated my work in the Keoladeo Ghana Sanctuary; and in Assam by Range Officer C. Chakravarty, who helped me considerably in the Kaziranga Sanctuary.

Numerous persons furnished me with information about local wildlife conditions, among them, Conservator of Forests G. Singh, about the Punjab; Game Warden B. Chandre, Rajasthan; Chief Conservator of Forests R. Joshi, Gujarat; Mr. V. Shukla and Mr. S. Thakur of

Allwyn Cooper Shikar Company and Mr. R. Dharmakumarsinhji of Bombay, Maharashtra; Chief Conservator of Forests P. Barua, Assam; Chief Conservator of Forests P. Rao, Andhra Pradesh; Conservator of Forests M. Ahmedulla, Orissa; Chief Conservator of Forests S. Shahi, Bihar; Mr. G. Hyde, United States Consulate, Calcutta, West Bengal; State Wild Life Officer M. Badshah and Mr. M. Krishnan, Madras; Wild Life Preservation Officer K. Mathew, Kerala; Assistant Wild Life Warden N. Negi, Uttar Pradesh; Chief Conservator of Forests R. Willan, Nepal; and Dr. P. Jay, Regional Primate Center, Davis, California.

I gratefully acknowledge the assistance of Mr. S. Wayman of *Life* magazine, who made the tiger observations in March, 1965, possible.

I am greatly indebted to several persons for identifying or analyzing specimens collected in Kanha Park and elsewhere: Dr. S. Mukerjee, keeper of the Central National Herbarium, Calcutta — plants; Dr. B. Biswas, Zoological Survey of India, Calcutta — rats and mice; Dr. R. Inger, Chicago Natural History Museum — amphibians and reptiles; Dr. K. Singh, Virus Research Center, Poona — ticks; Dr. H. Hoogstraal, Naval Medical Research Unit, Cairo — ticks; Dr. S. Prudhoe, British Museum, London — nematodes, trematodes, and cestodes; Dr. J. Sheals, British Museum, London — pentastomids; Dr. M. Andre, director of *Acarologia*, France — *Dinothrombium* mite; Dr. T. Maa, University of Taiwan, Formosa — hippoboscid flies; Mr. N. Usherwood, Agronomy Department, University of Maryland — soil samples.

A number of zoos were generous in providing me with unpublished information from their files: Mr. N. Bachkheti, Delhi zoo; Drs. D. Morris and R. Sadleir, Regent's Park zoo, London; Dr. E. Lang, Basel Zoological Garden; Mr. W. Conway, New York Zoological Park; Drs. T. Reed and J. Eisenberg, National Zoological Park, Washington, D.C.; Dr. L. Fisher, Lincoln Park Zoological Garden, Chicago; Gamekeeper Talbot, Woburn Abbey, England; and Mr. R. Baudy, Animal Training Center, Center Hill, Florida.

Several biologists gave me useful advice in planning the project or in writing up the results. I would like to thank Dr. W. Longhurst, Hopland Field Station, California; Dr. H. Buechner, Smithsonian Institution, Washington; and Dr. V. Flyger, University of Maryland.

Library facilities were kindly provided by the London Zoological Society and the British Museum.

Miss E. Monaghan, Johns Hopkins University, prepared the figures. All or parts of the manuscript were read and criticized by a number of persons who offered valuable suggestions and corrections for which I am extremely grateful: Dr. D. Klein, Cooperative Wildlife Research Unit, University of Alaska — chapter on chital and section on predator-prey relations; Dr. M. Altmann, University of Colorado — chapter on barasingha; Dr. W. Etkin, Albert Einstein College of Medicine, New York — chapter on blackbuck; and Dr. P. Leyhausen, Max-Planck Institut für Verhaltensphysiologie, Wuppertal, Germany — chapter on tiger. Dr. J. T. Emlen, University of Wisconsin, read the entire manuscript.

Finally, I would like to express my deep gratitude to my wife Kay, who assisted me in many ways both in the field and in the preparation of the report, and to my sons Eric and Mark, who, though they did not add materially to the project, contributed to it by making the work more enjoyable.

INDEX

MALE TIGER

TIGER CUB

TIGRESS